KEEPING YOUR PETS NATURALLY HEALTHY

KEEPING YOUR PETS NATURALLY HEALTHY

Holistic Care and Nutrition for Dogs & Cats

JUDY MORGAN DVM, CVA, CVCP, CVFT

Illustrated by Hue Grant

36 Paws Press

Published by 36 Paws Press
For more information, visit www.drjudymorgan.com

ISBN (paperback): 978-0-9972501-7-6
ISBN (ebook): 978-0-9972501-8-3

Book design by Christy Day, Constellation Book Services

Printed in the United States of America

Dedication

Every now and then you come across someone that shares your vision and makes up for your weaknesses. It is a true bonus when that person is also someone you love. This book is dedicated to Theresa Carpenter for being so meticulous in her research, making my life easier. I'm honored to call her my friend.

Table of Contents

Introduction

Nine years ago, I wrote my first book *From Needles to Natural: Learning Holistic Pet Healing* published in 2014. In that book I listed brand names for many products I was using in my practice. Sadly, many of those products are no longer available or the companies have changed hands, resulting in products becoming less than stellar. In this book I will not give very many brand names, as I never know when the tides will shift. Products I endorse and use for my own pets and patients can be found on www.drjudymorgan. com, which will be consistently updated with new products.

My goal with *Needles to Natural* was to inform pet owners that there were options for pet care that had less side effects and promoted healing rather than putting a band-aid on symptoms pets were experiencing. Since that time, I have interacted with thousands of frustrated pet owners dealing with chronic disease in their pets. Those interactions have enabled me to vastly expand my knowledge in holistic therapies. Writing an update to that book is long overdue.

In *Keeping Your Pets Naturally Healthy* I have attempted to address common medical issues seen in veterinary practice. It is not and never could be an exhaustive list of every malady that plagues dogs and cats, nor is it possible to list every possible therapeutic option. I have addressed each disease from a traditional and complementary standpoint, giving options for different types of treatment. My personal preference is to try food, herbs, and supplements before using medications with serious side effects. Before starting any regimen, please consult with your veterinarian, as herbs and supplements may interact with medications. Never stop your pet's prescribed medications without consulting your veterinarian.

For a complete list of vaccinations for dogs and cats, as well as recommended vaccination schedules, please refer to my previous book *Raising Naturally Healthy Pets: A Guide to Helping Your Pets Live Longer*, published in March 2023. A complete reference for parasite prevention and treatment from a holistic perspective can also be found there, along with information on finding a holistic veterinarian and how to compromise with your traditional veterinarian, if that is your only option. Dental care, training, socialization, and natural first aid remedies are also included in *Raising Naturally Healthy Pets*.

Throughout this book there are references to TCVM, Traditional Chinese Veterinary Medicine. Please refer to my previous book *Yin & Yang Nutrition for Dogs: Maximizing Health with Whole Foods, Not Drugs*, published in 2017, if you would like to gain further knowledge on using TCVM food therapy to help your pet return to a balanced state of good health. My social media sites contain a wealth of free information on this topic, as well.

1
The State of the Veterinary Profession

In the past three years I have had hundreds of people reach out to me and I've seen hundreds of social media posts with pet owners lamenting that they were unable to get an appointment with their veterinarian for weeks to months. Even worse, many times they were unable to be seen in an emergency, with emergency clinics diverting patients to hospitals much further away. Unfortunately, this can be a life-or-death situation and many pets have died while waiting to be seen. Emergency care cannot be guaranteed for pets right now and there is no hope for improvement any time soon.

Understaffing can lead to missed treatments, walks, and meals for those pets that are fortunate enough to be seen and admitted for care. I am not bashing the veterinary profession; I am pointing out irrefutable facts.

Current estimates show that by 2030 nearly 75 million pets in the United States could be without necessary veterinary care, as there is a projected shortage of 15,000 veterinarians. The reasons for this are many:

- Nearly 2,000 baby boomer veterinarians are retiring each year.
- Thousands of veterinarians and support staff left the profession during Covid due to the stress and inefficiency of practicing curbside medicine, as well as the fear of becoming ill.
- By 2030 the pet population is expected to be nearly 102 million dogs and more than 82 million cats in the United States.
- Enrollment and graduation at veterinary schools does not keep up with the projected need.
- Staff turnover is much higher due to client frustration and bad behavior toward veterinary staff. In 2020 the turnover rate for veterinary technicians was 23.4 percent a year, with veterinary turnover rate at 16 percent, which is much higher than it is for doctors in human health care. In understaffed clinics, staff members suffer distress at not being able to spend the time needed to provide their desired level of care and attention for each animal. The more stressed and over-worked they are, the more likely they are to quit.
- Low wages and high educational costs have led many to leave the field or turn toward other career opportunities.
- 30% of veterinarians surveyed want to work fewer hours (a few years ago this was 23%). The top two reasons are work-life balance and mental health, including stress, anxiety, and burnout. Most veterinary graduates are female, meaning there is a need to juggle work with child-care needs and family time.

In addition to having too few veterinarians available, there is also a movement toward corporate medicine replacing privately owned veterinary hospitals. The veterinary profession has tradi-tionally not been driven by money and has been considered one of the most trusted of the medical professions, but that attitude has changed dramatically in recent years.

Veterinary practices have become attractive targets for corporations and private equity groups. With investors' focus on the bottom line (profit), pet owners are seeing higher bills and declining care as a result. The focus on the bottom line may lead to too few staff doing too much work (resulting in more stress, burnout, and turnover), as employee salaries are the largest single cost in any veterinary practice. Veterinary costs have more than doubled in the past two decades, with the largest increases seen in the past three years, while the consumer price index showed a 149 percent increase between 2003 and 2023 (Bureau of Labor Statistics).

Recent estimates suggest at least 25 percent of companion animal practices and 75 percent of specialty veterinary practices, including emergency medicine, are now corporately owned. Mars Veterinary Health (yes, a candy company) started buying veterinary practices in 2007 and now owns more than 2,500 of them, including Banfield, Blue Pearl Specialty and Emergency Hospitals, VCA Animal Hospitals, Linnaeus and Anicura in the UK, and multiple hospitals in Singapore and Hong Kong. They also own one of the largest U.S. veterinary diagnostic laboratories, Antech, and one of the largest veterinary imaging companies (X-ray, ultrasound), Sound Technologies, as well as Asia Veterinary Diagnostics and Vetsource, an online pharmacy. IVC Evidensia, backed by a Swedish private equity group, owns 2,000 practices worldwide, while NVA, backed by a German private equity firm, owns over 1,200 veterinary practices.

Corporations often offer $100,000 sign-on bonuses and student loan repayment subsidies to veterinarians willing to sign a three-year employment agreement. Privately owned veterinary practices cannot compete with this. What the new corporate veterinary employees may not be aware of is that corporate management often has quotas that must be met, meaning pressure to see more patients and perform more procedures. The pressure on the veterinarian translates to pressure on the pet parent to authorize additional diagnostic tests or treatments.

What does all this mean for you, as a pet parent? It means you are having more trouble finding care for your beloved family members and when you do find care, the visit could quickly turn into a substantial financial challenge. How do you navigate this problem? The answer lies in education and prevention. My goal has always been to empower pet parents through education. If you can keep your pet healthy by feeding the correct diet and minimizing toxins to which your pet is exposed, you will have less need for ongoing, expensive veterinary care. Your veterinarian will always play an important role in your pet's life, but by taking proactive steps to maintain your pet's health, you can minimize the need for frequent veterinary visits and the associated costs.

2 Follow an Integrated Plan for Your Pet

Integration combines the use of traditional veterinary medicine with complementary therapies. It involves minimizing the overuse and misuse of conventional medications. Integrating chiropractic care, acupuncture, craniosacral therapy, physical therapy, cold laser, magnetics, homeopathy, homotoxicology, nutritional therapy, energy work, massage, and herbal therapies may allow the use of far fewer traditional medications that can have horrendous side effects.

First and foremost, feeding the proper diet is the foundation upon which any integrative pet care program begins. Minimizing harmful byproducts and chemicals is essential. You need to become a label reader. Know which ingredients are good and which are bad. Whether you are feeding commercial, home-cooked, or a raw diet, whole, fresh, organic food ingredients are best. If a food is suitable for human consumption and is something you would consider part of a healthy diet, your pet can probably share with you (see the chart on toxic foods for pets in the next chapter).

The second step in working toward a more holistic treatment plan for your pet is to minimize vaccinations. In the past, the veterinary community has advocated annual vaccinations for dogs and cats for common diseases like distemper, parvovirus, leptospirosis, and Lyme disease. More recently, research has shown that immunity from a single vaccination may last years or a lifetime. It is time to stop over-vaccinating our pets.

Vaccinations do not give instant protection from disease. The injection contains small amounts of the virus or bacteria that are killed or modified to prevent the injection from causing the disease. The animal's body recognizes the components of the organism and builds an immune response against the disease. Unfortunately, when the body is constantly bombarded with disease particles, preservatives in vaccines, and cell cultures in the vaccines, the immune system can go into hyper-drive, causing an overzealous response. This overzealous response can cause the immune system to react against the cells of the body. Diseases like autoimmune hemolytic anemia, autoimmune thrombocytopenia, masticatory myositis, lupus, arthritis, cancer, or any other inflammatory disease can be related to the constant stimulation of the immune system. See my book *Raising Naturally Healthy Pets* for a complete guide to vaccinations and vaccination recommendations.

Chronic use of medications can degrade the body's ability to recognize disease-causing organisms. The liver and kidneys are the filtration system for the body, constantly weeding out toxic substances. While medications may help treat one symptom or disease, they may cause other symptoms or set up a cascade of events that may eventually result in the demise of the individual.

Chronic use of heartworm preventatives and oral or topical pesticides for fleas and ticks can also affect the long-term health of your pet. These chemicals are neurotoxins and come with a long list of side effects that include long-term neurologic damage or death. Depending on where you live, internal and external parasites may be a big threat, but alternative, safer products are available. See my book *Raising Naturally Healthy Pets* for a complete guide to natural parasite prevention and treatment.

Environmental stressors contribute to disease by causing oxidative stress and inflammation, gene alterations and mutations leading to cancer and chronic disease, mitochondrial (the powerhouse of cells) dysfunction, endocrine disruption, altered intercellular communication, altered microbiome communities leading to allergies and infections, and impaired nervous system function. Exposure to pollutants in air, water, soil, and food can be difficult to avoid.

The effects of sound and light can also create problems. How often do you hear electronic buzzing or beeping in your household? Almost all appliances have audible signals that interrupt daily calm. The glow from electronic devices interrupts the normal circadian rhythm that dictates sleep and rest cycles. Set devices to silent when possible and turn off screens when not in use.

Electromagnetic fields cause oxidative damage to skin, organs, and bone marrow. These are emitted by everyday appliances such as microwaves, televisions, tablets, computers, cell phones, and wireless technology. In people, more serious issues such as heart disease, brain cancer, and pre-mature aging have been associated with EMF radiation. A study by Colorado State University of Veterinary Medicine found that proximity of high-powered power lines to the home resulted in an 80 percent increased likelihood of dogs developing lymphoma. Pets should not sleep near electronics including the television, refrigerator, computers, or other devices.

Other stressors include chemical exposure through use of cleaning agents, insecticides, fertilizers, and general household chemicals. Natural cleaning products are readily available which are less harmful. Simple dilute solutions of vinegar or lemon juice in water can be made inexpensively.

Sample Cleaning Product Recipes

- Fresh lemon degreaser:
- 2 cups water
- 2 tablespoons freshly squeezed lemon juice
- 1 tablespoon baking soda

Vinegar and vodka disinfectant with essential oils

- 1/2 cup white vinegar
- 1/2 cup vodka
- 10 drops lemon essential oil
- 10 drops lavender essential oil
- 1 1/2 cups water

Glass cleaner:

- 2 cups water
- 2 tablespoons white vinegar
- 2 tablespoons rubbing alcohol
- 5 drops peppermint essential oil

Bathroom cleaner:

- 1/4 cup baking soda
- 1 cup water

Hardwood floor cleaner:

- 1/2 cup white vinegar
- 1 gallon warm water
- 3 drops lemon essential oil

Confinement, stress, boredom, and solitary existence also contribute to chronic immune stress and disease in pets. Not only do pets suffer from these stressors individually, but they also mirror the stress of the owners. This emotional contagion, the mirroring of emotional or arousal states, is highly contagious within a household, causing increased levels of cortisol which suppresses the immune system and resistance to disease. In other words, calm down!

In addition to feeding good food and minimizing toxins for your pet, you need to know what is normal for your pet. The physical examination by your veterinarian, performed at least once a year and preferably twice a year, particularly once your pet is a senior, is the most important part of the veterinary visit. Detecting a heart murmur, aging changes in the eyes, high blood pressure, or small tumors allows you to get an early start on diagnosis and treatment of problems. Rather than waiting for an illness to become life threatening (and then not being able to get in to see a veterinarian), you may be able to make changes in food or lifestyle that will prevent further problems.

Laboratory diagnostics should be included in the annual visit. I recommend a complete blood count (CBC) to look for signs of anemia or increased white blood cells that could indicate infection, inflammation, or possible cancer. A complete chemistry screen will detect changes in liver or kidney function, electrolytes, blood sugar, heart muscle inflammation, and pancreatic function. A baseline thyroid hormone level can be used to help determine thyroid function, which is commonly low in any dog that is stressed or has another disease process in the body or may be high in older cats with hyperthyroidism. Take a urine sample to be analyzed for blood or protein in the urine, which could show signs of infection, bladder stones, bladder cancer, or kidney disease. A fresh stool sample should be tested twice a year for intestinal parasites (do not just routinely administer deworming medication). A heartworm test should be run at least once a year (two to four times if you live in a tropical climate with abundant mosquitoes).

Always ask for a copy of your pet's lab value results. Many times, subtle changes or trends in lab work can signal changes occurring internally that should be addressed early before disease progresses to more advanced stages. I have an online course available at www. drjudyU.com where you can learn what the lab values represent and what it means when they are high or low. Empowering yourself with knowledge enables you to have better conversations about your pet's health with your veterinarian.

Do not ignore dental disease in your pet. Dental tartar and bacterial infection under the gum line can contribute to heart and kidney disease. The bacteria in the mouth travel through the bloodstream and lodge on the heart valves or in the kidneys during blood filtration. Take care of your pet's teeth daily.

Proactive care is designed to keep your pet out of the emergency room. But let's face it, accidents can happen. However, chronic disease is preventable with the right care. To follow an integrated plan for your pets:

- Feed a species-appropriate diet with no preservatives, dyes, or chemicals. Recipes are provided throughout this book. More recipes can be found at www.drjudymorgan.com and in my book *Yin & Yang Nutrition for Dogs: Maximizing Health with Whole Foods, Not Drugs.*
- Feed high-quality proteins and low-carbohydrate diets.
- Limit the use of medications.
- Limit the use of vaccinations. For a complete list of recommended vaccine schedules and vaccines to avoid, see my book *Raising Naturally Healthy Pets.*
- Do not use chemical pesticides. For a list of alternative parasite prevention and treatment methods, see my book *Raising Naturally Healthy Pets.*

- Know what is normal for your pet by having annual veterinary examinations and laboratory testing.
- Know the problems encountered for your specific breed and take action to monitor and prevent problems.
- Prevent dental disease. For information on dental care and treatment and prevention of dental disease, see my book *Raising Naturally Healthy Pets*.
- Provide regular exercise.
- Keep your pet lean rather than heavy.
- Provide environmental stimulation and human interaction.
- Minimize environmental stressors.

3 Sterilization Options for Dogs and Cats

For the first twenty years I spent in veterinary practice I recommended spay and neuter for every dog and cat between six and eight months of age because that is what I was taught was appropriate. Animals coming from the local animal shelter were being sterilized as young as six weeks of age. Looking back, I feel bad that so much damage was done to so many animals by removing organs from their body that had very important functions and protected them from cancer, inflammatory diseases, arthritis, behavior disorders, and endocrine disorders. Once I discovered the importance of hormonal influence on health and longevity, I found there are ways to sterilize pets without removing that hormonal influence.

Sterilization Options for Female Dogs

Sterilization is the most common surgical procedure performed on pets in the United States. The main benefit of sterilization is population control and the reduction in euthanasia of unwanted dogs. The most common method of sterilizing female dogs is the traditional spay; however, there are other methods which may be more beneficial to your female dog. There are four methods I recommend, each with their own benefits and risks. The pros and cons of each method should be discussed with your veterinarian before proceeding with a sterilization.

An **Ovariohysterectomy, OVH, or traditional spay** is the most common sterilization procedure in the US. In this procedure, the ovaries (gonads) and uterus are removed. In female dogs, OVH eliminates the risk of pyometra (uterine infection), and pregnancy and heat cycles are eliminated. Removing the ovaries and uterus also eliminates the risk of a false pregnancy. False pregnancies mimic true pregnancies resulting in abnormal behaviors, as well as an increased risk of mastitis (mammary infection).

The **Ovariectomy, OVE, or laparoscopic spay** procedure involves removal of the ovaries, but the uterus remains intact. This sterilization method eliminates the risk of pyometra and pregnancy. Behavioral changes associated with "heat" are avoided. The advantages of an OVE over an OVH are less postoperative pain, complications, and recovery time.

Removal of the ovaries may protect the female dog against mammary tumors, uterine infections, and tumors (for OVH), mastitis (breast infection), transmissible venereal sarcoma, ovarian diseases (cancer, cysts, and infections), and chronic endometritis (inflammation of the uterine wall). However, a literature review on the connection between spaying and mammary tumors showed most studies had a high risk of bias. Of the four studies with only a moderate risk of bias, two found neutering to protect against mammary cancer and two found no association.

A Swedish study (where most dogs are not spayed or neutered) showed breed predisposition for mammary cancer and pyometra. Of 260,000 dogs, 20,423 were diagnosed with pyometra and 11,758 were diagnosed with mammary tumors. The top ten breeds diagnosed were the Leonberger, Irish Wolfhound, Bernese Mountain Dog, Great Dane, Staffordshire Bull Terrier, Rottweiler, Bullterrier, Doberman, Bouvier, and Airdale. Breed variations in incidence rate suggests genetic components in disease development.

A Norwegian study (where dogs are largely left intact) showed varying rates of mammary cancer development based on breed: 35.47 per 1,000 Boxer dogs, 3.87 per 1,000 in Bernese Mountain dogs, and 17.69 per 1,000 Bichon Frise' dogs. The mean age of mammary cancer development was 7 to 8 years.

Another Swedish study looked at the incidence of pyometra in five breeds with a high incidence of pyometra (Rottweiler, Collie, Golden Retriever, Labrador Retriever, and German Shepherd). In the Rottweiler, Collie, and Labrador Retriever, previous pregnancy showed protection against developing pyometra later in life. There was no protective effect found in Golden Retrievers and intermediate protection in the German Shepherd.

Any surgery that removes the gonads (ovaries in females) changes the animal in both positive and negative ways. There is mounting evidence supporting long-term health complications associated with surgical sterilization that includes gonad (ovaries) removal. Gonads are not just sex/reproductive organs; they are necessary endocrine glands for normal metabolic, behavioral, musculoskeletal, and anti-neoplastic (tumor/cancer) health.

The risks/disadvantages associated with OVH and OVE include:

- Higher risk of joint disorders—Female dogs that receive a traditional spay have a greater risk of joint disorders. For example, a study showed that spayed/neutered dogs had a 3.1 times higher incidence of patellar luxation. In females, neutering within the first year is also associated with a highly significant threefold risk of acquiring at least one joint disorder—up to 17% compared with 5% in females left intact or neutered beyond one year.
- Higher risk of cancer—A study of Golden Retrievers found that neutering at any time through 8 years of age increased the risk of osteosarcoma, hemangiosarcoma,

lymphoma and mast cell tumors by 3 to 4 times. A three-fold increase in transitional cell carcinoma of the urinary bladder for both sexes when neutered has been reported. In another study, cardiac hemangiosarcoma in spayed females was reported to be 4 times greater than that of intact dogs.

- Higher risk of developing autoimmune diseases—Studies suggest that ovary removal is associated with an increased risk for certain autoimmune disorders. The reproductive system and the immune system are highly interdependent. Female dogs are particularly at risk for atopic dermatitis, irritable bowel disease (IBD), and canine immune-mediated thrombocytopenia (ITP). Sterilized female dogs have a significantly greater risk of lupus (LUP) than their intact counterparts.

- Higher risk of urinary incontinence—Studies show that sterilized female dogs have a 5% to 20% higher risk of urinary incontinence.

- Changes in behavior—One of the most stated reasons to spay a dog is to reduce aggression. In practice, I have seen it go both ways. I have seen dogs "calm down" after being spayed; I have also seen dogs become more reactive and aggressive after being spayed. A survey conducted of over 13,000 dog parents (both neutered and intact) concluded that there was no association between neutering and aggression towards *familiar people*. The study also found there was a low but significant increase in the risk of aggression towards strangers for neutered dogs compared to intact dogs. This data was driven, though, by dogs neutered at 7 to 12 months of age. That age group showed they were 26% more likely to show aggression with strangers.

To reduce the risks associated with removing the ovaries, there are two recommended ovary-sparing sterilization procedures. As with any method, there are pros and cons.

Ovary Sparing Spay (OSS), also referred to as **hysterectomy**, removes the uterus and cervix, leaving one or both ovaries intact. This procedure eliminates the risk of pyometra and pregnancy, and it protects against some of the more serious cancers and immune-mediated diseases. This sterilization option is a wonderful option for those that want to eliminate the risk of pyometra, sterilize their pet, and keep hormones intact.

The risks/disadvantages associated with OSS include:

- Heat cycles continue—leaving the ovaries means the hormones are still intact so females will still be attractive to males. As such, she may show behavioral changes while in heat. However, removal of the entire uterus eliminates bleeding.
- Higher incidence of mammary tumors and cancer—The degree of risk depends on the breed. For example, a higher incidence of mammary tumors has been reported in poodles, English cocker spaniels and dachshunds. However, many of the studies are biased, as published by the British Small Animal Veterinary Association:

  "A commonly stated advantage of neutering bitches is a significant reduction in the risk of mammary tumours, however the evidence for this has not previously been assessed by systematic review. The objectives of this study were to estimate the magnitude and strength of evidence for any effect of neutering, or age of neutering, on the risk of mammary tumours in bitches. A systematic review was conducted based on Cochrane guidelines. Peer-reviewed analytic journal articles in

English were eligible and were assessed for risk of bias by two reviewers independently. Of 11,149 search results, 13 reports in English-language peer-reviewed journals addressed the association between neutering/ age at neutering and mammary tumours. Nine were judged to have a high risk of bias. The remaining four were classified as having a moderate risk of bias. One study found an association between neutering and a reduced risk of mammary tumours. Two studies found no evidence of an association. One reported "some protective effect" of neutering on the risk of mammary tumours, but no numbers were presented. Due to the limited evidence available and the risk of bias in the published results, the evidence that neutering reduces the risk of mammary neoplasia, and the evidence that age at neutering has an effect, are judged to be weak and are not a sound basis for firm recommendations."

© 2012 British Small Animal Veterinary Association.

🐾 Potential decrease in brain function—The uterus is thought to only be active during reproduction, but a fascinating rat model showed removing the uterus (hysterectomy) impacted brain functioning. The uterus is an organ that is part of the endocrine system. Removing it does not go without impact.

In **tubal ligation**, all organs stay intact, but there is zero risk of pregnancy. Tubal ligation is a sterilization method that does not remove the ovaries or uterus and may be a better choice for certain dogs, especially young ones. The dog still possesses the ability to maintain heat cycles and produce a steady level of hormones. This procedure is not well-known in veterinary clinics.

The risks/disadvantages associated with tubal ligation include:

- Heat cycles continue—As with OSS, leaving the ovaries means the potential for behavioral changes since the hormones are still intact. Regular heat cycles (including bleeding) will continue.
- Higher incidence of mammary tumors and cancer—The risks are the same for OSS, however there is controversy as to whether the incidence is higher for mammary cancer.
- Pyometra—Pyometra is a secondary infection that occurs because of hormonal changes in the female's reproductive tract. Pyometra can be fatal; the risk depends primarily on breed and age. However, the survivability of pyometra in a retrospective study was 97% in a non-specialized veterinary hospital setting.

There is always the option to leave a pet intact. I respect that this decision is the best choice for some dogs. When it comes to spay and neuter, *there is no one-size-fits-all solution*. Pet owners need to look at the pet and their lifestyle when making the decision. The goal is always to eliminate the chance of unwanted pregnancy while mitigating the risks and disadvantages of a particular sterilization method. For example, if your female dog is a breed that is at higher risk for mammary cancer, removing the ovaries (OVE) may be the best choice. It is important for you and your veterinarian to discuss the risks and benefits for your dog, as well as proper management, to decide on the best plan for lifelong well-being.

Diagnosing and Treating Pyometra

Pyometra is a severe bacterial infection in the reproductive tract that causes the formation of purulent (pus or containing pus) material to develop in the uterus. This occurs secondary to hormonal changes in female dogs and cats. Following a heat cycle, hormones change, making it easier for bacteria to enter the uterus, grow, and cause an infection.

Pyometra is caused by hormonal changes in the body that cause the uterus to fill with pus. Intact females that still have reproductive organs are more likely to get pyometra, especially when they are over age 6. A very common organism called E. coli, found in feces, usually causes the condition. There are hormonal changes which take place in the uterus during each heat cycle, and these make the infection more likely as pets get older.

Following estrus (heat), the hormone progesterone remains elevated for up to two months and causes the lining of the uterus to thicken in preparation for pregnancy. If pregnancy does not occur for several consecutive estrus cycles, the uterine lining continues to increase in thickness until cysts form within the uterine tissues (a condition called cystic endometrial hyperplasia). The thickened, cystic lining secretes fluids that create an ideal environment for bacterial growth. In addition, the muscles of the uterus cannot contract properly either due to thickening of the uterine wall or the high levels of the hormone progesterone. This means that bacteria that enters the uterus and fluids that have accumulated cannot be expelled.

During estrus, white blood cells, which would normally protect against infection by eliminating bacteria, are inhibited from entering the uterus. This normal occurrence allows sperm to safely enter the female's reproductive tract without being damaged or destroyed by these immune system cells.

Stump pyometra can occur in dogs and cats that have been spayed, if the doctor performing the surgery did not remove the entire uterus.

Progesterone-based drugs can also cause pyometra due to the changes they make in the uterus. In addition, estrogen or synthetic estrogen drugs will increase the effects of progesterone on the uterus. Drugs containing both estrogen and progesterone are sometimes used to treat certain conditions of the reproductive system. Any intact female receiving hormones must be carefully monitored for the development of pyometra.

Pyometra can be open or closed. In an open pyometra, the cervix is open, allowing the purulent discharge in the uterus to drain out through the vaginal opening. The discharge will usually be thick or bloody with a foul odor. The dog or cat may groom the hindquarter area excessively. In a closed pyometra, the cervix remains closed, trapping the pus inside the uterus. This type of pyometra is harder to diagnose; radiographs or ultrasound may be required for diagnosis. Closed pyometra is also more dangerous, as these animals become toxic more quickly and are subject to uterine rupture.

Pets affected with pyometra will usually drink more than usual, may have decreased appetite, and may be lethargic. They may vomit, have a bloated abdomen, and may collapse.

Symptoms generally appear six to eight weeks after going through a heat cycle for dogs, which cycle about every seven months. Pyometra most commonly occurs in cats that have been in heat within the past month.

A complete blood count (CBC) will usually show an elevated white blood cell count, with elevated numbers of neutrophils and band cells, which signal a bacterial infection. Blood glucose (sugar) and globulins may also be elevated.

In the past, the preferred treatment for pyometra was surgery. The veterinary surgeon usually performs an ovariohysterectomy (spay) to remove the infected uterus and ovaries. This surgery is more complicated than routine spay, however studies have shown high survivability over 97%, even in non-specialty clinic settings.

Pets diagnosed in the early stages of their illness are considered good candidates for a successful surgery. The risks of complications and extended hospitalization are higher if diagnosis is delayed.

After the surgery, typically, intravenous fluids (IV) are needed; the pet may remain hospitalized for two to three days on fluids and antibiotics.

Pyometra is a medical emergency that needs immediate treatment. If you notice symptoms or changes in your pet's behavior, call your veterinarian. Early diagnosis lowers the risks of complications. If left untreated, the disease will worsen to the point of dehydration, collapse, and death from septic shock. Closed pyometras that go untreated can result in uterine rupture, peritonitis, and a worse prognosis for recovery.

There is a medical approach to treating pyometra, although the success rate is highly variable and not without considerable risk and potential long-term complications.

Prostaglandins are a group of hormones that lower the level of progesterone in the blood, relax and open the cervix, and cause the uterus to contract, therefore expelling the bacteria and pus. They can be used to treat this disease, but they are not always successful and have some important limitations.

- Prostaglandins cause side effects including restlessness, panting, vomiting, defecation, salivation, and abdominal pain. The side effects occur within minutes after administration and can last for a few hours. They become progressively milder with each successive treatment.
- It takes approximately forty-eight hours for the prostaglandins to take effect, so pets that are severely ill and need immediate life-saving treatment are poor candidates.
- Because prostaglandins cause the uterus to contract, it is possible for the uterus to rupture and spill infection into the abdominal cavity resulting in the severely

life-threatening condition known as peritonitis. This is most likely to happen when the cervix is closed.

The use of prostaglandins to treat pyometra has variable rates of success. Prostaglandins do not prevent recurrence of the disease; successful breeding in the future is not guaranteed.

Aglepristone is a progesterone antagonist that has been used to treat pyometra in both dogs and cats. It is labeled for use to induce abortion after unwanted mating. In bitches with closed cervix pyometra, administration of Aglepristone is often followed by cervical opening within 24-48 hrs. There is no information on the effect of Aglepristone on pyometra in the queen (cat), but efficacy for this indication is thought to be the same as in dogs.

Homeopathic protocols exist for treatment of pyometra; work with a trained veterinary homeopath to be sure treatment is helping. TCVM (Traditional Chinese Veterinary Medicine) approaches to therapy may include acupuncture and herbal therapy. These modalities may be combined with traditional therapies.

Many dogs and cats can be bred after successful treatment for pyometra. The pet owner should be vigilant for any symptoms of pyometra after future heat cycles.

Sterilization Options for Male Dogs

The overwhelming majority of companion dogs in the United States are neutered, most before one year of age. Neutering is critically important for population control, reduction of some reproductive disorders, and offers convenience for owners. Most pet parents (and some veterinarians) assume there is one method of sterilization for male dogs. In fact, there are several, but only two that I recommend.

Castration (also known as *neuter* and *gonadectomy*), is the most common sterilization procedure in the US for male dogs. In this procedure, the testes (gonads) of the dog are removed. Any surgery that removes the gonads changes the animal in both positive and negative ways. In addition to population control, castration prevents testicular cancer and can minimize sexually driven behaviors. However, there is mounting evidence supporting the long-term health complications associated with surgical sterilization with gonad (testes) removal. Gonads are not just sex/reproductive organs; they are necessary endocrine glands for normal metabolic, behavioral, musculoskeletal, and anti-neoplastic (tumor/cancer) health.

The risks/disadvantages associated with castration include:

- Higher risk of joint disorders—Several studies show that neutering in the first year of life increases the risk of debilitating joint disorders. For example, in a study which examined the medical records of German Shepherd dogs examined over a 14.5-year period, 7% of intact males were diagnosed with a joint disorder, versus 21% of male dogs neutered prior to one year of age. Joint disorders such as hip dysplasia, cranial ligament tear or rupture (CCL), and elbow dysplasia are among the most common.
- Higher risk of cancer—A study of Golden Retrievers found that neutering at any time through 8 years of age increased the risk of osteosarcoma, hemangiosarcoma, lymphoma and mast cell tumors by 3 to 4 times. One study showed significantly higher rates of prostate carcinoma, prostate adenocarcinoma, prostate transitional cell carcinoma, and urinary transitional cell carcinoma in neutered dogs versus intact dogs.
- Higher risk of developing autoimmune diseases—Studies suggest that castration is associated with an increased risk for certain autoimmune disorders. The reproductive

system and the immune system are highly interdependent. Diseases such as atopic dermatitis, irritable bowel disease (IBD), autoimmune hemolytic anemia (AIHA), canine immune-mediated thrombocytopenia (ITP), pemphigus complex (PEMC), have been shown to be 2-4 times more than intact dogs.

- Changes in behavior—Castration has been advocated to make dogs more well-behaved companions. However, several studies have reported that castration neither prevents nor reduces dogs' aggressive behavior. While some studies suggest that castrated male dogs were significantly more likely than intact dogs to have bitten a person, other studies seem to suggest that castration prevents or improves the aggressive behavior of dogs.

Vasectomy is a less invasive procedure performed under general anesthesia. It involves cutting or tying the Vas Deferens, the tube which transports sperm from the testes to the urethra. The testes remain intact, but the dog is rendered infertile because the sperm is prevented from being ejaculated during copulation. This surgery can be performed on pediatric patients (dogs <6 months) without interfering with pubertal maturation. Keeping the sex hormones intact significantly reduces the risk of the joint disorders and cancers that can occur with castration. Studies also show a reduced incidence of obesity as well as adverse reactions to vaccines.

The risks/disadvantages associated with vasectomy include:

- Vasectomy is not effective right away. Dogs should be prevented from roaming or having contact with intact female dogs for 2 to 6 months following the procedure.
- Risk of testicular cancer—Just as with intact dogs, dogs rendered infertile by a vasectomy have some risk of developing testicular cancer. Malignant testicular cancer is not common.

- Disorders of the prostate—There is an increased risk of developing problems such as prostatitis (a bacterial infection), benign prostatic hyperplasia (non-cancerous enlargement of the prostate), prostatic cysts, and squamous metaplasia of the prostate (non-cancerous estrogen-producing tumors), although none of these are cancerous disorders. Prostate cancer is more common in dogs who have had the testes removed.
- Increased risk of hernia—Incidences of perineal (scrotum and anus) and inguinal (groin) hernia, as well as perineal adenoma (tumors in the anal region) are higher in dogs sterilized by vasectomy versus castration.
- Behavioral concerns—Although the dog is infertile, he will continue to have interest in females in heat. Taking him into public spaces may be a challenge as he will appear to be intact. There is also an increased risk of wandering and urine marking. There may be a risk of inter-dog aggression due to competition for available territory or availability of females in heat. Good training can solve all these issues.

I have made the decision to keep my male dogs intact. First and foremost, I am a responsible dog owner with small, passive Cavaliers. My only female dog is sterilized, and my dogs are either in a securely double fenced yard or on a leash. There is no risk of accidental breeding, and while everyone believes neutering will magically fix behavior problems, it can also make them worse. The main concern leaving my males intact is testicular cancer. Luckily, it is uncommon and considered highly treatable if found early.

Gonadectomy, or removing the testes, on the other hand, has shown to increase the risk of other serious concerns as explained above. Since behavior and accidental breeding are not a concern for me, neutering could potentially put my dogs at a higher risk of more serious cancers and disorders. I am confident leaving my male dogs intact is the right choice for me.

As with any procedure, there are risks associated with sterilization as well as leaving your male dog intact. Not all dogs have health problems after spaying or neutering. Unfortunately, in some dogs, neutering can greatly increase the chance of serious health problems. These risks depend on breed, age at the time of sterilization, size, sex, and genetics. Pet owners should know the pros and cons of these procedures in the context of their own dog and discuss these options with their veterinarian.

Sterilization Options for Cats

As I've said many times, cats are not small dogs! Like dogs, the primary reason for neutering (spaying/castrating) a cat is to control the population. Most shelters and rescue organizations neuter puppies and kittens before placing them for adoption. The reason is simple: a good number of pet parents—even when pre-payment is made—do not return for neutering at the appropriate time. However, unlike dogs, the considerations for neutering a cat differ greatly from those of dogs.

Spaying your female cat eliminates the possibility of pregnancy and pyometra (uterine infection). Neutering your male or female cat also ends mating behaviors that are stressful to cats and humans.

When in heat, female cats may display behavior such as loud and persistent crying and frequent rubbing and rolling on the floor. Your cat may also exhibit marking behaviors such as urinating outside the litterbox. An intact female's scent will attract male cats.

Unneutered male cats will wander from home in search of a mate and may not return. They may also spray inside the home and may be aggressive to owners, but many intact males are perfectly wonderful pets that do not spray and are very sweet. Feline immunodeficiency virus (FIV), which is more prevalent in intact tom cats, can be spread by sexual behavior and fighting; both FIV and the feline leukemia virus (FeLV) may be passed onto a queen's offspring.

However, aggression and spraying can also occur in spayed females and neutered males. Spaying and neutering are not a guarantee that your cat will not be aggressive or will not spray.

Neutering also reduces the risk of certain cancers in cats; namely, mammary, ovarian, and uterine cancer in females. Female cats have a 91% decrease in mammary cancer with spay prior to one year of age. Up to 96% of mammary tumors are malignant in cats. Ovarian and uterine cancers are not commonly seen. Spayed females no longer go into heat every 3 weeks for 5 days during the breeding season.

Removing the testes during castration reduces the risk of testicular cancer to near 0% in male cats. Neutered male cats also have a lesser risk of enlarged prostate gland and prostatic cancer, although prostatic disease is extremely rare in cats.

The recommended sterilization procedures for female cats include:

- An ovariohysterectomy (traditional spay) is the most common sterilization procedure in the US. Both the ovaries and uterus are removed during the procedure. Removing the uterus eliminates the risk of any future uterine disease, including infection (pyometra).

- In an ovariectomy procedure, the ovaries are removed while keeping the uterus intact. This sterilization option is more common in Europe and other locations. An ovariectomy is less invasive and faster than an ovari- ohysterectomy, so anesthesia time is shorter with an ovariectomy. Ovariectomy should be performed in young healthy females with a healthy uterus. Otherwise, an ovariohysterectomy (traditional spay) is recommended.

The recommended sterilization procedures for male cats include:

- Orchiectomy (castration) is the most common steriliza- tion procedure performed in the US for male felines. The testicles are removed, and patients are typically dis- charged the same day. The biggest advantage of castration is the reduction of sex-driven behaviors.
- During a vasectomy, the veterinarian cuts, ties, and blocks off the vas deferens tubes, preventing sperm from enter- ing the seminal stream during ejaculation. The procedure is potentially quicker and usually results in faster recov- ery than castration because the testicles are not removed. While the male cat is rendered sterile, he will retain his male sex-hormone driven behaviors such as roaming, urine marking, humping and aggression. Vasectomies are generally not taught in US veterinary schools.

Research from Tufts University shows that feral cats that undergo a vasectomy or hysterectomy could reduce a feral colony›s numbers more effectively than the traditional approach of neu- tering. This may be because vasectomized cats retain reproductive hormones and will continue to breed with females in heat. Because they are not able to reproduce, the females will come out of the heat cycle without being impregnated; this would also protect their turf from sexually intact competitors.

Risks and disadvantages of sterilizing cats include:

- Increased risk for diabetes: Cats have a 2- to 9-fold increased risk of developing diabetes mellitus after neutering, with Burmese cats reported to be especially susceptible. One hypothesis is decreased insulin sensitivity. Castrated cats have an increase in serum concentrations of insulin growth factor I, prolactin, and leptin, all of which are associated with metabolic rate and fat metabolism.

- Increased risk for obesity: There are known effects of neutering on the physiology and behavior of the cat that predispose it to obesity. Obesity and decreased insulin sensitivity go hand in hand. Sterilized cats can have increased body weight, increased body mass index, increased depth of the falciform fat pad (a type of abdominal fat), decreased activity and decreased metabolic rate. In addition to diabetes, obesity can open the door to a world of problems, including joint disorders, urinary tract problems, and cancer.

The best way to mitigate these risks is to feed a species-appropriate, low-carbohydrate diet to your cat. Studies have shown that a reduction of up to 30% of calories might be necessary to maintain a healthy weight on a sterilized cat. Cats may be less energetic post-sterilization and therefore burn fewer calories. Food intake should be controlled, meaning not leaving out food all day for cats to graze upon. Actively encouraging increased activity will help boost metabolism and burn calories.

Most veterinarians will recommend sterilizing a cat by 6 months of age. However, I recommend sterilizing cats once they are fully developed, and bones are finished growth (most likely around 9 months). Early spay/neuter results in the bone growth plates remaining open longer. Cats that are spayed or neutered prior to the closure of the growth plates have an increased incidence of growth plate fractures.

As with any procedure, discuss all your options with your veterinarian. There may be other health considerations to consider before deciding the best course of action. Sterilization is one of those areas where cats do differ from dogs...there appear to be many benefits to being spayed or castrated but fewer downsides.

Supporting Spayed and Neutered Pets

Spay and castration, the most common methods of sterilization in the US, are surgical procedures in which the sex organs (gonads) are removed. The ovaries and uterus are removed during a traditional spay and the testes are removed during castration. After many years of this practice, recent research in dogs has found that removal of the sex organs, along with its associated hormones, can result in significant health and behavioral issues for some pets. Gonad-sparing options for sterilization are available but unfortunately, they are not considered by most veterinarians, shelters, and rescue groups. Only a small percentage of veterinarians provide hormone-sparing sterilization. Many pet owners are not aware of health problems that occur due to loss of hormones. Given this reality, it is important to know how to support the health of a spayed or castrated pet to give them the best life possible.

To support your pet before surgical sterilization:

🐾 Do not vaccinate your pet within two weeks prior to or two months following sterilization surgery. When you drop your pet off on the day of surgery, be sure to tell the hospital staff that no vaccines are to be administered. Put your request in writing and get assurances that the note will be given to the surgical staff.

- Get a pre-op physical and lab work: Prior to the procedure, schedule a complete physical examination with your veterinarian. Pre-op lab work is critical! If not already a standard part of the complete exam, request full pre-op lab work (CBC, Chemistry panel, urinalysis). A thyroid blood test and a chest x-ray is also recommended if your pet is middle aged or older. Based on the results of these tests, the anesthetic protocol can be adjusted based on the organ function of the animal.

- Support the immune system—An optimized immune system will help speed up healing. Supplements such as probiotics, medicinal mushrooms, colostrum, vitamin C, and echinacea will provide excellent immune support.

The goal after surgery is complete healing with no post-surgical complications. Your veterinarian will send you home with discharge instructions and medications for pain.

- Limit activity in the days following surgery to avoid opening the incision. It is best to keep the pet away from other animals in the house until the incision is healed. Castration is a simpler procedure than spay. Pets undergoing castration without complications will often be discharged the same day. Pets undergoing spay may require an overnight stay in the hospital.

- Check the incision and keep it dry. Homeopathic Calendula 200 C, one dose given daily for five days, has a very positive effect on incision healing.

- Pain management—Veterinarians often prescribe
  NSAIDS (nonsteroidal anti-inflammatory drugs) for pain
  management. If giving an NSAID, watch for bloody or
  dark tarry stools, vomiting, diarrhea, or lack of appetite;
  if they are present, stop these medications immediately
  and call your veterinarian for an alternative medication.
  Do NOT give any over-the-counter medications for pain.
  Watch for signs of pain: flinching, hiding, unwillingness
  to move, or aggression. These behaviors can be a sign
  that a secondary infection is present. There are several
  options to aid in pain management including herbal
  formulas such as Dog Gone Pain and CBD products. A
  homeopathic alternative for pain management is Arnica
  1M, administered orally once every two hours (or less
  frequently) for the first 24 to 48 hours depending on the
  patient's comfort level. Acupuncture can provide significant pain relief.
- Probiotics are also important for recovery, especially if
  antibiotics are prescribed. Antibiotics are not necessary
  in routine surgical procedures performed in a clean
  hospital setting; however, many veterinarians routinely
  use them. A species- specific, high-quality probiotic
  containing billions of CFUs and multiple strains is
  recommended.
- Detox the liver and kidneys from the effects of anesthesia—To detox the liver from the anesthesia, the following
  can be given to your pet one week before and two weeks
  after the procedure:
    - Milk thistle: 100mg per 20 pounds of weight
      twice daily
    - NAC (N-acetyl cysteine): 250mg per 30 pounds
      of weight twice daily

- SAMe (S-adenosyl-L-methionine): 90-425 mg once daily 1 week before and 2 weeks following procedure on an empty stomach.
- B vitamins—good sources include salmon, organ meats, dark leafy greens, eggs, and goat milk.
- CoQ10 5 mg per pound of body weight twice daily
- Foods with sulforaphane—broccoli, brussels sprouts, kale, broccoli sprouts—1/8 to 1/2 cup daily for 10 days.

To detox the kidneys from the anesthesia, give your pet fresh or dried parsley. Dried parsley can be infused to make tea. Another great herb is dandelion root or leaves. The leaves can be chopped or ground and added to food. Dried dandelion root and leaves are also available in powder and tea.

Whether your pet was spayed/castrated four days or four years ago, it is important to support the endocrine system. The endocrine system consists of tissues and glands that release hormones into the bloodstream. A big part of endocrine balance comes from the hormones made in the testicles and ovaries. If these gonads were removed during sterilization, the remaining glands in the endocrine system must work harder to maintain hormonal balance. Certain levels of sex hormones are still needed for healthy biologic function throughout life. When the testes or ovaries are removed, the task of producing these hormones falls to the adrenal glands. In addition to potential adrenal gland issues, the effects of hormonal imbalances may include changes in bone growth and development, ligament and hip problems, urinary issues, immune system imbalances, and shorted lifespan. Ways to support the endocrine system include:

- Glandular support—In addition to the adrenal glands, other glands that support the immune system and balance hormones include tonsils, salivary glands, thymus, thyroid, pituitary, pancreas, and lymph nodes. Supplementing with natural hormone products such as melatonin can provide glandular support. Melatonin promotes healthy cortisol and estrogen levels. Veterinary endocrinologists are also recommending HMR (7-hydroxymatairesinol) lignans in combination with melatonin to support estrogen metabolism.

- Monitoring endocrine gland function- Blood tests that measure the number of circulating hormones in the blood are the most common tests used to detect disorders of the endocrine system. Many different hormones can be measured in the blood, such as cortisol, thyroxine, ACTH (adrenocorticotropic hormone), parathyroid hormone, growth hormone, and insulin. The adrenal glands and thyroid gland can be monitored using blood tests that measure the response of endocrine glands to stimulating hormones. A complete blood count and a urinalysis can also be used to determine problems with the endocrine system. The results of these blood tests may signal additional testing such as CT scan and MRI, radioisotope scan, and biopsy.

- Traditional Chinese Veterinary Medicine—Whenever surgery is performed on an animal, stagnation of blood circulation or a disruption in liver blood stores can occur. These liver imbalances can cause behavioral changes. After being spayed or neutered, many animals undergo what seem like personality changes. Some seem to be fatigued and have no interest in exercise—they just want to eat. This syndrome is caused by a deficiency of liver blood which is too weak to keep the Qi (life force) moving. Treatment is aimed at nourishing the blood and

Qi with herbs, foods, or massaging acupressure points. Chinese herbs such as Epimedium have been shown to increase testosterone levels in research animals. Deer antler velvet contains multiple substances including the female sex hormones estrone and estradiol and the male sex hormones including testosterone, androstenedione, and dehydroepiandosterone. Research in rats, using elk velvet antler, suggested the substance may have an androgen-like effect. It also contains substances that might help cells grow and function.

- Nutrition—A species-appropriate, high-quality raw or gently cooked commercial or home prepared diet will give your dog or cat the best chance at a long life, with or without gonads. Qi (energy) tonic herbs such as sage, thyme, licorice root, cinnamon, and ginger can be added in small quantities to any recipe. Jing means "essence" and is the foundation of life. If your dog or cat was spayed or neutered before reaching maturity, post-natal Jing is compromised. Jing tonics include eggs, bee pollen, small fish from the sea (sardines, mackerel), kelp, bone marrow and broth, fermented raw goat or cow milk, colostrum, Reishi mushrooms, and Vitamin D (always test before supplementing vitamin D, as overdoses are toxic to the kidneys).

- Hormone Restoration Therapy—Hormonal replacement is not a common treatment for dogs and cats, and most published accounts are focused on using hormone therapy to treat urinary incontinence. There is very little research on this process and standardized methods are not yet developed. One study published in 2021 focused on one 4-year-old dog who was suffering from progressive reduced mobility, rapid weight gain and fear of unfamiliar people following a pediatric neuter. He started weekly testosterone shots followed by gonadotropin-releasing hormone (GnRH) after three months. The dog has shown significant improvement in mobility, and his fear and anxiety were somewhat alleviated. The dog continues to receive hormone treatment, and his health is monitored through standard blood work, testosterone levels, and regular prostate exams. There is a need for more research to develop standard procedures and determine best practices for hormone restoration therapy.

Much has been learned about the health risks of spay and neuter in recent years. There is no way to reverse a traditional spay or castration; however, there are many options you can implement to support your dog's endocrine system. Take the time to do the research and then share that research with your veterinarian to determine a support protocol that is tailor-made for your pet.

Food is the Foundation of Life

Let me repeat: FOOD is the foundation of life.
Without a solid foundation, you cannot build a house.

For years, veterinarians have been telling clients to avoid feeding "people food" to their pets. Pet owners have been told to avoid adding anything to the bowl, as the diet would then become "unbalanced". Veterinarians have promoted filling bowls with brown, dry, processed balls of dead food instead, touting the "complete and balanced" myth: that all processed foods made by big pet food manufacturers are complete and balanced. In one study 94% of canned foods and 62% of dry formulations were not compliant with AAFCO (Association of American Feed Control Officials) guidelines. So much for complete and balanced.

Many players in the pet food industry are extremely dishonest about pet food ingredients. FDA is complicit in allowing illegal ingredients in pet food including diseased, putrid animal carcasses that have been left rotting in the sun. The pet food industry has spent millions of advertising and teaching dollars to convince veterinarians and the pet-owning public that the only way to provide a complete diet is to feed processed industrial food. Unfortunately, this is very far from the truth. Cats are carnivores and dogs are carnivorous omnivores and should be fed as they are genetically programmed, with species-appropriate diets. Dogs and cats have zero requirement for carbohydrates in their diet, yet most are fed diets containing at least 50 percent carbohydrates.

If a natural, species-appropriate diet is so great, why don't all veterinarians recommend feeding our pets this way? The truth is veterinary colleges don't focus on the role of diet in disease prevention. In addition, large pet food companies wield a lot of power over those schools and the veterinary industry. They pay large sums of money to have their products promoted to students, knowing that when they enter veterinary practice the new doctors will maintain product loyalty.

Unfortunately, since the advent of processed food for pets, the pandemic of degenerative health problems has escalated in dogs and cats. Chronic conditions such as cancer, obesity, allergies, and diabetes in pets today are skyrocketing. Veterinarians continually treat inflammatory and degenerative diseases, yet they fail to see any correlation between the highly processed diets and disease. In fact, they have been taught by the major pet food companies that the only way to treat chronic disease is to prescribe more processed industrialized foods, especially prescription diets. Prescription diets do NOT contain any medications and are no different from over-the-counter products, other than having a higher price tag.

Allergy symptoms and ear infections are two of the most often treated diseases in veterinary medicine. These are followed closely by dental disease, joint disease and arthritis, obesity, diabetes, behavioral problems, seizures, inflammatory bowel disease, pancreatitis, and cancer. These diseases have one thing in common: inflammation. Most industrial foods are highly inflammatory due to the high content of carbohydrates, gluten, preservatives, binders, dyes, and chemicals.

Pet food recalls in the past few years have included:

- Pentobarbital contamination (euthanasia solution). Rendering companies collect *used* cooking oil from restaurants, fast-food chains, and processing plants and meat-based waste from fat trimmings, bones, *inedible* scraps, *expired* or excess meat from supermarkets, butcher shops, meat lockers, slaughterhouses, packing plants, and other industrial locations. The waste is rendered and repurposed into biofuel, *animal food and pet food*, solvents, fertilizer, and more! According to the head of one of the largest rendering companies, in a speech given at an AAFCO meeting, it is nearly impossible to provide rendered meat products that do not contain pentobarbital. FDA has chosen to look aside and not confront this matter.

- Excess vitamin D in canned and dry foods. This created one of the largest recalls across many brands of food due to a mistake in formulation of the vitamin/mineral pre-mix added to food to make it complete and balanced. It took months for Hill's pet food to announce the recall of their products, even though other companies had taken that step earlier, resulting in kidney damage and death for thousands of dogs and cats.

- Aflatoxins in canned and dry food. Mold toxins are released from molds found on grains and legumes used in pet food. 60 to 80% of crops are infected by mycotoxins worldwide. They cause liver damage, seizures, cancer, and death. The toxins can be present even if there is no visible mold on the pet food; toxins survive cooking and heat processing. Grains are graded by quality; the lowest quality grains are used for pet food.

- Mold contamination. Improper storage and processing of food can result in mold growth. This can be seen in dry, canned, or refrigerated products.

- Bacterial contamination with Salmonella, E. coli, and Listeria. There are more recalls for bacterial contamination in dry kibble food than in raw food (68,000 tons of dry food compared to 900 tons of raw pet food between 2012 and 2019), even though the AVMA, AAHA, CDC, and FDA all warn against feeding raw pet food.
- Excess thyroid hormone. Pet food companies may use gullet meat from the throat which may also contain thyroid tissue. When the thyroid glands are not removed, active thyroid hormone is present in the food, causing symptoms of hyperthyroidism in pets (excessive thirst and urination, weight loss, increased appetite, restlessness, hyperactivity, elevated heart rate, rapid breathing, vomiting, and diarrhea). This has been found in dry kibble, canned food, raw food, and jerky treats.
- Plastic and metal pieces in food. Magnets are used in the pet food industry to pull metal out of the rough ingredients. The rumen (first stomach) of cows is notoriously filled with hardware and wire pieces, but metal can come from many sources.
- Insufficient thiamine. Thiamine (vitamin B1) is easily destroyed by food-processing techniques (up to 90% is destroyed). There have been at least five major pet food recalls involving nine brands of cat food. Symptoms include neurologic problems, blindness, weight loss, vomiting, and heart disease. Thiamine degrades during storage, with up to 57% loss within 6 months of storage of dry pet food, particularly when stored in open containers or in high heat.

Not only are recalls due to poor pet food quality an issue, but legal ingredients also allowed in pet food can cause chronic disease and cancer. These include:

- Carcinogenic (cancer-causing) preservatives. Ethoxyquin (not legally allowed to be added at the point of manufacture but can be added to meat or fish meal before arriving at the pet food plant and is therefore not listed on the pet food label), glyceryl monostearate, BHA (butylated hydroxyanisole), BHT (butylated hydroxytoluene), TBHQ (tertiary butylhydroquinone), propyl gallate, benzoic acid, sodium benzoate, sodium nitrate, and propylene glycol (banned in cat food because it causes anemia). Many of these are banned in Europe and Australia but are still used in the United States.
- Carcinogenic dyes. Blue dyes have been linked to brain and kidney tumors. Bladder tumors are associated with blue, red, and green dyes. Yellow dyes are linked to adrenal and testicular tumors. All dyes are associated with hypersensitivity reactions (allergies).
- Carrageenan comes from seaweed and is used as a thickener in moist foods. It can cause inflammation, lesions, ulcerations, and malignant tumors of the stomach and intestines.
- Rancid fats. Dry kibble pet food has minimal taste after extrusion and processing. Pet food companies make the food enticing by spraying "palatants" or flavor enhancers on the kibble. This can include generic animal fat which is a by-product of the rendering process and is a very low-quality fat. Storage for long periods, particularly in high heat in unsealed packaging, will result in rancid fats in the food.

Dogs given free-choice selection choose a diet with 50% protein, 45% fat, and 5% fiber. Cats choose a diet of 52% protein, 46% fat, and 2% fiber. Yet AAFCO has determined that the acceptable protein level for adult dog food is 18% and for adult cats is 26%. This is great for the pet food companies that prefer to use low-cost carbohydrates as fillers rather than having to use costly meats high in protein and fat, but at what cost to the dogs and cats eating those lower protein diets?

AAFCO also allows a fatty acid omega-6 to omega-3 ratio of 30:1. Ideal diets contain a ratio of 5:1. Omega-3 fatty acids have anti-inflammatory effects and are an essential component of the brain, eyes, skin, and joints. They support the cardiovascular system and endocrine system. Omega-3 fatty acids can help treat arthritis, chronic kidney disease, and heart disease. The three types of omega-3 fatty acids are:

- EPA (eicosapentaenoic acid) found in fish and marine products such as krill oil and algae

- DHA (docosahexaenoic acid) found in fish and marine products such as krill oil and algae

- ALA (alpha-linolenic acid) found in plant and nut oils

Omega-6 fatty acids are abundant in animal fat.

If feeding processed pet food is so bad, what can you do instead? The solution is a natural, species-appropriate diet free from artificial preservatives, added chemicals, and high-heat processing. There is good news for pet parents wanting to provide the best nutrition possible for their furry family members. Pet food is becoming increasingly like human food as most pet owners consider their pets to be part of the family. Over half of pet owners stated they want to feed fresh-made food in a Packaged Facts survey. Consumers are looking for pet food and treat options that are sustainable, traceable, and responsibly sourced. Fortunately, there are rising numbers of start-ups in the pet food sector, meaning more choices for high-quality products.

Each year, Susan Thixton, founder of Truth About Pet Food, compiles a list of trustworthy pet food companies using human-grade ingredients to prepare high-quality food. Pet food companies cannot buy their way onto the list; they must provide bills of lading for every ingredient they use as well as information about their handling and processing of food.

For those willing and able to make food for their pets, I have included recipes throughout the book for prevention and support of certain ailments. General guidelines when preparing food include:

- Meat in the recipes may be served raw or gently cooked. Practice safe food handling techniques including washing of hands before and after handling raw meat. After cutting raw meats, wash all surfaces with hot, soapy water.
- I recommend pre-portioning and freezing any extra food you don't plan to feed after 72 hours. Frozen food is best stored no longer than 3 months after freezing for optimal nutrition.
- All nuts, seeds, grains, tablet-based supplements, and produce used in the recipes should be finely chopped for better digestibility, bioavailability, and distribution. A food processor works great for this step!
- Fine powder supplements and oils should be thoroughly mixed into the recipe.
- Capsule ingredients should be opened for better distribution.
- Fish oils or other sources of omega 3 fatty acids should be added at the time of feeding or mixed into the food after cooking if meals are being gently cooked.
- Vegetables must be finely chopped, ground, or cooked for better nutrient absorption.
- Gently cooked means prepared on low heat in a slow

cooker, steamed, or baked at a low temperature (325 degrees Fahrenheit).

Nutritious Fresh Food Toppers

For those who do not want to prepare complete meals but would like to improve the nutritional content of their pet's diet, these super foods are great additions:

- Freshly caught wild fish or canned sardines in water—fish is loaded with naturally anti-inflammatory omega-3 fatty acids. Fish is also high in vitamin D, a fat-soluble vitamin that degrades quickly in processed food that is stored for long periods.

- Fresh berries—Blueberries and cranberries contain polyphenols which are powerful antioxidants that destroy inflammation-causing free radicals in the body. They can inhibit tumor growth, lower blood sugar, and decrease chronic inflammation. Anthocyanins in berries improve brain skills. Cranberries help prevent E. coli bacteria from sticking to the bladder wall, reducing urinary tract infections.

- Mushrooms—These are best served cooked, steamed or sauteed in coconut or olive oil. They contain antiviral, antibacterial, and antitumor properties. Mushrooms provide an excellent source of fiber as a prebiotic for good bacteria in the gut, improving the immune system. They help lower cholesterol and regulate blood sugar.

- Bone broth—This supports joint health and helps slow the progression of degenerative joint diseases. Rich in amino acids, it can also be used during recovery after illness or surgery. Bone broth helps heal leaky gut and decrease inflammation in the digestive tract.

- Dark leafy greens—These are rich in plant nutrients that are antioxidants and anti-inflammatory. They are high in calcium, iron, potassium, and vitamins A, C, and K. Greens are particularly useful for pets with liver disease or anemia.

- Eggs—These provide high quality protein and fat-soluble vitamins A, D, E, and K. One egg will supply about 75 calories.

- Grated ginger—Ginger fights cancer and relieves arthritis. It soothes the digestive system and decreases nausea. It can be used for motion sickness and nighttime tummy grumbles. Add 1/4 to 1 teaspoon, depending on the size of the pet.

- Pumpkin—This enhances immune health and strengthens the eyes. It is a great source of soluble and insoluble fiber which helps regulate bowel function.

- Raw local honey—Honey contains minute amounts of local pollen which can help desensitize against environmental allergens. Give 1/4 teaspoon per 20 pounds body weight daily. Honey is soothing to the throat and useful for treating a cough. Raw honey can be used topically to treat cuts and wounds (Manuka honey with high UMF factor).

- Turmeric—Curcumin is an active ingredient that is anti-oxidant, anti-inflammatory, antiviral, antibacterial, and antifungal. It is used to improve arthritis symptoms and to fight cancer. Absorption is enhanced when combined with black pepper, cinnamon, and coconut oil or bone broth to form Golden Paste.

GOLDEN PASTE

☐ 1 cup warm water

☐ 1/2 cup organic turmeric root powder

☐ 1/3 cup organic coconut oil OR 1/3 cup bone broth

☐ 1/2 tablespoon organic freshly ground black pepper

☐ 1 tablespoon organic Ceylon cinnamon

Place turmeric powder and water in a small saucepan on low heat on the stovetop. Stir until it forms a paste, usually about 5 minutes. Remove from heat and add the pepper and cinnamon, stirring to mix. Add the coconut oil or bone broth and stir well.

Store in an airtight container in the refrigerator and use within two weeks or freeze in ice cube trays. Mix 1/4 teaspoon for small dogs and cats up to 1 tablespoon for large dogs in each meal.

Homemade Meals for Pets

For those that enjoy spending time in the kitchen, recipes are provided throughout the book to support specific ailments or to maintain balance. Puploaf and Catloaf will support healthy adult dogs and cats for routine use.

HOMEMADE PUPLOAF

This is a balanced meal that can be fed to adult dogs. It is available commercially from Allprovide.com as gently cooked food.

- ☐ 1 pound 90% lean ground beef
- ☐ 4 ounces ground beef heart
- ☐ 3 ounces ground beef liver
- ☐ 8 ounces ground chicken or turkey gizzards
- ☐ 2 eggs ground with shell
- ☐ 4 ounces ground butternut squash
- ☐ 6 ounces ground vegetables including kale, spinach, broccoli, green beans, red pepper
- ☐ 3 ounces ground Shiitake mushrooms
- ☐ 2 ounces cranberries
- ☐ 1 teaspoon ground fresh ginger root
- ☐ 1 tablespoon flax seed oil
- ☐ 1 teaspoon kelp powder or 2 ounces of mussels
- ☐ 1 teaspoon sea salt
- ☐ 2 sardines, canned in water, should be added at the time of feeding as they smell bad when cooking.

Mix all ingredients together. May be fed raw or baked at 325 F for 30 to 45 minutes, depending on thickness and size of pan; should be lightly done, not over-cooked (juicy in the center). If your pet has a beef or chicken allergy, turkey or lean ground pork could be substituted.

Feed 2 to 3% of body weight per day, depending on activity level and size of dog (see recommended feeding chart). Food should be fed warm, not cold, from the refrigerator. Freeze any portion that will not be used within five days.

How much should you feed?

Dogs will consume an average of two to three percent of body weight per day, which converts to 20 to 30 calories per pound of body weight per day, depending on activity level, age, lifestyle, and breed. Larger breeds tend to need a lower percentage than smaller breeds with higher metabolism. Large dogs or inactive dogs may only need 1.5% of body weight fed daily.

Every pet is different. Feed based on ideal body weight, not the current body weight. Assess your pet with a critical eye at least once a week or weigh them to determine if there is too much weight gain or loss. Adjust the amount fed accordingly. Your pet should have a waist, meaning their underline tucks up behind the rib cage. You should be able to feel the ribs, not layers of fat over the ribs. Generally, people tend to keep pets too heavy. From a health standpoint, slightly underweight is healthier than slightly overweight.

RECOMMENDED FEEDING CHART

BODY WEIGHT		2% of BODY WEIGHT		3% of BODY WEIGHT	
<5 lb	<2.3 kg	1.6 ounces	45.4 grams	2.4 ounces	68.0 grams
5 lb	2.3 kg	1.6 ounces	45.4 grams	2.4 ounces	68.0 grams
10 lb	4.5 kg	3.2 ounces	90.7 grams	4.8 ounces	136.1 grams
15 lb	6.8 kg	4.8 ounces	136.1 grams	7.2 ounces	204.1 grams
20 lb	9.0 kg	6.4 ounces	181.4 grams	9.6 ounces	272.2 grams
25 lb	11.3 kg	8.0 ounces	226.8 grams	12.0 ounces	340.2 grams
30 lb	13.6 kg	9.6 ounces	272.2 grams	14.4 ounces	408.2 grams
35 lb	15.9 kg	11.2 ounces	317.5 grams	16.8 ounces	476.3 grams
40 lb	18.1 kg	12.8 ounces	362.9 grams	19.2 ounces	544.3 grams
45 lb	20.4 kg	14.4 ounces	408.2 grams	21.6 ounces	612.3 grams
50 lb	22.7 kg	16.0 ounces	453.6 grams	24.0 ounces	680.4 grams
55 lb	24.9 kg	17.6 ounces	499.0 grams	26.4 ounces	748.4 grams
60 lb	27.2 kg	19.2 ounces	544.3 grams	28.8 ounces	816.5 grams
65 lb	29.4 kg	20.8 ounces	589.7 grams	31.2 ounces	884.5 grams
70 lb	31.8 kg	22.4 ounces	635.0 grams	33.6 ounces	952.5 grams
75 lb	34.0 kg	24.0 ounces	680.4 grams	36.0 ounces	1020.6 grams
80 lb	36.3 kg	25.6 ounces	725.7 grams	38.4 ounces	1088.6 grams
85 lb	38.6 kg	27.2 ounces	771.1 grams	40.8 ounces	1156.7 grams
90 lb	40.8 kg	28.8 ounces	816.5 grams	43.2 ounces	1224.7 grams
95 lb	43.1 kg	30.4 ounces	861.8 grams	45.6 ounces	1292.7 grams
100 lb	45.3 kg	32.0 ounces	907.2 grams	48.0 ounces	1360.8 grams

DOG BODY CONDITION SCORE

THIN or FIT or FAT

1. VERY THIN
Very thin with ribs and pelvis prominent.

3. UNDER-WEIGHT
Below ideal weight with ribs and waist visible.

5. FIT
Good condition, can feel ribs, and has a waist.

7. OVER-WEIGHT
Above ideal weight, ribs hard to feel, no obvious waist visible.

9. VERY FAT
Very overweight with rolls of fat and large abdomen.

HOMEMADE CATLOAF

This is a balanced meal that can be fed to adult cats. This recipe provides 39 calories per ounce.

- ☐ 9 ounces chicken legs with skin and bone (use bone if feeding raw, remove bone and use meat and skin if lightly cooking or finely grind the bone so there are no sharp pieces)
- ☐ 6 ounces chicken hearts
- ☐ 4 eggs
- ☐ 5 ounces pork muscle meat 95% lean
- ☐ 4 ounces chicken liver
- ☐ 3 ounces mussels
- ☐ 2 ounces butternut squash ground or finely chopped
- ☐ 3 teaspoons flaxseed oil
- ☐ 2 teaspoons ground turmeric

If not using bone, add 1 tsp finely ground eggshell or organic eggshell powder for calcium requirements. An average 10-pound cat will eat 5 to 7 ounces per day, depending on activity level. Food should be served warm, not cold out of the refrigerator. Food can be stored in the refrigerator for up to four days; freeze in small portions any food that cannot be fed within that time.

How much should you feed?

There is no one-size-fits-all for feeding. Each cat is an individual with their own unique needs. Therefore, feeding amounts could vary as much as 50% above or below average. Less active adult and senior cats average about 20 calories per pound (45 calories per kilogram) of body weight per day. Active cats may need 30 to 35 calories per pound of body weight.

CAT BODY CONDITION SCORE

THIN or FIT or FAT

1.	VERY THIN	Very thin with ribs and pelvis prominent.
3.	UNDER-WEIGHT	Below ideal weight with ribs and waist visible.
5.	FIT	Good condition, can feel ribs, and has a waist.
7.	OVER-WEIGHT	Above ideal weight, ribs hard to feel, no obvious waist visible.
9.	VERY FAT	Very overweight with rolls of fat and large abdomen.

Feed based on ideal body weight, not the current body weight. Assess your pet with a critical eye at least once a week or weigh them to determine if there is too much weight gain or loss. Adjust the amount fed accordingly. Your pet should have a waist, meaning their underline tucks up behind the rib cage. You should be able to feel the ribs, not layers of fat over the ribs. Generally, people tend to keep pets too heavy. From a health standpoint, slightly underweight is healthier than slightly overweight.

Preparation and Storage of Food

My personal philosophy is that there is no "best" diet for all dogs or cats. Each has different requirements depending on breed, age, health, and lifestyle. My own pets eat a high-meat diet with added organs, vegetables, and fruit. The only dairy I use is raw fermented goat milk. My proportions lead toward 70 to 80 percent meat/bone/organs with 20 to 30 percent non-starchy vegetables and fruits for my dogs. Cats are fed less vegetables, generally only five to 7 percent of the diet.

Some pet owners add cooked grains or starchy vegetables to decrease costs or add bulk to the meal, while some pets require the addition of carbohydrates to the meal to decrease protein for specific medical indications or to maintain weight. I commonly use low-glycemic vegetables as a fiber source to feed gut bacteria.

Whether you choose to feed raw or gently cooked food is up to you. Some pets will have a preference. Either way, food should always be warmed at least to room temperature when fed. Cooked meals can be baked at low temperatures (325 F or lower) or prepared in a slow cooker, which uses lower temperatures and maintains moisture in the meal. Cooked bones should never be fed unless they have been ground to a very fine consistency.

Do not become complacent, feeding the same food over and over. Pets thrive on rotation, and it helps avoid having micro deficiencies or excesses that will create medical problems over time.

TOXIC FOODS

FOODS THAT MAY BE TOXIC TO YOUR PETS

Chocolate - Contains theobromine which can cause hyperactivity, seizures, tremors, irregular heartbeat, death

Macadamia Nuts - May cause vomiting, weakness, tremors, drunken walk, death

Grapes & Raisins - May cause vomiting, diarrhea, kidney failure, death; not all dogs are susceptible

Apricot, Peach, Cherry, Plum Pits - Contains cyanide; causes vomiting, shock, cardiac arrest, death

Onions/Scallions - Causes hemolytic anemia, vomiting, diarrhea, bloody urine; effects of eating onions are cumulative

Green Tomatoes, Tomato Vines, & Leaves - Causes vomiting, diarrhea, seizure

Raw & Green Potatoes - Causes vomiting, diarrhea, seizures, heart arrhythmias

Rhubarb - Causes tremors, seizures, heart arrhythmias, kidney disease, high in oxalates

Nutmeg - Causes tremors, muscle spasms, seizures, death

Persimmon Seeds - Causes vomiting, diarrhea, fever

Raw Dough or Yeast - Produces ethanol, causes liver failure, seizures, drunken gait, coma, death

Alcohol - Causes depression, weakness, liver failure, coma, death

Raw Salmon or Trout - Can carry parasites that causes salmon poisoning. Canned, frozen, or cooked is okay.

Avocado Peel - Causes vomiting, diarrhea, fluid accumulation

5 Allergies

Allergies are one of the foremost reasons pets are presented for veterinary care. Allergies are also one of the most frustrating problems for pet owners. Relentless scratching, ear infections, and skin infections are annoying as well as costly to treat. Pets suffering with allergies can lose weight from the constant motion of scratching and rubbing. Sometimes they smell so horrible it's difficult to stay in the same room with them. No one wants to pet their greasy, thickened, flaking skin.

Symptoms of allergies include itching, hives or bumps on the skin, red inflamed skin, swelling of the face, ears, lips, eyelids, or ear flaps, vomiting, diarrhea, sneezing, runny eyes, ear infections, constant licking, paw biting, poor coat quality, obsessive licking, hair loss, thickened skin, darkened skin, skin infections, scooting, and hot spots.

The skin is the largest organ in the body, providing protective covering against foreign invaders. The skin is normally covered in bacteria, fungal organisms, and viruses which form the microbiome; these healthy microorganisms play a role in defense against invading pathogens (the bad guys). Studies comparing healthy and allergic dogs and cats found that the two groups had varying levels of bacterial diversity. Healthy pets had *more* bacterial diversity than allergic individuals. The more diversity, the less infection occurs from pathogenic bacteria like *Staphylococcus pseudointermedius.*

Not only does alteration of the skin microbiome allow growth of pathogenic bacteria, it also has been associated with mast cell tumor growth.

Unfortunately, traditional treatments for allergic dermatitis (skin inflammation) destroy the skin microbiome. Antibiotics kill the pathogenic bacteria, but also kill the beneficial bacteria. At first, the bacterial skin infections will respond to antibiotics, but then return as soon as the antibiotics are discontinued. Over time, the bacteria become resistant and difficult to eradicate.

Antibiotics

Side effects from antibiotics can be more dangerous than just alteration of the microbiome. Some of these reactions include:

- Liver or kidney failure—tetracyclines, erythromycin, gentamycin, sulfa drugs
- Potassium deficiency
- Nutritional deficiencies—inhibit availability of Vitamins A and B, magnesium, zinc, and folic acid
- Hair loss—tetracyclines
- Light sensitivity—tetracyclines
- Anemia—sulfa drugs
- Joint pain and swelling—sulfa drugs
- Leaky gut syndrome—all
- Damage to teeth—tetracyclines
- Kidney failure—amikacin
- Bone marrow suppression—chloramphenicol, metronidazole
- Deafness—gentamycin, amikacin
- Destruction of the microbiome—all
- Allergies—cephalosporins
- Vomiting, diarrhea, anorexia—clavamox, doxycycline
- Cartilage destruction—enrofloxacin

- **ANTIBIOTIC RESISTANCE**
- Allergic reaction, anaphylaxis, collapse, trouble breathing
- Neurologic side effects, seizures—metronidazole, amino-glycosides, sulfa drugs
- Yeast infections

Alternatives to antibiotics can include:

- Diluted oil of oregano
- Manuka honey with high UMF
- Colloidal silver
- Olive leaf
- Essential oils
- Garlic
- Plantain, Goldenseal, Yarrow, Calendula, Turmeric
- Cranberry, D-mannose for urinary tract problems
- Immune support—mushrooms, herbs, probiotics
- Localized treatment vs. oral treatment

Harsh shampoos with detergents, antibacterial and antifungal ingredients, and chemicals strip the skin and coat of natural oils and the organisms that live there. Instead of using therapies that destroy the skin microbiome, treatment regimens should target normalizing the microbiome and restoring the skin barrier function.

Allergies can be caused by inhaled allergens like dust, mold, pollen, and even humans and other animals. Seasonal allergies are common and will be present only for certain periods of the year when the offending plant or tree is shedding pollen.

Conditions that may mimic allergic skin disease include endocrine disease, particularly in dogs. Dogs with hypothyroidism and Cushing's disease are prone to repeat skin infections. Blood testing should be performed to rule out these diseases if allergies suddenly seem to arise in older dogs. Neurologic conditions that lead to scratching may also be confused with allergies, particularly in brachycephalic (short-nosed) breeds prone to diseases such as syringomyelia and caudal occipital malformation syndrome.

Fleas and Flea Allergic Dermatitis

Flea allergy dermatitis is the most common cause of allergic dermatitis, where the pet is having a reaction to the saliva of the flea. One or two bites will result in itching for weeks. Always check for fleas and flea dirt with a flea comb if there is any suspicion. Flea dirt contains the eggs and poop of fleas; it looks like salt and pepper. Treatment for flea allergy dermatitis means ridding both your pet and the environment of all fleas but do this without the use of harsh chemicals! Only five percent of the flea life cycle is spent on the pet which means 95% of the life cycle is lived in the environment. Focus on the environment!

Giving your pet oral chemical pesticides will not prevent them from developing flea allergic dermatitis, as most chemicals do not repel fleas. The flea dies after ingesting the pesticide during a blood meal. Most topical pesticides do not repel either; the flea dies hours after contacting the chemical which means it has plenty of time to bite and consume a blood meal.

I prefer natural prevention for my pets. High quality essential oils made specifically for pets have worked well for my patients in the past. Be careful when applying essential oils; remember that your pet's sense of smell is much stronger than yours. Apply oils in a well-ventilated area and never spray around the pet's face. Do not use oils that are not specifically labeled for use on animals. Essential oils will help repel fleas.

Cedar oil has worked well for many of my clients. It is available for use on pets or in the environment. Not everyone likes the smell of cedar; there are many other essential oil products available. Essential oils will also repel mosquitoes. Lavender oil has been shown to repel ticks, while lemongrass oil seems to work particularly well against fleas. Peppermint oil will affect the nervous system of fleas and ticks without harming your pet. Many people use rose geranium oil and find it works well. Neem oil has been around forever and is another favorite. Rose geranium oil is safe to use full strength directly on the pet, but you will only need to apply one drop behind each shoulder blade and one drop near the base of the tail. Other oils should be diluted before applying to pets. Essential oils can be diluted in extra virgin olive oil or water and rubbed throughout the coat. They can also be diluted by putting a few drops in your favorite pet shampoo or conditioner. A bandanna with a few drops of diluted essential oil can also be used as a natural flea collar. Make sure the smell is not overwhelming, as this will be close to your dog's nose. If using essential oils on cats, be certain they are labeled for use on cats.

Coconut oil kills and repels fleas due to the ingredient lauric acid. Coconut oil can be rubbed through the coat and can be fed to the pets. I use 1 teaspoon per 20 pounds of body weight twice daily in the food. Coconut oil melts at 76 degrees, so rubbing it between your hands will make it into a liquid that you can rub through your pet's coat. It moisturizes skin and helps kill yeast too.

Another great option is garlic for dogs and cats. I have used this in the past in my barn for the horses. We still had flies, but the horses eating it were bothered a lot less than the horses that were not. A lot of people claim dogs and cats will die when fed garlic, but that simply is not true. Fresh crushed garlic can also be added to your pet's diet for flea protection. Anywhere from 1/2 clove to 2 cloves daily would be considered safe, depending on the size of the dog. A good rule of thumb would be no more than 1/2 clove per 20 pounds of body weight daily, with a maximum of 2 cloves for any size dog. Cats can be given 1/2 a small clove three times a week. However, if you have a pet that has a history of hemolytic anemia, it would be safer to avoid the use of garlic in any form.

I do not recommend using Brewer's Yeast tablets for flea prevention. Brewer's yeast basically contains B vitamins, but they are processed and degraded. B vitamins supplied naturally through a healthy diet will be more effective.

Beneficial nematodes can be used to kill flea larvae in your yard. Remember, the squirrels, rabbits, mice, and other small critters outside can be harbingers of fleas. Nematodes will not survive in hot, sunny areas of the lawn, but the fleas do not like those areas either. So spread these little guys in the shady, moist areas where the fleas are most likely to be found.

Food-grade diatomaceous earth can be sprinkled in the environment or on the pet. Be careful when using it, as you do not want your pet to inhale the dust. DE works by dehydrating the fleas and ticks; it will also be drying to your pet's coat. I prefer to use essential oil sprays made specifically for dogs or cats on the pet and use DE in the environment.

Many people claim vinegar works well. It can be added to the drinking water at the rate of 1 teaspoon per quart of water. We used to make a mixture of white vinegar and Skin So Soft to use on our horses. They had shiny coats and smelled great! Vinegar can also be diluted in water in a 1:1 mixture and sprayed on the coat.

Do not forget the old-fashioned flea comb. The teeth are very close together and will remove fleas and flea eggs. Put the fleas in a bowl of dish soap as you remove them, as this will kill them. These are particularly good for cats because it is a lot harder to bathe a cat. Comb your pets daily if you have any evidence of flea activity.

Vacuum. A lot. Vacuuming will help remove the fleas, eggs, and larvae in the environment. Be sure to get in the corners, under the furniture, and in the crevices under the sofa cushions if your pet sleeps on the furniture. Wash pet bedding often in hot water. More information can be found on flea treatment and prevention options at www.drjudymorgan.com.

Canine Atopic Dermatitis

A study from Finland found identifiable dietary, genetic, and environmental factors that play a role in development of canine atopic dermatitis—a fancy name for allergies that cause skin disease, inflammation, and itching in dogs. A total of 2,236 dogs were included in the study, which began in 2009. Canine atopic dermatitis is considered an incurable inflammatory and allergic skin disease in dogs, affecting up to 10% of the dog population with usual onset of symptoms between one and three years of age.

There is a genetic component to canine atopic dermatitis which can be passed down from either parent, with the most frequently affected breeds reported to be West Highland White Terriers, Boxers, English Bulldogs, Dalmations, Golden Retrievers, French Bulldogs, Bull Terriers, German Shepherds, and English Springer Spaniels. I would add American Bulldogs to this list.

The Finnish study looked at factors affecting prenatal and early postnatal development of the immune system to determine potential risk factors in addition to genetic factors. Their findings support what I have found to be true in daily practice; many findings matched similar risk factors in children. Early nutritional and environmental exposures are crucial for the programming of the immune system and therefore predisposition to allergy later in life.

Factors that contributed to development of canine atopic dermatitis included:

- Maternal history of canine atopic dermatitis (one study showed up to 65% of offspring will develop allergies if one or both parents suffered with allergies, while healthy parents gave rise to only 11% of pups developing allergies).

- Dogs with greater than 50% white-colored coat were at high risk of developing allergies.

- Pups delivered to mothers that were fed non-processed meat diets (raw diets or home-made meat-based diets) resulted in lower risk of developing allergies than pups whose mothers were fed ultra-processed carbohydrate-based diets (dry kibble). Heat processing of food causes denaturation of food proteins, which promotes immunogenicity and allergenicity. Dogs fed non-processed meat diets have been shown to have a greater variety of microbial populations in the gut, leading to stronger immune function.

- Maternal deworming during pregnancy resulted in less allergies in the pups. Worm infection of the mother during pregnancy has been reported to have a long-lasting impact on the fetal immune system development and disease development later in life.

- Pups started on a non-processed meat diet as their first food had a lower risk of developing canine atopic dermatitis than pups feed ultra-processed carbohydrate diets (kibble). Improved microbial populations in the gut of raw-fed puppies stimulate immune tolerance development, protecting against allergies later in life.

- Pups with sunlight exposure for one or more hours per day during the first one to two months of age showed a significantly lower risk of developing allergies.

- Pups exposed to grass and dirt in the first two months also showed lower risk of developing allergies. Pups house totally indoors in urban environments developed significantly more allergies.

This study adds good evidence to what veterinarians see in daily practice. Dogs with canine atopic dermatitis should be removed from breeding programs. Feeding meat-based, non-processed diets during pregnancy and at weaning can help populate the gut with microbial diversity that will lead to a stronger immune system. Playing outside is important in the early development of the immune system as well. While this study looked only at dogs, the same parameters should apply to cats suffering with allergies (this is less common in cats overall).

Traditional Treatments for Allergies

Traditional treatments used in veterinary practice to treat allergies rarely cure the problem. They are aimed at diminishing symptoms, not resolving the root cause. Immune suppression is the basis for most treatments. Drugs that are used and their side effects can include:

- Steroids: Undesirable side effects include increased thirst and urination, vomiting, diarrhea, aggression, panting, diabetes, liver disease, Cushing's disease, blood clots, pancreatitis, stomach ulceration, immune suppression, poor wound healing, and infections. Steroids should not be used in patients with diabetes, seizures, congestive heart failure, high blood pressure, kidney failure, stomach or duodenal ulcers, or if infected with the herpes virus (cats). Long-acting steroid injections are particularly problematic (Depo-medrol).

- Antihistamines: Side effects include dry mouth, dizziness, restlessness, lethargy, and nausea. They can cause trouble with urination and heart arrhythmias. Antihistamines should not be used in patients with heart disease, high blood pressure, thyroid disease, kidney disease, liver disease, or glaucoma.

- Cyclosporine (Atopica): Side effects include vomiting, diarrhea, lack of appetite, anaphylactic allergic reaction, shock, liver failure, bone marrow suppression, kidney disease, tremors, seizures, immune suppression, infections, poor wound healing, viral papilloma formation, cancer, and uncontrolled *Demodex* infection (mites). It is unsafe for use in pets under six months old or who have infections, cancer, or kidney disease. Not to be used in breeding or pregnant animals. Do not give vaccines while on this drug. This drug also interacts with other common medications including antibiotics, antifungals, antacids, cardiac drugs, and antiseizure medications.

- Oclacitinib (Apoquel): FDA approval only for dogs but has been used off-label in cats. Side effects include vomiting, diarrhea, anorexia, behavior changes, aggression, hyperreactivity, liver failure, bone marrow suppression, seizures, immune suppression, infections, poor wound healing, viral papilloma formation, and uncontrolled *Demodex* infection. Unsafe for dogs under twelve months ole or who have infections or cancer. Likely to predispose the pet to cancer development.

- Cytopoint injection: This only works 60 to 70 percent of the time and usually stops working after a few injections as the body will make antibodies against the active ingredient. Side effects include vomiting, diarrhea, lethargy, behavior changes, hyperexcitability, urinary incontinence, immune suppression, immune-mediated hemolytic anemia, liver damage, clotting disorders, anaphylactic reactions, and shock. It should not be used for small dogs under 8 pounds or dogs used for breeding or who are pregnant.

- Hydrolyzed diets: These prescription diets have limited ingredients or hydrolyzed proteins (proteins that have been broken down into smaller particles). These diets are not made for long-term use and do not provide proper nutrition for growing pets. They always contain a long list of synthetic vitamins and minerals and questionable ingredients like canola oil, soy, carrageenan, and brewer's rice. They are exorbitantly expensive.

The Root Cause of Many Allergies

If all the traditional treatments are so toxic, what can be done to alleviate the suffering associated with allergies? Unfortunately, in traditional medicine, much focus is put on suppressing symptoms and treating the skin, but there is another underlying problem that must be addressed to help combat the disease.

Pets with allergies not only show an imbalance in the skin microbiome, but also show an imbalance in the gut microbiome. There are many tests available to analyze the distribution of bacteria within the gut that will show just how out of balance the microbiome has become. Repairing the microbiome can take a considerable amount of time. Fecal transplants are becoming more common; a healthy fecal sample is fed or instilled into the bowel of the pet that has microbiome dysbiosis (out of balance) to replace the missing microbes. This does not even require a veterinary visit as fecal transplant capsules are now available.

In addition to repairing the microbiome, inflammation in the gut must also be repaired. Up to 90% of immune system function lies within the gut. *Leaky gut* is a term that describes the results of bowel inflammation. In a healthy pet, the intestinal walls serve as a barrier, keeping foreign materials such as bacteria, toxins, and food particles out of the body's circulation. When food is eaten and broken down, only small nutrient particles are absorbed into the bloodstream. In a pet with leaky gut, the barrier function of the intestines is compromised due to inflammation and swelling, allowing larger particles and microbes to cross the intestinal walls and enter the body's circulation.

Leaky gut syndrome can be caused by any insult to the intestines such as infection, trauma to the abdomen, exposure to toxins, over-vaccination, stress, mycotoxins, poor diet, and use of medications. Gastrointestinal signs may include vomiting, flatulence, soft stools, or weight loss, but they do not always occur. Leaky gut syndrome is associated with inflammatory bowel disease, arthritis, allergic skin disease, hepatitis (liver inflammation), pancreatitis, cancer, and behavioral issues including aggression. These diseases all have inflammation as the common denominator.

Alternative Treatment Options

First and foremost, if feeding dry kibble, switch to a species-appropriate diet (this will be a recurring theme throughout the book). True food allergies are not very common, but some pets will do better on certain proteins. Food sensitivities or intolerances can occur over time. This is not a true "allergy" but can cause similar symptoms of ear infections, itching, redness, and paw-licking.

When trying to determine if food is a contributing factor, it is best to switch to a novel protein—one to which the pet has never been exposed. The most common ingredients in pet food are chicken, beef, peas, corn, rice, and potatoes. Years ago, lamb was considered a novel ingredient, but it has become widely used.

Novel proteins now include rabbit, duck, alligator, emu, kangaroo, goat, and quail. If you cannot switch away from feeding kibble, be sure to read the complete ingredient list, as a novel protein may be listed first, but a common ingredient may be listed further down.

Many allergic pets will react to the synthetic vitamin and mineral ingredients added to pet food to make it balanced. This is why I prefer to feed whole foods without synthetic additives. It may be difficult to find commercial foods with novel ingredients that do not contain synthetic additives, which is why many pet owners turn to preparing food for their pets.

Discontinue all medications, if possible. Medications should never be stopped without consulting with your veterinarian, as doing so may cause severe issues for your pet. If your pet has been on immune-suppressant drugs, stopping them quickly can have deadly consequences; many may need to be slowly eliminated.

Provide a diet that contains healthy fiber, as fiber is the food (prebiotic) for the beneficial bacteria in the gut microbiome. Fiber can be provided using non-starchy, dark leafy greens, pumpkin, flaxseed, inulin, or apple pectin. Probiotics (beneficial bacteria) can be added to the diet to repopulate the gut. I am a big fan of soil-based products that also contain fulvic and humic acids. Look for products with a very high (in the billions) CFU count (colony forming units) that do not include poor-quality inactive ingredients such as Animal Digest or rice bran.

There are many supplements that can help repair gut damage and alleviate allergy symptoms. Choose one or two to try; do not give all of them at the same time. These are not meant for long-term use. Commercial preparations may include a combination of a few ingredients. Dosages may vary when using commercial products; most herbs are very safe when high quality products are used so exact dosing is not critical. Some to look for include:

- L-Glutamine—This is an amino acid that nourishes the cells lining the gut wall, helping with their growth and repair. It is found naturally in spirulina, broccoli, and asparagus. It can be dosed at 20 mg per pound of body weight per day for both dogs and cats.
- N-Acetyl Glucosamine—This form of glucosamine comes from shellfish and can also be found in bone broth. While normally used to support joint health, it also promotes growth and healing of the gut lining. Dose at 15 mg per pound of body weight per day for dogs and cats.
- Licorice root—This is an anti-inflammatory herb. It also helps nourish intestinal cells. It should be given in the deglycyrrhized form. Licorice root tea can be given at 1/2 teaspoon for small dogs and cats up to 2 teaspoons for large dogs once or twice daily. Dried herb powder can be given at 20 to 60 mg per pound three times daily.
- Aloe Vera Juice—This juice (must be from the gel of the inner leaves) promotes tissue and cell regeneration and is anti-inflammatory. It can also form a coating to protect the cells of the gastrointestinal tract. Dose at 1 to 4 teaspoons daily, depending on size of the pet. Do not use aloe vera for more than one to two weeks.
- Slippery Elm—This makes a coating that lines the intestines to protect them and decrease inflammation. The dose is 10 mg per pound of body weight two to four times daily. The powder can be mixed with water to make a sludge that can be mixed with a small amount of food. Medications should be given 1 to 2 hours before a dose of slippery elm, since the mucilaginous coating it creates can inhibit their absorption. Slippery elm paste (powder mixed with cold water) can also be used as a poultice for hot spots and rashes.

- Marshmallow root—This herb provides relief from inflammation and irritation in the digestive tract. It encourages healthy growth of intestinal microflora while lubricating and soothing inflamed mucous membranes in the intestines by creating a coating like the properties of Slippery Elm. This is best fed between meals as a tea but can be added to meals at a dose of 1/4 teaspoon for cats and small dogs up to one teaspoon for large dogs two to three times daily.
- Chamomile flowers—This herb fights inflammation, expels gas, is antispasmodic, expels worms, and stimulates digestion. Be sure to purchase chamomile in forms specifically made for pets, as it can be toxic. Avoid use in pregnant animals. It can also be used as a topical ointment or poultice by mixing with coconut oil or shea butter. Dried herbs should be dosed at 50 mg per pound of body weight up to three times daily or 2 drops per pound of body weight of an alcohol tincture up to three times daily.
- Ginger root—Warms the digestive tract, excellent for nausea and digestive upset. Dose is 25 to 35 mg of fresh grated root per pound of body weight twice daily. It can be mixed with food.
- Quercetin—Quercetin is a natural antihistamine. 5 to 10 mg per pound of body weight can be given twice daily. Quercetin is found naturally in blueberries, apple skin, and parsley. Quercetin is often combined with Bromelain.
- Curcumin (turmeric root)—This is a potent anti-inflammatory and stimulates circulation and digestion. Dose at 1/8th to 1/4 teaspoon dry powder per ten pounds of body weight twice daily mixed in food. It can also be given as

Golden Paste: 1/4 teaspoon for cats and small dogs up to one tablespoon for large dogs twice daily.

- Milk thistle—This boosts the ability of liver cells to filter toxins from the blood and decreases allergic response. The dose is 5 mg per pound twice daily.
- Nettles—can be used as dried whole herb, tea, or tincture to help itchy dogs.
- Dandelion root and leaves can help flush toxins and allergens from the body.
- Red clover—used for lymphatic drainage. It helps flush allergens from the body.
- Digestive enzymes—These can be plant or animal origin. Enzymes help the body to correctly digest food. Adding beef or pork pancreas is also an option.
- Mushrooms—Reishi is the preferred mushroom to combat allergies and support the digestive system. Chaga is also effective for digestive support. Both also support the immune system. Mushrooms are a great source of prebiotic fiber. The mushrooms can be gently sauteed in olive or coconut oil and added to the diet or can be given as an extract in powder form at 100 mg per ten pounds body weight per day.
- Colostrum—Colostrum contains over 90 immune factors; it improves allergy symptoms by inhibiting immune cells that cause allergic reactions. It is also anti-inflammatory and can reduce histamine levels. Give 1/8th teaspoon per 25 pounds body weight twice daily.
- Omega-3 fatty acids—High-quality fish, krill, or algae oil can calm inflammation. Give 100 mg of EPA and DHA combined for every 10 pounds body weight per day. One sardine contains approximately 100 mg of EPA/DHA.

Topical Treatment for Allergic Dermatitis

As stated earlier, it is important to re-establish a healthy skin microbiome. Shampoos used for bathing should not contain harmful chemicals including:

- Artificial colors—synthesized from petroleum and linked to organ damage and cancer, as well as allergic reactions.
- Artificial fragrances—synthetic ingredients that have been linked to cancer.
- Phthalates (may be labeled as "fragrance")—these are hormone disruptors.
- Preservatives—hydantoin, urea, isothiazolinones, quaternium chemicals, parabens which are associated with allergic reactions, cancer, and reproductive issues
- Surfactants—cocamide-MEA and triethanolamine, sodium lauryl sulfate, laureth sulfate, stearalkonium chloride; these are thought to carcinogenic and strip the oils from the coat and skin.
- SD alcohol 40 or SD-40—Alcohol dries the skin and burns when it contacts open abrasions.
- Humectants—PEG or polyethylene glycol, propylene glycol; skin irritant, drying.
- Chlorhexidine—antibacterial that destroys the skin microbiome, irritant.

Do not use human shampoos (including baby shampoo) on your pet. Look for shampoos made with coconut oil, olive oil, Jojoba oil, shea butter, aloe vera, apple cider vinegar, and pet-safe essential oils. Always check the label to make sure the shampoo is safe for cats as some dog-safe shampoos are not safe for bathing kitties. Do not bathe excessively.

Another option is a Thera-Clean or microbubble bath which

is available at many grooming salons. Microbubble cleansing was developed in Japan and researched at the University of Tokyo. The system produces millions of tiny bubbles that carry oxygen and negative ions that gently remove trapped dirt, bacteria, yeast, and allergens from the coat and hair follicles without soaps, chemicals, or abrasives. Because the microbubble system gets into the hair follicles it can be very effective at eliminating *Demodex* mite infestations.

Topical creams or salves should not contain petroleum-based ingredients or chemical preservatives, dyes, or fragrances (see the list under shampoo ingredients to avoid). Coconut oil by itself can be very soothing and has antibacterial properties against pathogenic bacteria. Essential oils, beeswax, Carnauba wax, Manuka honey, and herbs may be included in high quality products.

If your pet develops a hot spot or oozing sore, do not use alcohol or peroxide to clean the wound. Clip hair away from the area and flush with saline solution. Alcohol burns and peroxide kills healthy cells, delaying healing and leading to more infection.

HOMEMADE SALINE SOLUTION

☐ 1 cup boiling water

☐ 1/2 teaspoon sea salt

☐ Mix ingredients together and stir to dissolve; allow to cool. Make a fresh solution each time you need it.

Ear Infections Related to Allergies

There are basically two kinds of infections that are commonly seen in ears: yeast or bacteria. It is imperative to determine what kind of infection is present, so you know how to treat the problem. Your veterinarian should always perform cytology, looking at a stained slide under the microscope using some of the debris from the ear canal. This can determine whether yeast or bacteria make up most of the infection and can also indicate if there are multiple agents present.

Most common symptoms include scratching or rubbing the ears, foul odor coming from the ears, redness, heat, and pain. Some pets may shy away when you try to pet their head, others may yelp or try to bite when the ears are touched. Long-eared dogs like spaniels tend to be more prone to ear infections than dogs with upright ears, as there is little air circulation in the ear canals of the floppy-eared dogs. Bacteria and yeast grow well in warm, dark, moist environments—just like the ear canal.

A healthy pet with no allergy problems should have minimal problems with ear infections. Getting water in the ears can lead to bacterial infections; this is commonly seen with dogs that swim a lot or after grooming or bathing if water enters the ear canals. Applying a dropper of witch hazel before and after swimming and bathing will dry any moisture in the ear canal. Bacterial infections most commonly show up as yellow or green discharge from the ears that looks like pus, with a very foul odor and significant pain. If bacteria are present, a culture and sensitivity should be sent to the lab to determine which antibiotic would be best to treat the infection.

Yeast infections, on the other hand, tend to have a brown or dark gold greasy discharge (seen in the photo above). The yeast is usually described as smelling like "corn chips" or "Fritos". These infections may not be quite as painful but do seem to cause more scratching. Yeast and bacteria are always present in the ears and on the skin as the natural microbiome. When there is a yeast overgrowth, the body is not able to deal with the infection. Many pets will develop an allergy to the yeast, causing more itching, swelling, and pain.

Chronic yeast infections are commonly associated with food intolerance, particularly protein intolerance (proteins are not found just in meats; grains and legumes also provide significant levels of protein). Yeast feeds on sugar; sugar is a breakdown product of carbohydrates. Diets high in carbohydrates will feed the yeast overgrowth. By changing the diet from a high-carbohydrate product (i.e.- dry kibble) to a more species-appropriate, meat-based diet, many pets will show significant improvement in chronic yeast infections. Foods that contain sugar, dextrose, high fructose corn syrup, honey, maltodextrin, white potatoes, sweet potatoes, grains, peas, chickpeas, and lentils provide a growth source for the yeast. Anti-fungal additions to the diet such as oregano, garlic, calendula, spearmint, and turmeric may help your pet fight the yeast. If your pet is not able to fight off the yeast infections with changes in diet, bathing, and ear cleaning, the immune system needs to be strengthened.

Careful cleaning of the external ear canals to remove debris should be performed when there is a lot of discharge. Never use cotton swabs in the ear canal. Daily cleaning can be very painful, and many pets will not allow cleaning until the infection has diminished. Medications should not be applied directly after cleaning, as cleaning agents may interfere with active ingredients in the medicated drops. All hair should be shaved surrounding the ear canal to allow air flow.

A drying agent should be used to flush the ears after cleaning. I recommend never using cleaning agents that contain dyes or fragrances, water, or peroxide. Peroxide breaks down into hydrogen (the bubbles) and water. Cleaning with water leaves water in the ear canal, which sets up the scenario for more infection.

Most infections can be cleared quickly with careful cleaning and appropriate treatment, along with a diet change if yeast is the predominant problem. Ear infections that are not treated for long periods of time will result in swollen ear canals that may develop calcified scar tissue, diminished hearing, and possibly rupture of the ear drum. The sooner an infection is treated, the better the chance for recovery.

Natural products that I have found to be helpful may contain enzymes, witch hazel, essential oils, colloidal silver, and aloe vera.

For those with pets that suffer with allergies, improving the diet, bathing with natural products to soothe the skin, adding supplements to decrease inflammation, and restoring gut health may help. I do not recommend using drugs that harm the immune system.

Allergies are frustrating to live with, frustrating to treat, and often lead to euthanasia or surrender of affected dogs. Don't give up but be realistic in your expectations. Many pets will improve significantly with changes in diet and supplements, but some will suffer with lifelong outbreaks.

SAMPLE RECIPES FOR NOVEL PROTEIN DIETS

Canine recipe for adult dog:

- ☐ 16 ounces 95% lean rabbit
- ☐ 2 ounces duck liver
- ☐ 2 ounces dandelion greens finely chopped
- ☐ 1/2 teaspoon kelp powder
- ☐ 100 IU vitamin E

- ☐ 300 IU vitamin D
- ☐ 1 teaspoon eggshell powder
- ☐ 1 teaspoon turmeric
- ☐ 1 capsule 15 mg zinc

This recipe provides 36 calories per ounce of food. This is a low-fat diet. Supplement with omega-3 fatty acids at the time of feeding. It may be served gently cooked or raw. See chapter 4 for feeding guidelines.

FELINE RECIPE FOR ADULT CAT:

- ☐ 13 ounces duck gizzard
- ☐ 7.5 ounces duck liver
- ☐ 2.5 ounces dandelion greens finely chopped
- ☐ ¾ teaspoon eggshell powder
- ☐ 1/2 teaspoon kelp powder

This may be served gently cooked or raw. Provides 25 calories per ounce. See chapter 4 for feeding guidelines.

6 Autoimmune Disease

Autoimmune disease occurs when the immune system reacts against the body. It sees a part of the body as "foreign" and attacks those cells. Diseases in dogs and cats include a long list of possibilities:

- Polyarthritis
- Pemphigus
- Lupus
- Hemolytic anemia
- Thrombocytopenia
- IBD
- Thyroiditis with secondary hypothyroidism
- Addison's disease
- Masticatory myositis
- Symmetrical lupoid onychodystrophy
- and many others

Triggering factors may include genetics, over-vaccination, use of harmful chemicals and pesticides, environmental pollutants, leaky gut, and an imbalance in body systems.

Each of these diseases is associated with heat in the body. They may also be associated with Blood Deficiency from a TCVM standpoint. Symptoms will vary, depending on which organ system is being affected and may include:

- Low-grade fevers
- Spiking fevers
- Joint pain
- Lethargy
- Brittle or broken nails
- Muscle wasting
- Panting, rapid shallow respiration
- Pale gums
- Bruising, bleeding
- Oozing sores
- Vomiting
- Diarrhea

Symptoms will worsen during hot weather, just like turning up the heat under the frying pan on the stove. Disease will be aggravated by feeding energetically warming or hot foods (lamb, chicken, venison, dry kibble).

Most often, pets with these diseases will be treated with immune-suppressing drugs such as steroids, cyclosporine, and others (prednisone, prednisolone, Atopica, Apoquel, etc). While suppressing the immune system will decrease symptoms and hopefully, stop progression of disease, this does not actually cure the disease in most cases. The immune system needs to be re-set to function optimally.

From an alternative perspective, feeding energetically cooling diets made with organic, fresh foods can be extremely beneficial. Cold-water, wild-caught fish will make an excellent protein base. Rabbit is also a good choice. Duck or grass-fed beef, which are great blood tonics, may also be beneficial. For dogs and cats with hemolytic anemia, add Blood tonics like dark leafy greens, egg yolks, and sardines, along with the herbal formula Si Wu Tang (also called Four Substance) at 0.5 grams twice daily.

As 80% of the immune system lies within the bowel, it is imperative to feed an organic, clean diet that decreases inflammation. Add good probiotics to an easily digestible (home cooked) diet. Coconut or MCT oil (1 tsp per 20 pounds body weight per day) can also help strengthen the bowel.

Herbal alternatives to steroids include plant sterols (similar benefits without the horrible side effects) and palmitoylethanolamide (PEA) which binds to cells in the body to decrease pain and inflammation.

Antioxidants, including CoQ10 (5 mg per pound of body weight twice daily), can decrease inflammation by decreasing free radicals in the body and decreasing oxidative stress.

For skin lesions, healing salves should not include petroleum-based products. Cold laser therapy can be very helpful in getting lesions to heal. Chemicals should be avoided for these pets, including all flea and tick chemicals.

These pets should no longer receive vaccinations. Vaccinations stimulate the immune system and can be overwhelming, particularly if multiple vaccines are given at one time. Remember, one injection may contain more than one vaccine, like DHLPP which contains 8 antigens.

Acupuncture can be very beneficial for these pets, as well as the use of herbs. Cooling herbs such as kelp, coptis, rhubarb, winter melon, gentiana, and honeysuckle can work very well. Gui Pi Tang and Wei Qi Booster can be very effective at rebuilding platelets in dogs with thrombocytopenia. Si Wu Tang helps build blood, which is necessary in cases of hemolytic anemia and lupoid onychodystrophy. Work with a veterinary herbalist to choose the best formula for your pet.

Autoimmune disease is not a death sentence. Knowing signs and symptoms to watch for can help get your pet diagnosed sooner. By strengthening the immune system and avoiding triggers that will aggravate the disease, your pet can enjoy a long life by achieving a cure. Never stop immune suppressant medications abruptly. Work with your veterinarian to formulate a plan to wean the pet off medications as you are working to restore balance to the immune system.

Barney, a middle-aged Maltese dog, was presented to me after a diagnosis of immune-mediated thrombocytopenia (IMTP). His owner was frustrated about spending money for repeated testing to monitor Barney's platelet counts and expensive medications to suppress the immune system, especially since Barney's platelet count remained low. Barney had received vaccinations annually his entire life, including many for diseases to which he had no exposure. He was given chemical pesticides monthly and eating dry kibble.

I prescribed Gui Pi Tang and Wei Qi Booster, along with a home-prepared diet (Puploaf). Within four weeks, Barney had normal platelet counts, was no longer anemic, and was back to his usual energetic self. He was weaned off all immune suppressant medications within a month. Barney continued to do well for eight months and no longer needed to have blood testing repeated.

A year later, Barney was returned to the clinic. The owner had gotten tired of making food for Barney and had gone back to feeding him dry kibble. Within a month, Barney was again suffering with IMTP with very low platelet counts. Herbal and dietary therapy was reinstituted. The owner refused to use the immunosuppressant drugs, but Barney was able to return to good health using only the herbs and dietary therapy.

Unfortunately, this cycle repeated multiple times. The owner would make food for a few months, then stop. Each time, Barney would return with active IMTP. This case shows the power of diet in transforming disease.

I have cured many cases of symmetrical lupoid onychodys-trophy (dry, brittle nails that fall off which is extremely painful) using herbs, supplements, and dietary therapy. Owners unwilling to change the diet were never able to effect a cure for their dogs, while those willing to prepare or purchase human-grade raw or gently cooked diets had great success. Dogs supplemented only with omega-3 fatty acids recovered as well as dogs given cyclsosporine in one study, which shows that providing meals with lower omega-6:omega-3 ratios are beneficial. AAFCO allows ratios of 30:1, while ideal is 5:1.

While some pets must remain on immune-suppressing drugs, it may be possible to decrease or eliminate doses by supplying high-quality nutrition, supplement, and herbal support.

7 Endocrine Diseases

Endocrine glands secrete hormones that affect the body in various ways, regulating metabolism, hair growth, muscle strength, digestion, reproduction, and pretty much everything the body does.

The most common endocrine disorders seen in veterinary practice include diabetes mellitus, obesity, hypothyroidism (dogs), hyperthyroidism (cats), Cushing's disease (dogs), and Addison's disease (dogs, not as common). Yes, I did say obesity is an endocrine disease. Fat cells produce hormones that can contribute to other diseases like diabetes and hypertension.

Improved diagnostic capabilities have allowed more cases of these disorders to come to light. However, I think we also see more endocrine disorders in pets and people due to the horrible diets of fast food, processed food, and chemicals in our environment. Many of the meats we eat come from animals that have been fed antibiotics and hormones to increase growth rate. Most pesticides and herbicides sprayed on crops and lawns, as well as flame retardants and plastics, are endocrine disruptors, meaning they interfere with normal endocrine gland function by mimicking, blocking, or interfering with the hormones of the body which are part of the endocrine system. These chemicals are associated with a wide array of health issues. Our endocrine systems are overloaded and working hard all the time which leads to imbalances and disease.

Most of these diseases have symptoms that overlap. One of the earliest and most common symptoms is increased thirst. The body tells the pet to drink more, which means there is internal heat and inflammation. There seems to be some genetic predilection, as well. Some diseases are associated with weight gain like hypothyroidism (underactive thyroid) and Cushing's disease (overactive adrenal and/or pituitary gland). Others can be associated with weight loss, like diabetes (pancreatic disease) and Addison's disease (underactive adrenal gland). Many times, pets will have more than one endocrine disease at the same time. Hypothyroidism, Diabetes, and Cushing's disease commonly occur together.

Hypothyroidism

Hypothyroid disease, or an underactive thyroid gland, is the most common hormone imbalance in dogs that is treated by veterinarians. This is extremely rare in cats. The thyroid gland is responsible for metabolism so when it doesn't function properly the body slows down. Pets become sluggish and gain weight. The cycle of hair growth and shedding is interrupted, and many dogs develop bald patches, particularly along the flanks. The hair will become dry and brittle and lack shine. Skin and ear infections are commonplace. Some dogs become anxious, depressed, aggressive, or develop seizures. These dogs seek warmth.

When I was in high school, we had a female Doberman that my mother wanted to breed. My mother loves puppies and we had no clue that breeding should only be undertaken after purchasing a high-quality dog and performing health testing. The dog only had two pups in the litter. Infertility is a symptom of hypothyroidism. Once the dog was placed on thyroid supplements, she was able to have a normal-size litter.

Primary hypothyroidism is caused by autoimmune thyroiditis—the immune system attacks the thyroid gland. Decreased production of thyroid hormones may also occur with age. Some pets will drink and urinate more often. Large breeds seem to be affected more often; Dobermans, Labradors, and Greyhounds lead the list. Environmental and food toxins, vaccinations, and medications contribute to the constant attack on the thyroid gland.

Older dogs with untreated thyroid disease may also develop laryngeal paralysis as a complication. Laryngeal paralysis may be related to the autoimmune disease that affects the thyroid gland. This disease syndrome has been given the name Geriatric Onset Laryngeal Paralysis Polyneuropathy or GOLPP. Polyneuropathy affects many nerves leading to poor swallowing function and progressive hind-end weakness.

The folds that close over the larynx, or airway, do not open and close properly due to decreased nerve function. The dogs make a loud roaring noise when breathing heavily and may cough and choke when drinking water since water gets into the airway. These dogs are at high risk for swelling of the laryngeal tissues and difficulty breathing secondary to environmental factors like high heat and humidity, and stress factors like obesity and exercise.

They have increased incidence of aspiration pneumonia. They develop hind-end weakness, an unsteady gait, and loss of muscle mass. Treatment with thyroid supplementation does not correct laryngeal paralysis. This disease most commonly affects Labrador Retrievers, Newfoundlands, Borzois, Golden Retrievers, Greyhounds, German Shepherd Dogs, and Brittany Spaniels.

Diagnosis of hypothyroidism requires blood testing for different thyroid hormones and antibodies against the thyroid gland (T3, T4, freeT4, AAT3, AAT4). Cholesterol and triglycerides are commonly elevated in hypothyroid dogs. Most routine laboratory tests only test for total T4. This is not an accurate test for diagnosing hypothyroidism. The best laboratories for testing thyroid disease are the Endocrine Diagnostic Laboratory at the Michigan State University Veterinary School and Hemopet in California.

Treatment usually consists of:

- Supplemental synthetic thyroid hormone, levothyroxine, starting at 0.05 to 0.1 mg per 10 to 15 pounds optimal body weight given twice daily. The medication should not be given with food. It should be given one hour prior or two hours after feeding to ensure proper absorption. Most clients are never told this.
- Natural thyroid hormone supplementation is available but rarely used. The brand names include Armour Thyroid, Nature-Throid, NP Thyroid, and WP Thyroid; it is made from desiccated porcine thyroid (dried pig thyroid).
- Feeding a healthy species-appropriate whole food diet (more protein, less carbs) that is minimally processed.
- Decreasing (or stopping) vaccine usage.
- Supporting the immune system with vitamin D (found in cod liver oil, sardines, eggs, kefir, and beef liver).
- Kelp as a source of iodine which is required for thyroid function (1/4 teaspoon for small dogs, 1/2 teaspoon for medium dogs, 1 teaspoon for large dogs). If preparing home-made meals, be sure to incorporate an iodine source in the meals.
- Omega 3 fatty acids—give 20 to 30 mg per pound of body weight daily of EPA and DHA combined.
- Licorice root, Rehmannia, and Ashwaganda are commonly included in herbal thyroid supplements.
- Vitamin A (50 to 100 IU per pound of body weight daily), ester-C (100 to 500 mg daily, dosed to bowel tolerance— lower dose if diarrhea develops), and Vitamin E (400 to 1,000 IU per day) are also important to support endocrine function.
- Some supplements contain ground thyroid gland, which can add thyroid hormone without synthetic supplementation.

🐾 Thyroid hormone levels should be closely monitored, as over or under-supplementation can have dire consequences. Some laboratories have specific test codes that must be used when testing pets that are taking medication. Timing of testing may be linked to when the medication was given. Be sure to ask your veterinarian.

SAMPLE DIET FOR HYPOTHYROID DOG

- ☐ 1 pound beef 90% lean
- ☐ 2 ounces beef liver
- ☐ 2 ounces beef heart
- ☐ 3 ounces carrot finely chopped or grated
- ☐ 5 grams crushed garlic
- ☐ 3 ounces parsley chopped
- ☐ 4 ounces kale chopped
- ☐ 4 ounces Shiitake mushrooms chopped
- ☐ 1 can or 3.5 ounces of sardines
- ☐ 4 teaspoons flaxseed oil
- ☐ 1/2 teaspoon kelp
- ☐ 1 teaspoon ground eggshell

Provides 33 calories per ounce. See chapter 4 for feeding guidelines. May be feed raw or gently cooked. Add oil after cooking if not feeding raw.

Hyperthyroidism

Hyperthyroidism, an overactive thyroid gland, is a disease of cats. When seen in dogs it is almost always related to a malignant functional thyroid tumor (but has also been seen in dogs inadvertently fed diets containing thyroid glands). Cats develop adenomas or benign enlargement of the thyroid gland; they rarely have malignant thyroid tumors.

Thyroid hormone is responsible for metabolism, so increased levels will effectively "rev the engine". Symptoms may include hyperactivity, increased thirst and urination, vomiting, diarrhea, increased appetite with weight loss, excessive vocalization, racing heart rate, high blood pressure, and possibly a palpably enlarged thyroid gland on the neck.

Testing to confirm suspected thyroid disease in cats may include a blood test for T3, T4, and free T4. Liver and cardiac enzymes will often be elevated on routine chemistry screens. The average age at the time of diagnosis is 8 to 13.

Causes of hyperthyroidism are still not completely known. A relationship has been theorized between this disease and PBDE's (polybrominated diphenyl ethers) which is a chemical flame retardant used in many industries and BPA (bisphenol-A) which is a chemical used to coat the inside of pet food cans. The BPA may not be the cause of the problem, as PBDE is found in ocean fish from pollution; the association may be the chemicals in the fish, not the can. The amount of iodine in cat foods may also play a role, as well as the addition of soy which can disrupt thyroid function.

Treatment for hyperthyroidism consists of four options.

1. A twice-daily medication called methimazole can be given as a pill, liquid, or transdermal gel. Methimazole will stop

production of thyroid hormone but will not shrink the thyroid tumor. Side effects include suppression of the bone marrow with low red and white blood cell production, liver failure, vomiting, anorexia, fever, and allergic dermatitis. Cats taking this medication need to be monitored with bloodwork every few months. This is probably the most common form of treatment. Many cats with thyroid disease have underlying kidney disease which will become apparent when the thyroid disease is treated.

2. Surgery is a less commonly used option for treatment. Removal of the thyroid gland should only be performed by a highly skilled surgeon in a specialty center. Accidental removal of the parathyroid glands which are very small and lie next to the thyroid gland can have devastating results, including death. If the entire thyroid gland is removed the cat will need to be given thyroid supplements for life. Many hyperthyroid cats have cardiac or kidney disease and are not good candidates for surgery.

3. Radioactive iodine therapy has become more popular as the primary form of treatment for this disease. While the initial cost may run well over one thousand dollars, this cost may be less than the money that will be spent on medications and monitoring when treating with drugs. Treatment consists of an injection of radioactive iodine under the skin. The iodine is concentrated in the thyroid gland causing selective destruction of the gland tissue. A small percentage of cats may become hypothyroid after treatment, requiring thyroid hormone supplementation. An equally small percentage may need a second injection of radioactive iodine if their tumor was particularly large or if it was malignant (only 2 to 3% of tumors in cats are malignant). The cats must stay in

a lead-lined room for three days after treatment, so owners are not exposed to any radioactive particles.

4. The fourth method of treatment is relatively new. Hill's pet food company has added Y/D to the alphabet soup. This is a diet which is severely deficient in iodine, decreasing the availability of iodine to the thyroid gland, resulting in decreased production of thyroid hormone. While decreasing hormone production will help diminish symptoms, the diet does nothing to diminish the size of the thyroid tumor, which can continue to grow and potentially become malignant over time. The diet may cause the tumor to enlarge, as hormones like Thyroid Stimulating Hormone will detect decreased levels of iodine and cause the thyroid to work even harder. Iodine deficient diets in people cause goiter, which is benign enlargement of the thyroid gland. Could cat foods actually be causing this disease by providing too little iodine? And by restricting iodine levels further, are we adding to the problem? The dry formulation of Y/D contains soy products, which may have contributed to the development of hyperthyroidism initially. The entire body is also being deprived of iodine, which may have unknown repercussions. This diet cannot be fed to healthy cats without thyroid disease, so owners of multiple cats will have to separate cats at feeding. Use of this diet is not recommended for hyperthyroid cats.

Alternative treatments for hyperthyroidism in cats can be helpful.

🐾 A high quality, high moisture diet (frozen raw, home-cooked, or rehydrated freeze-dried raw) should be the basis for treatment.

- Yin tonifying (cooling) meats—see energetics chapter—are needed: rabbit, duck, grass-fed beef, liver, and clams are good protein sources.
- Liver support is essential, as liver enzymes are commonly elevated with this disease. Milk thistle (5 to 10 mg per pound twice daily) and/or SAM-e (90 mg daily) may be helpful.
- Foods high in vitamin A like carrots, kale, spinach, and barley grass should be added in small amounts if the cat will eat them. They can be cooked and minced or fed raw.
- L-Carnitine (250—500 mg twice daily) for cardiac support; also found in high quantities in red meats.
- Taurine (250—500 mg two to three times daily) for cardiac support; also found in high quantities in red meats, poultry, eggs, dairy products, and fish.
- Home cooked diets for cats can be hard to balance and must include sufficient carnitine and taurine.
- Herbs to balance thyroid function: Bugleweed has been shown to decrease output of thyroid hormone by the thyroid gland. Dosage will depend on the product used. Hawthorn can help lower blood pressure and decrease work of the heart. Many cats will be too sick at the time of diagnosis to be treated with herbal therapy alone.
- Acupuncture can help balance the immune system and lower blood pressure, as well as support the kidneys and liver.
- Hyperthyroid cats should no longer be vaccinated.

The hardest thing about using alternative treatments is getting them into the cat. Most cats do not enjoy being medicated. Powders and liquids can be added to meals in most cases.

Hyperadrenocorticism

Hyperadrenocorticism or Cushing's disease, caused by over-production of hormones by the adrenal gland, is being diagnosed in dogs with ever-increasing frequency; it is rarely seen in cats. Symptoms include increased thirst and urination, excessive panting, hair loss, muscle weakness, pot belly, liver enlargement, and chronic skin or urinary tract infections. The adrenal gland is ruled by the pituitary gland; the disease can stem from either gland. Hormones released from the adrenal gland include cortisols similar to prednisone as well as lesser estrogen, progesterone, and testosterone types of hormones.

One of the earliest indicators of adrenal gland dysfunction is an elevation in serum alkaline phosphatase (SAP or ALP) on the chemistry panel. The best test of adrenal gland function is performed at the University of Tennessee veterinary diagnostic laboratory; I recommend sending all samples to that lab. They will test for an array of hormones, not just cortisol. By performing a Dexamethasone suppression/ACTH stimulation combination test, it is usually possible to discern whether the excess hormone production is originating in the pituitary or the adrenal glands. Some dogs will have normal cortisol level on testing but will have abnormal levels or estrogen, progesterone, or testosterone hormones; this is called Atypical Cushing's. Unless all hormones are tested, the diagnosis may be missed.

This disease can be caused by a tumor in the adrenal gland (may be more common in large breeds), a tumor in the pituitary gland (may be more common in small breeds), or by over-administration of steroids. If testing reveals primary adrenal production, an abdominal ultrasound is recommended to rule out an adrenal gland tumor. Adrenal gland tumors can be highly malignant and aggressive and difficult to remove surgically.

Pituitary gland tumors are much more common, occurring in

about 85% of dogs with Cushing's Disease. These are benign, slow growing tumors that usually do not spread to other areas of the body. Surgical removal of pituitary tumors has been performed rarely using a procedure called transsphenoidal hypophysectomy.

Dogs with Cushing's disease commonly have high blood pressure; this should be monitored and treated if needed. Blood pressure can be lowered with herbal medications containing hawthorn, acupuncture, or traditional medications. These dogs may also have elevated calcium levels which can lead to production of bladder and kidney stones. Dogs with high calcium levels should be x-rayed to check for the presence of stones. Pancreatitis is a common complication.

Traditional treatments for hyperadrenocorticism include harsh medications including mitotane (Lysodren), ketoconazole (Nizoral), selegiline or L-Deprenyl (Anipryl), and trilostane (Vetoryl). Dogs taking these medications must be monitored closely for reactions. The medications work by stopping production of hormones by the adrenal gland cells. Side effects are common, including vomiting, diarrhea, anorexia, liver failure, kidney failure, weakness, collapse, tremors, seizures, hypoadrenal crisis, and diminished hearing (I had one patient become deaf on selegiline; luckily hearing returned on discontinuation of the drug). Considering most dogs with this disease have significant liver dysfunction it seems odd to use medications that can cause liver failure. I rarely used these drugs in my practice (I can remember two dogs treated with these drugs and I was not the one who prescribed them).

Luckily there are quite a few alternative treatments available for this disease, particularly if caught early.

- Melatonin 3 mg twice daily for small dogs, up to 6 mg twice daily for large dogs; decrease dose if pet is too sleepy or lethargic.

- Flax seed lignans or HMR lignans 20 to 40 mg once daily.
- Glandular products including ground adrenal, pancreas, and thymus glands.
- Antioxidant vitamins A (50 to 100 IU per pound of body weight daily), Ester C (100 to 500 mg daily dosed to bowel tolerance—decrease dose if diarrhea develops), and E (400 to 1,000 IU per day)
- CoQ10 100 to 400 mg daily as an antioxidant.
- Si Maio San, Ophiopogon, Liu Wei Di Wang, or Rehmannia Chinese herbal formula at 0.5 gm per 10 to 20 pounds body weight twice daily. Your holistic veterinarian will choose the herbal formula that best fits your pet.
- Acupuncture to lower blood pressure and increase energy and muscle strength.
- Hawthorn berry to lower blood pressure; feed 1 teaspoon of ground berry per one pound of food fed or 1/2 teaspoon of hawthorn tincture daily.
- Diet issues must be handled; good quality protein sources, minimal or no carbohydrates, plenty of leafy green vegetables, lower in calcium to prevent formation of bladder stones.
- No more vaccines should be given, and stress should be kept to a minimum.
- Liver function should always be supported with milk thistle at 5 to 10 mg per pound of body weight twice daily and SAMe at 90 mg for small dogs, 225 mg for medium dogs, and 400 mg for large dogs.

Hypoadrenocorticism

Hypoadrenocorticism or Addison's disease is the opposite of Cushing's disease. It is more common in dogs but can affect cats.

The adrenal gland does not produce enough cortisol and/or min-eralocorticoids (hormones that regulate salt and water balance). Middle aged female Poodles are the most affected, although it can be seen in almost any breed. Symptoms include vomiting, diarrhea, lethargy, anorexia, dehydration, kidney failure, muscle weakness, tremors, and collapse. When in crisis these pets need to be treated immediately or face certain death. Electrolyte imbalances, includ-ing high potassium levels, will slow the heart rate and can cause heart function to cease.

Diagnosis of this disease can be elusive. Pets are commonly presented for vague, repeated episodes of vomiting and diarrhea. Commonly, symptoms occur during times of stress or increased activity. Normally the adrenal gland is responsible for the "fight or flight" response that increases heart rate and metabolism when the body is stressed. Without those hormones the body is no longer able to fight or flee.

Bloodwork may show low sodium and high potassium lev-els, elevated BUN or creatinine (kidney enzymes), and low red blood cell count. These tests are not diagnostic but may be early indicators warranting further diagnostics. The definitive test for diagnosis is the ACTH (Adrenocorticotropic hormone) stimula-tion test. ACTH is a gel that is injected to stimulate the adrenal gland to produce hormones. A blood sample is taken before and after giving the injection to determine how well the adrenal glands respond. A pet with Addison's disease will have no response to the ACTH gel, confirming the diagnosis.

Causes of Addison's disease include auto-immune disease, in which the body attacks the adrenal glands, or the overuse of steroids for treatment of other diseases. Constant stress and bombardment with dietary and environmental toxins can cause the adrenal glands to shut down. When steroids, particularly long-acting injections, are used for treatment, they suppress the normal production of steroids by the adrenal glands. When used for prolonged periods of time and then suddenly withdrawn the body does not have time to respond and the animal can crash in Addisonian crisis. Overuse of long-acting injections of steroids can permanently shut down the adrenal glands.

Treatment of Addison's disease consists of replacing the hormones the adrenal gland is not producing. Low doses of prednisone are usually given daily to replace cortisone. If mineralocorticoid supplementation is necessary, fludrocortisone (Florinef), a tablet that is given daily, or desoxycorticosterone pivolate (Percorten-V), can be given as an injection every 25 days to replace the mineralocorticoids. Not all pets with Addison's disease will require mineralocorticoid supplementation.

During times of stress (boarding, holidays, dog shows, veterinary appointments, etc.) additional or increased dosing of prednisone may be required. Kidney and liver function, along with electrolytes, must be monitored frequently to ensure proper dosing of the medications (I recommend at least every three months once the pet is stabilized and more often during the initial treatment period). Herbal and glandular supplements can help treat Addison's disease. Feeding liver, kidney, and spleen which are glandular organs can help decrease the auto-immune process that attacks other glands. Dandelion, parsley, spirulina, and nettle can be fed, as well as herbal licorice root.

In some cases, Addison's disease is caused by genetics, so dogs diagnosed with this disease should be removed from breeding programs and the parents may also need to be removed.

- The best way to prevent Addison's disease is by avoiding stresses on the immune system. Avoid stressful situations like boarding or crowded events.
- Feed a healthy, species-appropriate diet with no artificial

preservatives, dyes, or chemicals. Include secreting organs liver, kidney, and spleen in the diet.

- Minimize vaccinations, medications, and parasiticides which will stress the immune system.
- Once diagnosed, support with glandular products, antioxidant vitamins (A, C, and E), and herbals will help keep the immune system in the best shape possible.
- Support the immune system with colostrum and medicinal mushrooms (Reishi, Maitake, Cordyceps, Chaga).

Diabetes Mellitus

Diabetes mellitus is a common malady that afflicts dogs and cats. I cringe when I see an obese dog or cat because I know it's only a matter of time until diabetes becomes the diagnosis for that pet. A study from the United Kingdom showed Border Terriers, West Highland White Terriers, Cocker Spaniels, Tibetan Terriers, Cairn Terriers, and Samoyeds are considered high-risk breeds for diabetes.

Diabetes is a condition that occurs when the body cannot use glucose (a type of sugar) normally. Glucose is the main source of energy for the body's cells. The levels of glucose in the blood are primarily controlled by a hormone called insulin, which is produced by the pancreas. Insulin helps cells in the body use glucose or energy. Without insulin, the sugar stays in the blood and is useless to the cells. Without glucose, muscle wasting and weight loss will occur.

We once adopted a Miniature Pinscher who was obese, blind, and diabetic. Unfortunately, his owners were not able to afford his treatment. He was being fed a low-quality corn-based kibble which made it impossible to get his blood sugar regulated. The first thing I did was change his diet to a species-appropriate raw food. His blood sugar was easy to regulate with the diet change and his insulin requirement dropped from 20 units twice daily to 3 units twice daily. By spending more money on food, I was able to spend less money on treatment and the dog was able to lose the extra weight he was carrying.

Risk factors associated with diabetes include:

- Sedentary lifestyle
- Obesity, which may be related to the sedentary lifestyle (recent data show an increase in canine obesity of 37 percent between 2007 and 2012 and a 32 percent increase in canine diabetes over the same period).
- Diets high in carbohydrates which increase the workload of the pancreas, which produces insulin.
- Medications, like steroids
- Female dogs are twice as likely to be diabetic as male dogs
- Male cats are 1.5 times as likely to be diabetic as female cats
- Breed disposition: dachshunds, beagles, schnauzers, poodles, Labrador retrievers, Cocker spaniels, and possibly Burmese cats
- Age over 8 years
- Concurrent diseases such as pancreatitis, Cushing's disease, kidney disease, and periodontal disease

Symptoms of diabetes include:

- Increased thirst and urination
- Weight loss
- Wry coat with dandruff
- Recurring skin infections
- Recurring urinary tract infections
- Cloudy eyes or cataracts
- Muscle atrophy
- Weakness

Initially the pet may be hungry, wanting to eat more, but eventually they will have decreased appetite. If the pet is in advanced stages of diabetes at the time of diagnosis, the following may be seen:

- Lack of appetite
- Vomiting
- Increased thirst and urination
- Sweet odor to breath
- Ketones in the urine indicate ketoacidosis, a very dangerous condition that may require hospitalization.
- Dehydration
- Weight loss
- Diabetic neuropathy usually affects the hind legs, the dog or cat will walk flat-footed on the hind legs.

Diagnosis of diabetes is made through blood testing and urinalysis. The normal blood sugar for dogs and cats is 80 to 120. Cats are unique because a stressed cat may have an elevated blood sugar as high as 200 to 225. Testing urine will give more evidence as to whether the pet is truly diabetic. If glucose is found in the urine, it is more likely the pet is diabetic. Blood sugars above 225 generally indicate a pet has become diabetic. A fructosamine level gives a more accurate determination of the average level of sugar in the blood over a 7-to-10-day period with one simple blood test.

Once a pet is diagnosed as being diabetic, treatment will generally involve daily injections of insulin, although there is an oral medication now available for cats called Bexacat. Bexacat should not be used in cats who have previously been treated with insulin, are receiving insulin treatment, or who have insulin-dependent diabetes mellitus, as serious adverse reactions can occur. Bexacat should not be initiated in cats who are not eating well, dehydrated, or lethargic when diagnosed with diabetes mellitus. Cats treated with Bexacat may be at an increased risk of serious adverse reactions which can be fatal.

Insulin comes in two strengths: U-40 and U-100 which indicates how many units of insulin each ml contains. The syringes you use must match the insulin you use.

The pancreas normally produces insulin. The insulin drives the glucose, or sugar, into the cells of the body to serve as fuel for the cells to function. Without insulin, the glucose stays in the blood stream, resulting in high glucose levels when performing a blood test. The excess sugar in the blood stream will then spill over into the urine when the blood is filtered through the kidneys. High levels of sugar in the urine will predispose the dog or cat to urinary tract infections (bacteria love the high-sugar environment).

The goal is to give enough insulin to drive the sugar (glucose) into the cells to be utilized as energy, but not so much insulin that the blood sugar drops too low. The brain is very dependent on glucose for its nutrition, so any changes in mental state could mean hypoglycemia (low blood sugar). Symptoms of low blood sugar include:

- Tremors
- Weakness
- Wobbliness
- Seizures
- Coma
- Death

If you suspect your pet is suffering from low blood sugar, offer food or smear syrup or sugar water on the gums. Low blood sugar is an emergency and should not be ignored. It is very important to monitor blood sugar levels often when your pet is first diagnosed.

Glucometers can be purchased for monitoring at home; your veterinarian can instruct you on obtaining blood samples. Most of our clients use the vein along the edge of the ear. A small drop of petroleum jelly placed next to the edge of the ear, followed by a quick stab with a needle or lancet, will allow a drop of blood to bead up on the jelly which can be used to measure the blood sugar.

There are also glucose-monitoring devices that can be attached to your pet—the MiniMed iPro2 and the Abbott Freestyle Libre. These devices make it easier for pet parents to monitor diabetic control at home. The stress of frequent blood sampling is avoided, and data can be captured any time during the day.

It will be very important to work with your veterinarian to ensure your pet is well regulated to keep the blood sugar as close as possible to the normal range of 80 to 120.

Feeding a diet that promotes ideal blood glucose levels is also important in managing your diabetic pet. Diets should have low starch content, as starch breaks down to sugar, increasing the "glycemic" or sugar load. Diets high in meat content, along with insoluble fiber and low-glycemic vegetable matter, will help keep blood sugar well maintained. Dry kibble is rarely, if ever, the correct choice for maintaining a diabetic pet. Raw or freeze-dried diets generally work very well for dogs and cats; canned low-glycemic foods would be another option if they will not eat raw or freeze-dried food. Avoid any foods that contain added sugar or foods that fall into the semi-moist category.

The body will thrive on routine, preventing spikes and drops in blood sugar. Pets should be fed every 12 hours. If your pet will not eat or is vomiting, check with your veterinarian before giving an insulin injection. Having a slightly high blood sugar for a day or two is much better than having a drop in blood sugar resulting in hypoglycemia.

Skin and urinary tract infections are more common in pets with diabetes. It is important to have the pet well-regulated with insulin injections to keep blood sugar levels stable. Monitor urine regularly for infection.

SAMPLE DIET FOR DIABETIC DOG
(ALSO CUSHING'S)

- ☐ 1 pound 93% lean ground turkey
- ☐ 3 ounces turkey or chicken liver
- ☐ 2 ounces kale, spinach, or collards finely chopped
- ☐ 2 ounces red or green cabbage, broccoli, or cauliflower finely chopped
- ☐ 2 stalks celery finely chopped
- ☐ 2 eggs without shell
- ☐ 1 teaspoon fresh grated ginger root
- ☐ 1 teaspoon ground eggshell
- ☐ 1/2 teaspoon kelp
- ☐ 1 ounce oyster or 1 zinc capsule 15 mg
- ☐ 1 teaspoon turmeric

Provides 24 calories per ounce. Feed appropriate amount twice daily (see chapter 4). May be fed raw or gently cooked.

SAMPLE DIET FOR DIABETIC CAT (ALSO
HYPERTHYROIDISM)

- ☐ 8 ounces boneless skinless chicken thigh
- ☐ 4 ounces boneless chicken breast with skin
- ☐ 2 eggs without shell
- ☐ 4.5 ounces chicken liver

- ☐ 2 ounces pork muscle 95% lean
- ☐ 1 ounce kale finely ground
- ☐ 1 ounce butternut squash finely ground
- ☐ 1 ounce oyster
- ☐ 4 teaspoons ground sunflower seed
- ☐ 1.5 teaspoons turmeric
- ☐ 1 teaspoon ground eggshell
- ☐ ¾ teaspoon salmon oil
- ☐ 1/2 teaspoon kelp

Provides 34 calories per ounce. Feed appropriate amount twice daily (see chapter 4). May be fed raw or gently cooked.

Pancreatitis

Pancreatitis simply means inflammation of the pancreas; it affects thousands of dogs and cats every day. It can come on acutely or it may be a chronic condition that progresses over time. The pancreas is a vital organ on the right side of the abdomen adjacent to the stomach. The pancreas produces enzymes to assist in food digestion and hormones such as insulin, which regulates blood sugar or glucose metabolism. The digestive enzymes are secreted into the small intestine, and the hormones enter the bloodstream. When the pancreas becomes inflamed, the digestive enzymes are spilled into the surrounding area in the abdomen, causing damage to the liver, bile ducts, gall bladder, and intestines.

While the usual blame is a high-fat meal, getting into the trash, or other dietary indiscretion, there are many factors that may play a role. Some pets will develop acute pancreatitis with no changes in diet or dietary indiscretion. While the symptoms may suddenly progress to an acute presentation, there has often been sub-clinical, simmering inflammation or imbalance in the body going on for some time.

We adopted a 16-year-old Cocker Spaniel who suffered from infections in his ears, eyes, and skin. He also had repeated bouts of pancreatitis. The pancreatitis was not due to being fed a high-fat diet; it was due to chronic inflammation throughout his body. The pancreatitis was just one more organ being affected by it. By clearing up his infections and placing him on a whole-food, home-prepared diet, he was able to spend the next two years without any pancreatic issues.

Abdominal trauma around the pancreas, high calcium levels in the blood, obesity, toxins, and some drugs (steroids, diuretics, antibiotics, and non-steroidal anti-inflammatory medications) may all contribute to the syndrome. Dogs with Cushing's disease are particularly prone to pancreatitis, as they have high circulating cortisol (steroid) levels. In cats, over 95% of cases have no obvious underlying cause. Inflammation of surrounding organs including the small intestines, stomach, liver, and gallbladder may contribute to inflammation in the pancreas.

Chronic bouts of pancreatitis or even one bout of acute pancreatitis may be enough to cause the pancreas to stop producing insulin, leading to diabetes. Pets fed high-carbohydrate diets have chronic pancreatic stress, as the pancreas works overtime producing enzymes to break down the starch. Fat has been incriminated as causing pancreatitis, however many pets do very well on high-fat diets, while some that are fed low-fat diets still have flares of pancreatitis. Ketogenic diets contain up to 70% fat, but they are fed raw; it is rare for a keto-fed pet to develop pancreatitis. Cooked fats undergo oxidation, which causes inflammation. Raw fats are less likely to cause pancreatitis if they are not rancid or oxidized.

Although pancreatitis can occur in any dog breed, it occurs more frequently in the Miniature Schnauzer, Miniature Poodle, Yorkie, and Cocker Spaniel. Inflammation of the pancreas is also more common in females than in males, and more common in elderly dogs.

Symptoms may include restlessness after eating, assuming a prayer position with the hindquarters in the air, drooling, nausea, lip-licking, regurgitation, vomiting, diarrhea, loss of appetite, fever, weight loss (more common in cats), dehydration, lethargy, and mild to moderate abdominal pain. Pancreatitis can be life threatening if not treated appropriately, particularly in a severe acute attack.

Any underlying disorders that might contribute to pancreatitis should be ruled out, including laboratory testing for calcium and cortisol levels. Drugs that might be contributing to the disease should be discontinued as soon as possible, if possible.

Diagnosis can be difficult, particularly in cases of chronic pancreatitis. Laboratory testing can give clues, but abdominal ultrasound is the best diagnostic tool. Lipase and amylase levels in the blood are not entirely diagnostic; the SPEC-CPL (Specific Canine Pancreatic Lipase) test is more accurate for dogs and the fPLI (Feline Pancreatic Lipase Immunoreactivity) test is more accurate for cats.

The four main goals of treatment are the management of dehydration, nausea, pain, and providing nutrition. Treatment may require the use of intravenous or subcutaneous fluids, depending on severity. Anti-nausea, anti-diarrheal, and pain medications or herbal preparations may need to be instituted. Antibiotics are rarely indicated as pancreatitis is usually a sterile process (unless there is a secondary sepsis or other infection). Acupuncture can help dramatically for some pets.

Once the vomiting is controlled it is important to get the pets to eat as quickly as possible. Years ago, pets would be fasted for 5 to 7 days, but this has been shown to be detrimental to recovery. The earlier the pet gets back to eating, the better the prognosis for a good recovery. Feeding tubes may have to be placed to ensure adequate caloric intake.

Recovery can be enhanced by using:

- Antioxidant therapy with vitamins E at 300 to 600 IU daily and C at 1,000 mg per 30 pounds body weight daily.
- SAMe 90 mg for cats and small dogs, 225 mg for medium dogs, and 400 mg for large dogs once daily, given on an empty stomach.
- Omega-3 fatty acids can decrease inflammation. Encapsulated forms are generally tolerated better than liquids in this case.
- Vitamin B12 can be given by injection 1/4 ml weekly for small dogs and cats up to 1 ml for large dogs or can be given daily orally at 250 mcg for small dogs and cats up to 750 mcg for large dogs. Beef liver contains 60 mcg of vitamin B12 per 100 grams and is considered the best food source of vitamin B12. This vitamin will improve appetite, supports the gut microbiome, and boosts immunity.

SAMPLE RECIPE FOR PANCREATITIS IN DOGS

- ☐ 16 ounces ground turkey 93% lean
- ☐ 6 ounces turkey gizzard
- ☐ 3 ounces beef liver
- ☐ 2 ounces beef pancreas

- ☐ 3 teaspoons grated fresh ginger root
- ☐ 4 ounces butternut squash finely chopped or ground
- ☐ 3 ounces cabbage, kale, green beans, or zucchini mixed and ground
- ☐ 4 ounces Shiitake mushrooms chopped
- ☐ 2 ounces asparagus
- ☐ 3 teaspoons flaxseed oil
- ☐ 300 IU vitamin D3 (3 drops of Rx Vitamins Vitamin D3)
- ☐ 1 teaspoon ground eggshell powder
- ☐ 1 teaspoon kelp powder
- ☐ 1 teaspoon ground turmeric powder
- ☐ Provides 30 calories per ounce. See chapter 4 for feeding directions. May be served raw or gently cooked. Add oil after cooking if not feeding raw.

SAMPLE RECIPE FOR PANCREATITIS IN CATS

- ☐ 8 ounces skinless boneless chicken breast
- ☐ 8 ounces chicken gizzards
- ☐ 8 ounces chicken liver
- ☐ 3 ounces pork muscle meat 95% lean
- ☐ 1 teaspoon grated fresh ginger root

- ☐ 2 ounces green beans
- ☐ 1/2 teaspoon cod liver oil
- ☐ 1 capsule 15 mg zinc
- ☐ 1.5 teaspoons ground eggshell powder
- ☐ 1/2 teaspoon kelp powder
- ☐ 1/2 teaspoon ground turmeric powder

Provides 30 calories per ounce. See chapter 4 for feeding directions. May be served raw or gently cooked.

Obesity

Obesity is an epidemic among pets. It is estimated that over 60% of the pets in America are overweight or obese. I can attest to this based on the photos I see on social media. One of the most challenging cases I had in clinical practice was getting a Labrador retriever to lose half his body weight. Scanlan was a seeing eye dog for one of my clients. When the owner obtained Scanlan he weighed 65 pounds but over the course of a few years ballooned to 130 pounds! He could no longer fit into his harness and had no energy to work. The owner fed weight-loss kibble and used a drug called Slentrol for three months, to no avail. Scanlan developed diarrhea from the drug but never lost any weight. We were finally able to get Scanlon below 100 pounds over a course of three months with a diet change from kibble to a species-appropriate raw diet.

Is obesity just a matter of "looks" or does it cause health problems? Because obesity in pets and humans is such an overwhelming problem, scientists have started taking a hard look at the causes and consequences of obesity. Some of the facts are shocking and should scare us enough to get us to sit up and pay attention.

Many veterinary studies have shown that obesity in dogs and cats increases the risk of health problems. These problems can include arthritis, cruciate ligament tears, and degenerative joint disease, diabetes mellitus, abnormalities in circulating lipid profiles (triglycerides, cholesterol), cardiac and respiratory diseases, urinary disorders, reproductive disorders (decreased fertility), cancer (mammary tumors and transitional cell carcinoma), dermatological diseases, and anesthetic complications.

These conditions not only shorten the expected lifespan of the affected animals, but also decrease their quality of life, so obesity in cats and dogs has considerable potential to cause suffering for both the animals and their guardians. A 2.8-fold increase in mortality (death) has been shown in obese cats (8 to 12 years old) compared to lean cats. A large lifetime study of Labrador Retrievers found that a moderately overweight group of dogs lived nearly two years less than their leaner counterparts.

Obesity may cause disease, but it may also be the result of disease. For example, hypothyroidism decreases metabolism and activity levels, resulting in obesity. Cushing's disease causes weight gains due to a cortisol-driven increase in appetite. And while obesity predisposes pets to develop arthritis, it is likely that arthritis promotes the development of obesity due to the animal's decreased ability to exercise. Neutering may also play a role in obesity, as metabolism tends to decrease when hormones are reduced. Without careful attention to correct calorie intake, these pets often become overweight. Overuse of pharmaceutical drugs like steroids can also cause obesity. Certain breeds are more prone to obesity, including Labrador Retrievers, Cavalier King Charles Spaniels, Scottish Terriers, Beagles, and Cocker Spaniels.

Fat cells are a necessity in the body. They are part of the endocrine, or hormonal, system in the body. They help regulate metabolism, energy intake, and fat storage. Fat cells secrete many proteins that control various metabolic functions. One hormone that is produced, called Leptin, regulates food intake. The hormones produced by these cells activate an enzyme that increases fat oxidation and reduces insulin resistance. This enzyme is also activated during exercise.

As pets become obese and their fat cells enlarge, fat tissue undergoes molecular and cellular alterations affecting systemic metabolism. These alterations include the release of pro-inflammatory proteins. This in turn leads to insulin resistance which leads to diabetes in human studies.

How do you know if your pet is obese? Most Americans, when surveyed, did not realize their pets were overweight. Overall, we tend to keep our pets at an unhealthy weight. Your pet should have a "waist" behind the rib cage; the underline should not be a straight line from under the front legs to the back legs. You should be able to feel the ribs, with just a modest covering of muscle. There should not be an indentation over the spine; you should be able to feel the tops of each backbone with muscle along the back, not fat. (See the charts in chapter 4.)

How do you get your pets to lose weight if they are carrying a few extra pounds? Many people really struggle with this. My first recommendation is to feed a species-appropriate diet. Most pets will automatically lose weight when they change from a high-carbohydrate diet to a meat-based, low-glycemic diet. Continuing to feed dry kibble filled with carbohydrates will make weight loss very difficult or impossible. Kibble diets that are "low calorie" or made for weight loss are a waste of money—these kibbles are filled with undigestible fiber or cellulose (sawdust, basically). Add a high-quality probiotic to the diet to keep the bowel healthy and improve digestion. Do not starve your pet by cutting back the amount of kibble in the bowl. Not only will you be cutting back calories, but you will also be cutting back nutrients, leaving your pet malnourished. Obese cats will develop hepatic lipidosis, or fatty liver, if they are starved; this is often fatal. Weight loss should be gradual; expect to take months to reach ideal weight if your pet is obese.

If your pet is acting hungry or sluggish, have a blood test run to rule out metabolic problems such as hypothyroidism, Cushing's disease, or diabetes.

Get your pet to move more by walking, swimming, or playing. If your pet is arthritic, use low impact exercise. Swimming is best, but not all pets like to swim. Physical therapy using an underwater treadmill can be wonderful exercise.

You can steam or cook vegetables like green beans, broccoli, or kale and add to the meals to make them feel like they are getting more to eat without adding calories. Use fresh fruits and vegetables or dehydrated pieces of liver or lean meat as treats. Don't hand out "cookies" made with carbohydrates that are high in calories.

By keeping your pets lean and well-muscled throughout life, you can help them avoid many problems that are commonly seen in senior animals. Grab the leash and head out for a walk. Kitty owners can use laser lights, wind-up toys, or teach cats to play fetch. Exercise needs to be part of the daily routine for both of you.

SAMPLE WEIGHT LOSS DIET FOR DOGS

- ☐ 8 ounces white fish (sardine, cod, flounder, tilapia)
- ☐ 8 ounces boneless, skinless chicken breast
- ☐ 2 ounces chicken liver

- ☐ 8 ounces vegetable medley finely chopped (cabbage, zucchini, kale, carrots, green beans, red peppers)
- ☐ 2 eggs without shell
- ☐ 1 teaspoon fresh grated ginger root
- ☐ 1 teaspoon eggshell powder
- ☐ 1/4 teaspoon kelp
- ☐ ¾ teaspoon ground turmeric powder
- ☐ 1 oyster or 1 zinc 15 mg capsule

Provides 22 calories per ounce. See feeding guidelines in chapter 4. Feed based on the desired weight, not the current weight. May be fed raw or gently cooked.

SAMPLE WEIGHT LOSS DIET FOR CATS

- ☐ 8 ounces whitefish (sardine, cod, flounder, tilapia)
- ☐ 8 ounces boneless, skinless chicken breast
- ☐ 3 ounces duck liver

☐ 2 eggs without shell

☐ 2 ounces vegetable medley finely chopped (cabbage, zucchini, kale, carrots, green beans, red peppers)

☐ 1/2 teaspoon cod liver oil

☐ 1/2 teaspoon nutritional yeast

☐ 1.5 teaspoons eggshell powder

☐ 1/2 teaspoon kelp

☐ 1 zinc 15 mg capsule or 1 ounce oyster

☐ 1.5 teaspoons turmeric

Provides 29 calories per ounce. See feeding guidelines in chapter 4. Feed based on the desired weight, not the current weight. May be fed raw or gently cooked.

Supplements to enhance weight loss include:

- Vitamin C—prevents accumulation of fat in liver cells; citrus fruits or Vitamin C powder made for pets may be used. Give approximately 15 mg per pound of body weight.
- Garlic—blocks intestinal cholesterol absorption. (The original study showing garlic as toxic to dogs used 5 grams of garlic per 2.2 pounds of body weight per day; that's about a teaspoon per pound or 6 to 8 cloves to a 10-pound dog!) The dose for dogs is 1 teaspoon per 30

pounds body weight per day of fresh garlic. Do not use it in cats or dogs with a history of hemolytic anemia. Cats can safely eat 1/16th teaspoon every other day.

- Ginger—antioxidant, appetite suppressant, aids digestion, increases metabolism. Feed 1/4 teaspoon fresh grated ginger root per ten pounds body weight once or twice daily.
- Turmeric—fights inflammation associated with obesity. Best given in the form of Golden Paste. (See recipe in chapter 4.)
- Omega-3 fatty acids (fish, krill, calamari, algae oil)— decrease triglycerides; dose is 30 mg of DHA and EPA per pound of body weight daily.
- Spirulina or chlorella—rich in vitamins B, C, and E, copper, zinc, manganese, and fiber; aids digestion, metabolism, removes toxins, prevents fat absorption. There are no specific dosing guidelines. Be sure to select a product that has been tested for contaminants such as heavy metals. 1/4 to 1 teaspoon can be safely given, depending on the size of the pet.

8 Mobility Disorders

One of our wonderful rescue Cavaliers came to us with some issues associated with her spine. Her owner had turned her over to rescue because Shayna would cry every time she was picked up and sometimes when she would run or jump. The owner could not afford to have diagnostic testing to determine the problem and potential surgery for treatment. Shayna's owner had confined Shayna inside for two years, forcing her to use piddle pads, and never taking her out to play. When Shayna arrived in foster care the first thing she discovered was the doggy door. She would run outside to play but she would not come back in through the door. She would sit outside and bark. It wasn't that she couldn't come back in; she wanted everyone else to come out to play. It was spring and the maple tree seed "helicopters" were falling from the trees and floating on the wind. Shayna would chase them for hours, if allowed. By the time we adopted her, Shayna had already earned the nickname Crazy Shayna.

Of course, since I was a veterinarian, the rescue group thought I would be the perfect person to adopt Shayna. Maybe I would be able to cure her pain with chiropractic or acupuncture. I wasn't so sure that was an option. You see, Shayna was very crooked. When she looked at you, her head was a bit cocked to one side. One eye was always looking up while one was always looking down. When she laid down her hind end laid on the side and her front end laid on her sternum. Her spine was as straight as it could get when she was in that position. X-rays of Crazy Shayna's spine showed the worst case of scoliosis I have ever seen. Her spine was an S-curve. One side of her rib cage was shorter than the other. There was no acupuncture or chiropractic manipulation in the world that would fix the problem! Despite her affliction, Crazy Shayna led a very normal life. She took supplements and medications to manage her pain and only got to play with her frisbee (her absolute favorite pastime) for a few minutes at a time.

In addition to Scoliosis, Wobbler's Syndrome, Intervertebral Disc Disease, Degenerative Myelopathy, Degenerative Lumbosacral Stenosis, osteoarthritis, infections, cancers, and inflammatory diseases of the joints and spine are commonly seen in veterinary practice. Some disorders have specific breed predilections, others are widespread. Sometimes high doses of steroids or anti-inflammatory drugs can provide relief for these disorders; other times pets are rushed to surgery. My preference is to use natural pain relief therapies whenever possible before resorting to medications that may have disastrous side effects.

Pain Assessment

Chronic pain can significantly affect daily living activities in our pets. Currently there are no biomarkers (biochemical or physiologic parameters) that reliably correlate to chronic pain. Physiologic biomarkers, such as blood pressure, heart rate, and cortisol levels, have very low specificity because circumstances other than pain such as fear, anxiety, and stress can also affect these markers.

Objective measurements are not widely used in veterinary practice. These might include force plate measurements, computerized gait analysis, and activity monitors. Unfortunately, even if these were utilized widely, they may only give insight into mobility parameters, with no measurement of internal pain. The most common chronic pain condition encountered in dogs and cats is osteoarthritis (OA); other conditions that can cause chronic pain include intervertebral disk disease, chronic pancreatitis, cancer, and other illnesses.

Things to consider when determining pain level in your pet include:

- Ability to play
- Appetite
- Gastrointestinal function
- Hygiene (ability to maintain cleanliness, urine or stool incontinence)
- Interaction with family members
- Presence of pain (flinching when touched, tension in the body, vocalizing)
- Sleep (increased, decreased, interrupted by pacing or wandering)

One owner assessment questionnaire that has been widely used was developed in Finland by the University of Helsinki researchers. By filling out the questionnaire weekly, a pet owner can determine whether their dog's mobility is improving or declining from week to week. Another assessment questionnaire has been developed by the canine arthritis association.

A more complete assessment of pain may be made using the BEAP pain scale created for pet hospice patients. By assessing appetite, ability and desire to move around, facial expressions, body weight, and vocalizations a pet owner can determine changes in pain scores from week to week.

The Feline Grimace Scale, developed by researchers at the University of Montreal, has gained wide acceptance and use among veterinarians to determine the pain level a cat may be experiencing.

The accurate assessment and management of pain is essential

in ensuring the best quality of life for animals. The recognition and evaluation of pain remains a major limiting factor in pain management for pets. There is good evidence that facial expression can be a useful, valid, and reliable tool for recognizing and evaluating pain in humans and other animals. Both the sensory and emotional components of pain have been demonstrated to affect facial expression. Many of the mammalian species studied to date have similar facial expression responses to pain.

The researchers categorized, tested, and scored five facial action units indicative of pain in cats:

- Ear position: Ears facing forward, ears slightly pulled apart, or ears flattened and rotated outward.
- Orbital tightening: Eyes opened, eyes partially opened, or eyes squinted.
- Muzzle tension: Muzzle relaxed (round), muzzle mildly tense, or muzzle tense (elliptical)
- Whisker position: Whiskers relaxed and curved, whiskers slightly curved or straight, or whiskers straight and moving forward.
- Head position: Head above the shoulder line, head aligned with the shoulder line, or head below the shoulder line or tilted.
- A cat with no pain has ears standing up, eyes round and wide open, a rounded muzzle, relaxed whiskers, and head above the shoulders.
- A cat experiencing some pain will have eyes squinted, ears more to the side, less curvature in the whiskers, a less-rounded muzzle, and head at the shoulder level.
- Cats with more severe pain will have eyes squinted or shut, ears flat to the sides, straight or upwardly curved whiskers, more tension in the muzzle, and head below the shoulders.

Once it is determined the cat is experiencing pain, the next step is to determine the cause. Arthritis, urinary infection or blockage, dehydration from kidney disease, gastrointestinal upset, and wounds are some of the possibilities. If you suspect your cat is showing signs of pain, a trip to your veterinarian for a full examination, bloodwork, and radiographs should be arranged.

Determining quality of life can be difficult for pet owners and veterinarians. By using these tools weekly, it is possible to document changes in pet comfort that may help make decisions regarding improved pain management to improve quality of life.

Intervertebral Disc Disease

Recent studies of Intervertebral Disc Disease have shown alternative therapies combined with medication or surgery have a superior response and recovery when compared to medical or surgical treatment alone. Alternative therapies can include acupuncture, electrical stimulation, cold laser therapy, and physical therapy, along with herbal supplements and food therapy. Disc disease can occur in cats or dogs but is more common in dogs.

A speaker at a veterinary conference for acupuncturists recently referenced quite a few studies showing the same rate of return to function for dogs with ruptured discs with or without surgery. Some dogs will never walk again, even with surgery. Some dogs with complete loss of hind end function will relearn to walk, even without surgery. I have had patients in both categories. Dogs with complete loss of deep pain perception in the limbs (pinch the toes to see if they respond) are generally thought to do better with surgical decompression of the spine. Surgery must be performed within the first 48 hours of pain loss to have the best outcome. Unfortunately, up to fifty percent of dogs suffering one ruptured disc may have a second or third episode in the future. Proper diet, weight loss, and controlled exercise are important in preventing recurrence.

Roscoe, a Bassett Hound, originally came to me with back pain and decreased function of his hind legs but was still able to walk. Roscoe was obese, weighing over 70 pounds. He had been over-vaccinated for years and was eating a very poor diet. I treated Roscoe with chiropractic, acupuncture, and herbs which helped his back pain, but the more important problem was obesity which was contributing to inflammation and decreased mobility. Roscoe's parents took on the weight loss challenge and succeeded in having him lose over 20 pounds using healthy home cooked meals. Along the way Roscoe also tore an anterior cruciate ligament in his hind leg and needed treatment with herbs and laser for that. He did very well for over a year and then became very painful again. Over the course of a few weeks his condition deteriorated, and he was unable to walk. His parents opted for surgery on his back and within a few weeks he was up and running.

Obviously, long backed breeds like Dachshunds and Bassett Hounds are predisposed to disc disease. But many other breeds are prone to similar problems, including Beagles, Cocker Spaniels, and Shih Tzus. All these breeds are prone to obesity, which may contribute to the disease. The best prevention is to control weight, feed a healthy diet, and avoid things that will cause inflammation in the body (sugars and chemicals, including preservatives and dyes). Disc problems can occur in the neck as well as the back; avoid the use of collars if your dog pulls on the leash when walking.

Treatment for degenerative disc disease can include:

- Cage rest (baby playpens can work well if you do not have a crate)
- Steroids, aspirin, and nonsteroidal anti-inflammatory medications (These cannot be used together! Pick one or the other!) These drugs can cause stomach and intestinal ulceration, kidney failure, and liver failure.

- Muscle relaxers—methocarbamol at 30 mg per pound divided into 3 doses daily.
- Herbal medications –American or Chinese combinations; choice will depend on tongue and pulse diagnosis performed by a trained veterinary herbalist; check www.tcvm.com or www.AHVMA.org to find a veterinarian trained in acupuncture and herbal therapy.
- Traditional pain medications—tramadol or gabapentin are commonly used. Tramadol is only effective in 20% of cases. Gabapentin has many side effects including lethargy, drowsiness, stumbling, incoordination, depression, cognitive impairment, gastrointestinal upset, and behavior changes. The drug can also cause deficiencies in vitamin D, vitamin B1, and folate. Gabapentin should not be used in pets with kidney or liver disease.
- PEA—palmatoylethanolamide—The dose is 100 mg for dogs and cats under ten pounds, up to 2,000 mg daily for large dogs.
- Homeopathic remedies—arnica, hypericum, calendula
- Weight control
- Massage, Reiki, physical therapy
- Stem cell or Platelet Rich Plasma therapy
- Golden Paste—see recipe and dosing in chapter 4.
- Bone broth—1/8th to 1 cup once or twice daily based on the size of the pet.
- Deer Antler Velvet—500 to 1500 mg daily.
- Green lipped mussels—may be fed as freeze-dried treats, powders, or whole mussels in food.
- Omega 3 fatty acids—Fish, algae, krill, or calamari oil or phytoplankton. Give 30 to 60 mg per pound of body weight of EPA and DHA added together.
- CBD oil or treats—usually dosed at 1 mg per 10 pounds body weight 2 to 3 times daily.

- Acupuncture and electroacupuncture
- Cold laser therapy
- Chiropractic care or Veterinary Orthopedic Manipulation
- Physical therapy including underwater treadmill.
- Carts—www.eddieswheels.com
- Hind end lifts and harnesses—Ruffwear www.ruffwear. com and Help 'Em Up harnesses
- Puppy stairs to decrease jumping or falling off furniture (my favorites are the original Puppy Stairs which can be ordered from www.puppystairs.com)
- Surgical Decompression

Degenerative Myelopathy

Degenerative myelopathy (DM) is also known as chronic degenerative radiculomyelopathy (CDRM). It is a progressive disease that affects the spinal cord and eventually the brain stem and cranial nerves, which results in complete paralysis. If not euthanized, the pet will eventually succumb due to paralysis of the rib muscles and difficulty breathing.

The symptoms result from degeneration of the white matter of the spinal cord. The white matter contains the nerve fibers responsible for transmitting signals from the brain to the limbs and sensory information back to the brain. The fatty myelin sheath surrounding the nerve fibers is destroyed and eventually the nerve fibers also deteriorate. DM is like some of the forms of human amyotrophic lateral sclerosis (ALS) more commonly known as Lou Gehrig's Disease.

One theory for the cause of DM is that the immune system itself attacks the nervous system causing degeneration. But according to veterinary neurologist Dr. Joan R. Coates, one of the leading experts in this condition, DM is not an inflammatory disease. Degenerative myelopathy patients do not benefit from immunosuppressive drugs such as cyclophosphamide, prednisone, and azathioprine. She states that DM is like oxidative stress which characteristically has a release of free radicals resulting in cell degeneration.

A genetic mutation of SOD-1 (super oxide dismutase—a free radical scavenger found in abundance in the central nervous system) has been found in affected animals. DNA testing can be performed to determine whether a dog is at risk for the disease. Results are labeled as N for normal or DM for degenerative myelopathy. A result of N/N means the dog will not develop DM and cannot transmit it to their offspring. A result of N/DM means the dog will not have the disease but is a carrier and can transmit this variant to 50% of their offspring. Breeding two carrier dogs has a predicted outcome of 25% DM-affected puppies. Dogs with DM/DM may develop the disease and will transmit the genes to all their offspring.

While cats can be affected by this disease, it is very rare. Breeds commonly affected include German Shepherds, Corgis, Siberian Huskies, Collies, Bernese Mountain Dogs, Boxers, Chesapeake Bay Retrievers, Golden Retrievers, Kerry Blue Terriers, Miniature Poodles, Rhodesian Ridgebacks, Standard Poodles, and Wirehaired Fox Terriers. Any breed can potentially be affected.

The disease generally starts at mid- to late age, but dogs have been affected as young as four years old.

Symptoms may be subtle early in the disease. The disease affects the nerves to the hind legs first. Dogs may appear clumsy or be weak in the hind end; they may drag their feet causing the nails to wear down. They may sway when standing or cross their hind legs. As the disease progresses, they will knuckle over or have trouble placing their feet when walking. The hind limbs may tremble, and the muscles will start to atrophy or waste away. Disease progression continues until the dog is unable to stand or walk. Eventually they will become urine and fecal incontinent. The disease will progress to the forelimbs in later stages. Progression is slower in smaller breeds.

Affected dogs generally lose the ability to walk within six to twenty-four months from diagnosis. Dogs with DM are not painful; weakness is the issue.

This disease may be suspected based on breed, medical history, physical examination, and diagnostic tests. The diagnosis is made by eliminating other causes of hind end weakness. Radiographs, CT scans, or MRI can be used to rule out problems such as hip dysplasia, intervertebral disc disease, spondylitis, cruciate tears, and chronic arthritis. If one of these other problems is also present, it can contribute to the patient's loss of function of the hindquarters. DNA testing is recommended for any at-risk breed displaying clinical signs consistent with DM. Biopsy of the spinal cord is the only way to definitively diagnose DM.

While there is no cure, diet and exercise appear to play key roles in slowing or halting disease progression. Studies have shown that physical therapy increases average survival times in pets with DM. Underwater treadmill therapy is highly recommended if available. Dogs suffering with arthritis or other painful disorders in addition to DM should be treated for pain. Other options that may help include:

- The best therapy for these dogs is exercise. This can include leash walking, swimming, physical therapy, and underwater treadmill.
- Hind end support lifts can make life easier for the owners and pets. There are many great products available; I really like those made by Ruffwear and Help 'Em Up harnesses, which are available from many online outlets.
- Carts—www.eddieswheels.com

- Electroacupuncture for nerve stimulation seems to help these dogs retain feeling in their feet.
- Walking on rough surfaces for tactile stimulation may be helpful.
- If the pet is dragging its feet, protective boots should be used to avoid abrasions and wounds. Ruffwear www. ruffwear.com and Therapaws www.therapaw.com are two good sources for these.
- The use of cold laser therapy is still being explored for these dogs.
- Toe Grips can be applied to the nails to give added traction.
- No-Knuckling Training Socks and Resistance Bands can help.
- Chiropractic adjustments, massage, and energy therapies (Reiki, TTouch, craniosacral, vibrational therapy, etc.) will help with blood and nerve flow.

Since this disease may (or may not) be caused by immune system dysfunction, a healthy anti-inflammatory diet and supplements can play a key role in treatment. A raw or home cooked diet free from preservatives, dyes, and chemicals can help decrease inflammation. The diet should contain high quality proteins and be low in carbohydrates.

Supplements can include:

- Aminocaproic acid. Westlab Pharmacy may be a good source for this.
- B-complex vitamins—100 mg daily or 1 tablespoon of nutritional yeast
- Vitamin C—up to 3000 mg daily
- Vitamin E—up to 2000 I.U. daily
- Selenium—up to 100 micrograms daily

- CoQ10 200 to 400 mg twice daily depending on the size of the pet.
- Omega 3 fatty acids dosed at 20 to 40 mg per pound of body weight (best source for this case may be borage or evening primrose oil).
- Ginger—1 tsp dried, ground, given twice daily.
- Garlic—1 fresh, crushed, raw clove twice daily for large dogs, 1/2 clove for smaller dogs, given every other day.
- Bromelain—400 to 500 mg twice daily
- Curcumin—400 to 500 mg twice daily, can be given as Golden Paste
- Grape seed extract—50 mg daily
- Green tea—1 capsule twice daily
- Avoid the use of chemical parasiticides like topical flea and tick preventatives and oral ivermectin.
- N-acetylcysteine (NAC) at 75 mg/kg divided (or 600 mg three times daily for dogs under 50 pounds and 1200 mg three times daily for dogs over 50 pounds) into 3 doses per day for 2 weeks, then 3 doses every other day. Westlab Pharmacy in Gainesville, Florida, can compound this product. It also available from human supplement companies.
- Epsilon-aminocaproic acid (EACA) 500 mg twice daily, from Westlab Pharmacy.

Dogs that are down must be supported to avoid pressure sores. Frequent turning and inspection for any irritated areas must be performed. If the dog is unable to urinate or defecate on its own, the owner must learn to express the bladder and bowels. Incontinent animals must be kept immaculately clean. Getting the pet outside for environmental enrichment is a good idea.

Osteoarthritis

Another name for osteoarthritis is degenerative joint disease. Pets with arthritis may show pain or discomfort in many ways. Common symptoms in dogs include:

- Becoming less active
- Sleeping more
- Interacting less with the people and animals around them
- Whining, crying, groaning
- Aggression, snapping when approached
- Panting
- Pacing because they can't find a comfortable position to lie down
- Slower getting up
- Difficulty using stairs or jumping into the car
- Stiffer when walking or running
- Limping
- Loss of appetite due to pain

Diagnosis of arthritis is based on physical examination and radiographic evidence of degenerative joint disease. Cats suffer from arthritis as often as dogs but are less likely to show symptoms. Over 90% of cats aged 6 to 20 have damage in at least one joint and 90% of cats over age 12 have evidence of osteoarthritis. Age is the number one factor in developing arthritis, but obesity, injuries, poor conformation, and genetic predisposition can play a role. An increased risk is seen in Maine Coon, Persian, Scottish Fold, and Siamese cats.

Symptoms in cats may include:

- Reluctance or hesitance to jump up or down
- Reduced height when jumping
- Difficulty going up or down stairs

- Bunny-hopping with the hind legs or going sideways up and down stairs
- Limping
- Stiffness especially after sleeping
- Walking with the tail down instead of up like a flag
- Difficulty using the litter box or avoiding the box
- Reduced levels of activity
- Hiding or sleeping more than normal
- Less time spent on grooming, clumpy coat from decreased grooming
- Increased vocalization
- Flinching when touched
- Irritability, aggression
- No symptoms at all

There are many treatments available for arthritis, including surgery if the problem is severe.

The most important treatments for arthritis are weight control, exercise in moderation, and pain management. Ideally, a pet with arthritis should maintain a very lean body mass, as extra weight will put more stress on the joints. Even a five-percent weight loss can have dramatic effects on mobility scores. The easiest way to help your pet lose weight is to lower the amount of carbohydrates in the diet, meaning little or no dry food, adding meat protein and vegetables to decrease calories.

Generally, arthritic pets will already be limited in their activity because of pain, but these pets still need exercise. If the pet remains inactive, the muscle groups will start to shrink because they are not being used. As the muscle groups shrink, the pet becomes weaker and more inactive. This then becomes a cycle of inactivity. Exercise is needed to maintain muscle tone and to promote joint health. Controlled walks, swimming, and physical therapy are good exercises that can promote muscle tone and joint mobility. High impact activities such as chasing a ball for prolonged periods may cause too much pain. The key is controlled exercise. Swimming and the use of underwater treadmills are excellent forms of exercise without putting pressure on painful joints.

Pain management is a broad category which includes multiple aspects of both traditional and alternative medicine. Many owners will give aspirin or over-the-counter anti-inflammatory medications to pets, not realizing that aspirin commonly causes stomach ulceration and many of the medications are toxic in pets. Newer NSAID medications are available through veterinarians, but many pets cannot tolerate these medications and many pet owners are afraid to use them due to the possible side effects. Steroids have been used by some doctors, but I prefer to use them for very specific cases, and only as a last resort. There are many side effects associated with steroids, including liver damage, diabetes, and increased thirst and urination.

A new class of drugs has recently been introduced for dogs and cats, anti-NGF (nerve growth factor) antibodies. NGF activates and perpetuates pain by increasing the release of additional pain and inflammation mediators. By targeting NGF, the antibody reduces pain signals. The medication is given by injection (Librela for dogs, Solensia for cats) to provide pain relief from osteoarthritis for four to six weeks. The most common side effects are vomiting and injection site pain, however serious side effects including rapidly destructive joint disease and problems with nerve function have been seen in human trials using the same class of drug. Deterioration or joints in humans were made worse when an NSAID was combined with anti-NGF. The injections should not be used in pregnant or breeding animals. This type of therapy has only been marketed for a short time; long-term side effects remain to be seen.

From a more holistic way of thinking, there are many alternatives available to treat the pain and inflammation of arthritis. I recommend any pet with symptoms or evidence of degenerative joint disease should be started on a nutritional joint supplement containing glucosamine, chondroitin, and hyaluronic acid. Glucosamine acts as a mild anti-inflammatory. Chondroitin inhibits destruction and promotes production of cartilage components. Hyaluronic acid contributes to joint lubrication. There are, literally, thousands of products available on the market. When choosing a product for your pet, be sure to do research on the product you want to use. Human supplements can be used in pets but may not be as readily absorbed and used by the pet's body.

Nutraceuticals (nutritional supplements) are not regulated by the FDA, so you are at the mercy of the company selling the product. Do not rely on website testimonials! (After all, I'm pretty sure my mother would write a pretty good testimonial for me on my website.) The product may, or may not, contain the ingredients listed on the label. One study done years ago showed there were very few products that contained the same level of therapeutic agents in the supplement as they showed on the labels. Some had none, some had more, and some had less.

Studies have shown that starting these agents early for breeds that may be prone to developing arthritis may have a protective effect for the joints. Dosage for glucosamine should be around 15 mg per pound of body weight per day (1500mg for a 100-pound dog, 750 mg for a 50-pound

Hyaluronic acid should be dosed at 2 to 20 mg per day, depending on the size of the dog. I dose any dog over 50 pounds with 20 mg daily. Chondroitin should be given at a dosage of 10 to 15 mg per pound of body weight daily (about the same as the glucosamine). MSM (Methylsulfonylmethane) is found in many joint supplements and has been shown to significantly reduce inflammation in joints. Dosages for MSM should be similar to glucosamine, at around 15 mg per pound of body weight per day.

Polysulfated glycosaminoglycan injections (Adequan, Chondro-protec, Cartrophen, and Ichon are a few of the trade names) have also proven to be highly effective in my opinion. These products contain the building blocks of joint fluid and will help block some of the inflammatory causes of degenerative joint disease. When looking at the joint fluid of an arthritic joint, the fluid will be thin, watery, and possibly bloody. A healthy joint will have a thick, sticky, clear lubricating fluid. Injections of PSGAG's help the body make a better joint fluid. PSGAG injections should not be given within two weeks of a surgical procedure, as it may decrease clotting ability.

Injections are given under the skin or in the muscle once or twice weekly for four weeks. In my practice, we continued monthly maintenance injections. I used Adequan injections twice weekly on my daughter's retired 35-year-old show pony that was so arthritic he could barely walk from the barn to the paddock. By the time I had given his sixth injection he galloped across the field chasing the other horses!

Omega 3 fatty acids, when given in high doses, have been shown to protect the body from inflammation. I recommend all pets with arthritis should take omega 3 fatty acid supplements. The active ingredients in Omega-3 supplements are eicosapentaenoic acid (EPA) and docosahexaenoic acid (DHA). Add the milligrams of these two together to get the milligrams of active omega 3 in the capsule. If the product does not list the actual milligrams and instead gives a percentage of active ingredients, avoid it.

I currently recommend a sixty-pound dog be given about 2,400 milligrams daily. Be careful of the source of fish oil, as many products can have high levels of mercury, lead, PCBs, and other contaminants. Some pets do not like the taste of the oils; natural sources such as wild-caught salmon or sardines can be fed. Vitamin E must always be given along with fish oils or omega-3 fatty acids because vitamin E levels in the blood will drop when omega-3's are fed. Most prescription products will have vitamin E added.

Vitamin C has been shown to be beneficial for pets with arthritis by decreasing inflammation, which in turn decreases pain. Pets must be given bio-available, buffered vitamin C, not over-the-counter human products. Vitamin C will cause diarrhea if dosed too high. If your pet is prescribed this vitamin and develops diarrhea, decrease the dose to the level the pet can tolerate. Small dogs and cats usually tolerate 150 to 500 mg twice daily, while large dogs can usually take 500 to 1000 mg twice daily. Start low and increase gradually. If the pet develops diarrhea, decrease to the last dosage that causes no side effects.

Herbal anti-inflammatory products have become more popular in the last decade. Herbs that may decrease pain and inflammation include willow bark (do not use in cats as it contains salicylate, the active compound in aspirin), devil's claw, feverfew, yucca, Boswellia, turmeric, ashwagandha, arnica, and garlic. There are many products available, but again, these are not regulated by any government agencies.

Herbs can and do have side effects, just like prescription medications. Please consult with a veterinary herbalist prior to using these products. Many herbal products cannot be used along with traditional medications, so always ask if products can be used together!

Duralactin is a supplement made from the dried milk protein of hyperimmunized cows. This product blocks the white blood cells responsible for inflammation from migrating, attaching to, and participating in reactions that cause pain and inflammation in the body, particularly in the joints. There have been no side effects associated with this product and it does not cause gastrointestinal upset.

Duralactin is available in vanilla flavored wafers that smell like cake. It is also available in a soft chew that contains glucosamine, MSM, and Omega-3 fatty acids. Personally, I do not feel the levels of these additions are high enough for therapeutic value, so I like to use the vanilla wafer and supplement the glucosamine, chondroitin, and Omega 3 fatty acids separately. I'm also not a fan of the inactive ingredients in the soft chews. For cats the product is available as a capsule, liquid, or paste.

My favorite arthritis treatments in the past few years have been the nontraditional therapies including acupuncture, acupressure, and chiropractic. Acupuncture and acupressure can be used to decrease pain and inflammation and help with improved mobility. All pets with arthritic joints will benefit from chiropractic care since the pain in the joints affects mobility and results in improper movement of the spine. Once animals have a chiropractic adjustment and mobility is restored to the spine, the lower limbs move in a more fluid manner. Think of the spine as a "slinky" that should be mobile at every joint. When watching people or animals run, the spine should be relaxed, allowing fluid motion of the limbs. A "locked" or stiff spine will result in a stilted gait which puts more pressure on the joints. Watching a horse from behind, the tail head should naturally swish side to side during the walk or trot. I love seeing animals move before and after treatment. Clients are continually amazed the first time they see the free movement of their horse or pet after an adjustment.

Massage to loosen tight, contracted, painful muscles in spasm can help immensely. There are many professional massage therapists available to work on pets, but I usually gave my clients home massage techniques to perform between visits. Once I am able to release muscle spasms in the office with acupuncture, chiropractic, or myofascial release, the pet will maintain the benefits of therapy much longer if the owner continues the work at home with daily massage. Generally, pets will enjoy gentle massage along both sides of the spine and over the hips. Start with very light pressure, gradually increasing to a level your pet will tolerate. A good reference for home acupressure treatments is a book called *Four Paws, Five Directions* by Cheryl Schwartz.

Cold Laser Therapy has recently become commonplace and many traditional veterinarians are starting to perform this treatment. There are many levels of cold laser available for use and, unfortunately, this is another place where you need to do your homework and be sure the laser being used will be beneficial and not harmful. Some lasers can burn the skin when not used properly. Others have minimal power and are not effective. High power class IV lasers were only approved for use by the FDA in 2005. This is the category I recommend using because of their ability to penetrate deep into the tissues and joints.

Wavelength and power are the determinants of strength and effectiveness of the laser. Lasers work by using specific wavelengths of light that stimulate blood flow, release oxygen from the red blood cells, release energy to heal tissues, and stimulate acupuncture points. This results in decreased pain, increased wound healing, neurologic repair, and decreased production of scar tissue. Besides arthritis, cold laser therapy can be used to heal infected wounds, infected ears, chronic lick granulomas, sprains, strains, and fractures, as well as to speed healing after surgery. New uses for cold laser therapy are constantly being developed.

Treatment using cold laser therapy usually consists of five to seven treatments performed over two to three weeks, then follow up as needed. If high level lasers are being used, the operator, the person holding the animal, and the animal should wear protective goggles to prevent damage if the laser were to be accidentally pointed at the eyes.

Physical therapy for both cats and dogs has become a prominent specialty in veterinary practice in the past ten years. The use of specific prescribed exercises, pools, treadmills, and underwater treadmills have helped animals recover from surgery, arthritis, and traumatic injuries much more quickly than they would without therapy. Many owners with dogs used for show, agility, dance, and strength work use physical therapy techniques to keep their pets strong and in great shape. When choosing physical therapy for your pet, use a reputable therapist trained by one of the licensed centers currently in operation. Don't hesitate to ask for credentials and referrals from other clients.

Newer therapies including stem cell regeneration and enhanced platelet therapies are more complicated because they involve anesthesia and surgical procedures but are showing great promise. My first client to request Stem Cell Therapy owned a giant German Shepherd named Roxy. Roxy weighed over 110 pounds and had been born with elbow and hip dysplasia. I had been treating Roxy for over five years with joint supplements, Adequan, herbal supplements, and chiropractic, but her arthritis was progressing and she was starting to show lameness. The owner reluctantly started using low doses of Rimadyl, which made Roxy more comfortable, but we were both worried about the long-term effects of using an NSAID. When I mentioned Stem Cell Therapy, Roxy's owner was thrilled at the possibility of decreasing pain and increasing mobility for his beloved girl.

When we radiographed Roxy's joints we found bad elbows, stifles, and hips. The joints were some of the worst I had ever seen on x-ray, and I was impressed that Roxy was maintaining her current level of mobility. Roxy was sedated and multiple vials of fat were removed from under the skin over her chest and behind her shoulder. The fat cells were shipped to California, processed to harvest the Stem Cells, and they were shipped back to us. The cells were then injected into Roxy's hips, stifles, and elbows, with one dose given intravenously. Within two weeks I received multiple phone calls and text messages proclaiming Roxy was running like a puppy. Roxy had Stem Cells injected an additional time and she continued to do well for quite a few years.

I have also performed Platelet Rich Plasma therapy. The procedure is much simpler than Stem Cell Therapy in that no harvesting of fat cells is required. A blood sample is processed and filtered to isolate a platelet-rich fraction and that is then injected into the arthritic joints. The first patient I treated with PRP, a young dog with hip dysplasia, did very well, showing a decrease in pain and an increase in mobility.

Orthopedic, heated, or magnetic pet beds can also help relieve pain for many pets. Some arthritic pets are worse in cold weather, while others will be worse in hot weather. (Most of us associate cold wet weather with joint pain, but that isn't always the case.) There may be times when pets seem very comfortable even though they have severe arthritis, like Roxy, but there will also be times when you will need every tool in the toolbox to keep the pet moving.

Treatment options for pets with arthritis include the following:

- Feed a healthy, species-appropriate diet free from dyes, chemicals, or preservatives to decrease inflammation. The diet should contain high quality proteins and be low in carbohydrates.
- Weight loss, if needed.
- Controlled daily exercise.
- Golden Paste (see chapter 3)—natural anti-inflammatory and pain relief
- Bone broth—natural source of collagen to support joints
- Homeopathic arnica, hypericum, calendula, ruta, Symphytum

- Green lipped mussels 5 mg per pound daily
- Deer Antler Velvet 50 mg per pound daily
- Colostrum—provides over 70 growth factors for cellular support, give 3 to 5 mg/pound daily.
- PEA (palmatoylethanolamide)—dose is 100 mg for dogs and cats under ten pounds, up to 2,000 mg daily for large dogs.
- CBD oil and treats
- Omega 3 fatty acids dosed at 30 to 50 mg (some holistic veterinarians recommend up to 200 mg) per pound of body weight along with vitamin E at 1 to 2 IU per pound of body weight daily.
- Natural anti-inflammatories such as Duralactin given twice daily.
- Joint supplements containing glucosamine, chondroitin sulfate, and MSM, dosed at 15 mg per pound once daily.
- Hyaluronic acid dosed at 2 to 20 mg per dog once daily (Conquer).
- Polysulfated glycosaminoglycan injections (Adequan, Cartophen, Ichon, Chondroprotec) given once or twice weekly for four weeks, then once a month.
- Vitamin C—150 to 1000 mg twice daily based on the size of the cat or dog and bowel tolerance.
- Cold laser therapy.
- Chiropractic adjustments or Veterinary Orthopedic Manipulation
- Acupuncture, Electroacupuncture, or acupressure
- Herbal anti-inflammatory medications
- Chinese herbals—check www.tcvm.com to find a veterinary practitioner in your area.
- Stem Cell Therapy
- Platelet Rich Plasma Therapy

- Massage
- Acupressure—*Four Paws, Five Directions* by Cheryl Schwartz
- Physical therapy including underwater treadmill
- Orthopedic, heated, or magnetic beds
- Pain management with steroids, NSAIDS, opioids, or other medications as a last resort.

Cruciate Ligament Tears

The word **cruciate** means 'to cross over' or 'form a cross'. The cruciate ligaments are two bands of fibrous tissue located within each stifle (knee) joint. They join the femur and tibia (the bones above and below the knee joint) together so that the knee works as a stable, hinged joint.

One ligament runs from the inside to the outside of the knee joint and the other from the outside to the inside, crossing over each other in the middle. In dogs and cats, the ligaments are called the cranial and caudal cruciate ligament. In dogs, the most common knee injury is a rupture or tear of the cranial cruciate ligament. Ruptured cruciate ligament is not a common ailment in cats; it usually occurs because of trauma.

The two most common causes of cranial cruciate rupture are trauma and degeneration of the ligaments within the joint. Acute or traumatic cruciate rupture is caused by a twisting injury to the knee joint. This occurs most often when the dog is running and suddenly changes direction. This places most of the body weight on the knee joint, and excessive rotational and shearing forces are placed on the cruciate ligaments. A cruciate ligament rupture is usually extremely painful, and the knee joint becomes unstable, resulting in lameness.

A more chronic form of cruciate damage occurs due to

progressive weakening of the ligaments because of repeated trauma or arthritic disease. Initially, the ligament becomes stretched or partially torn and lameness may be only slight and intermittent. With continued use of the joint, the condition gradually gets worse until a complete rupture occurs. Sadly, 40 to 60% of dogs that have cruciate disease in one knee will develop the same problem in the second knee.

Manganese deficiency has been associated with ligament weakness and injuries. Manganese activates the enzymes that are needed to build collagen. Dogs cannot make manganese so it must be provided in the diet. Manganese is found in liver, mussels, ginger, kelp, hemp seeds, pumpkin seeds, spirulina, pineapple, spinach, kale, oysters, sardines, hair, feathers, and wool. The herbicide glyphosate (Roundup) has been shown to reduce uptake of manganese; avoid feeding grain-filled kibble that may have GMO produce or meat from confinement-raised animals that were fed GMO grains. So not supplement synthetic manganese, as too much manganese can be neurotoxic; the mineral should be provided through whole food ingredients.

Obesity, inactivity, poor conformation, and having luxating patella (kneecap) can contribute to strain on the cruciate ligament. Ligaments weaken with age and neutered animals are more likely to have cruciate tears. Diagnosis is made by palpation of the joint; radiographs will show fluid in the joint but will not show the ligament itself.

There are many surgical options for repair of torn cruciate ligaments. Cats and small dogs may heal enough to have a stable joint with confinement and rest for a period of eight to twelve weeks. My cat, Mittens, had a traumatic injury and tore his cruciate ligament. After twelve weeks of confinement and not being allowed to climb or jump he was able to resume normal activities with no lameness.

Custom knee braces are a newer option for pets that cannot undergo surgery, or the owner wants to avoid surgery. My office manager had an older beagle with significant heart disease that ruptured her cruciate. A custom brace was made which the dog wore very comfortably. Three months later she ruptured the cruciate ligament in her other leg and had to wear a second brace. After six months in braces the knees had healed enough that the dog was able to walk and run normally without the braces. A good brace will cost around $1,000. Even with the cost of two braces, the cost was significantly less than two surgical repairs which generally average $3,000 to $5,000 each.

For those wanting to avoid surgery, rest, acupuncture, cold laser, chiropractic care, and use of many of the same supplements recommended for arthritis can result in return of function. Stem cell therapy, enriched platelet therapy, and prolotherapy can also be used successfully. Physical therapy is an important adjunct to healing. Weight control is a critical piece of the healing puzzle.

Mobility Support

One big problem for older arthritic dogs is slipping and sliding on wood, laminate, or tile floors. Many dogs will not walk on slippery surfaces for fear of falling. Not only is the sliding scary, but it can also be dangerous, resulting in torn ligaments and muscles and broken bones. "Toe-Grips" are small, thick, rubber bands that can be placed around the properly trimmed nails of dogs to help them "get a grip" on slippery floors. Charlie was our first pet to wear them and once he realized he wouldn't fall he ran everywhere in the house. Toe grips can be ordered online and are easy to apply, but you may want to ask for help from a veterinarian or technician the first time you try. Soak the bands in alcohol and they slip on easily. Once the alcohol dries, they should stay in place if sized correctly. Toe grips will need to be replaced as the nails grow out or the bands wear through. Charlie was not very active, so his bands stayed in place for months.

Another method to decrease slipping is by using rubber boots that can be applied to the paws with Velcro closures. Boots should not be left on for long periods of time, as they will trap moisture and lead to infections between the toes. They are great for use on long walks or for dogs that drag their toes or feet causing abrasions. Sizing is important; follow directions for whichever product you choose.

I had rubber floors throughout my veterinary clinics to minimize slipping for pets and people. I loved them but most people are not going to put rubber floors in their homes. An inexpensive alternative is the use of rubber "tiles" that can be purchased at home supply stores. They come in multiple sizes and colors and can be locked together like puzzle pieces. Most people use them in children's playrooms. These are much better than throw rugs, unless you get rugs with rubber backing that will not slip.

Caring for dogs that have mobility problems can be challenging for the caretaker. It is crucial that you lift the dog without hurting the dog or yourself, especially with large breeds. Harnesses are available to support the dog comfortably and keep you from hurting your back when lifting. I have had great success with both the Help 'Em Up harnesses and harnesses from Ruffwear. There are harnesses available for the front end, the back end, or both. Don't use a towel or leash around the middle of the dog; it will cause pain to the dog and you.

Two- and four-wheel carts are available for pets with paralysis or extreme weakness. Our Cavalier King Charles Spaniel, Charlie, had a four-wheel cart for the last three years of his life. His arthritis was so bad that he could not walk without the support of the cart. With the cart, he was able to run and chase the other dogs and go for walks with the pack. It is critical that the cart be fitted to the pet. Most websites have instructions for measuring the pet to assure correct fit. A cart that is not balanced will put strain on the spine and musculature.

- Toe Grips www.toegrips.com
- Rubber boots—Ruffwear www.ruffwear.com or Thera-paws www.therapaw.com
- Puppy stairs and ramps—www.puppystairs.com
- Body lifts—Help 'Em Up harnesses and www.ruffwear.com
- Carts www.eddieswheels.com

Just Say No to NSAIDs

NSAIDs, or nonsteroidal anti-inflammatory drugs, are commonly used to decrease pain and inflammation for both humans and animals. You might recognize these in your own medicine cabinet with names like ibuprofen (Advil) and naproxen (Alleve). Both can be deadly to pets, so please don't share. Your pet might be placed on any number of these, which include carprofen (Vetprofen, Novox, Rimadyl), deracoxib (Deramaxx), firocoxib (Previcox), piroxicam (Feldene), or meloxicam (Metacam). While these drugs have eliminated much pain and suffering for pets (mostly dogs, cats are very sensitive to these drugs, although Metacam and the new drug, Onsior, are available for cats), they can also have serious side effects, including death. Common uses for the medications include ACL tears or other strains/sprains, post-surgical pain management, arthritis, and trauma. They are also commonly included in some cancer treatment protocols.

The risks of NSAID use are serious. If your pet is placed on an NSAID drug, you need to monitor closely for any of the following signs and stop administration of the drug immediately:

- decreased appetite
- vomiting
- excessive drooling or nausea

- diarrhea
- black, tarry stools
- abdominal pain
- lethargy
- pale gums
- seizures

These symptoms could be an indication of more serious side effects which can include:

- kidney failure
- liver failure
- stomach or intestinal ulceration
- stomach or intestinal perforation
- death

These drugs should NEVER be combined with steroids, aspirin, or other NSAIDs, as the risk of side effects and death are much higher. If your pet is given one NSAID and the doctor wants to change your pet to a different NSAID, you should wait a MINIMUM of 5 to 7 days between drugs. If your pet has gastrointestinal side effects like decreased appetite, vomiting, or diarrhea, do NOT mask the symptoms by giving additional drugs like Pepcid, metoclopramide, metronidazole, famotidine, or sucralfate. If your pet is suffering from GI symptoms and is taken OFF the NSAID, then antacids and stomach protectants can be given. The combination of antacids and NSAIDs can cause a rare reaction in which the stomach wall swells to the point of obstructing the GI tract. (I never would have known about this, but it happened to my office manager's dog while being treated by another veterinarian.) If an NSAID is prescribed for one of your pets, please do not share it with other pets in the household. Many NSAIDs cannot be given to cats and the dosage range for dogs is very narrow. Small weight differences can be significant when dosing the drugs.

While I do believe pain management is an important part of proper pet care, I also believe owners need to be well informed of the potential side effects. I am always amazed when I see a new client with a pet that has been given steroids and NSAIDs together. Owners need to be aware of the dangers. Always ask questions about interactions between medications.

SAMPLE DIET TO HELP ARTHRITIS IN DOGS IF WORSE IN WINTER

☐ 1 pound venison

☐ 1 pound boneless chicken thigh with skin

☐ 8 ounces sweet potato

☐ 4 ounces beef kidney

☐ 4 ounces cabbage

☐ 3 ounces beef liver

☐ 3 teaspoons ground turmeric powder

☐ 3 teaspoons hempseed

☐ 3 teaspoons ground eggshell or bonemeal powder

☐ 1 teaspoon cod liver oil

☐ 1 teaspoon kelp

☐ 1/2 teaspoon sea salt

☐ 1 capsule zinc 15 mg or 1.5 ounces oyster

Provides 37 calories per ounce. May be fed raw or gently cooked. Follow feeding guidelines in chapter 4.

SAMPLE DIET FOR CRUCIATE LIGAMENT INJURIES

☐ 10 ounces ground beef 90% lean

☐ 6 ounces beef heart

☐ 2 ounces beef liver

☐ 4 ounces kale

☐ 2 eggs

☐ 2 ounces dandelion greens

☐ 2 ounces crab

☐ 1 ounce fresh parsley

☐ 1.5 teaspoons ground eggshell or bonemeal powder

☐ 1 teaspoon ground hulled hempseed

☐ 1/2 teaspoon kelp

This diet provides 31 calories per ounce. May be fed raw or gently cooked. Follow feeding guidelines in chapter 4.

SAMPLE DIET TO HELP ARTHRITIS IN CATS

- ☐ 8 ounces venison
- ☐ 4 ounces salmon
- ☐ 4 ounces beef liver
- ☐ 1 ounce oysters (or 1 zinc capsule 15 mg)
- ☐ 2 teaspoons bonemeal or eggshell powder
- ☐ 1/2 teaspoon kelp
- ☐ 1 teaspoon grated fresh ginger root
- ☐ 1 teaspoon ground turmeric powder
- ☐ 1 teaspoon ground hulled hempseed
- ☐ 100 IU vitamin E
- ☐ 500 mg taurine

This recipe provides 33 calories per ounce. May be fed raw or gently cooked. Follow feeding guidelines in chapter 4.

9

Syringomyelia and Chiari Malformation

Our first "foster failure" (a foster dog that wins your heart and you can't possibly send them to another home, so you keep them) was a ruby red Cavalier from Indiana. He was given up by a puppy mill breeder in Indiana who walked into a veterinary office and "dropped off" five old females and one old male that were no longer capable of producing puppies. At least she didn't send them to auction. The ruby red boy was adopted by a woman who was on vacation in Illinois and thought he was cute. By the time she drove him home from Illinois to Pennsylvania, she had decided she didn't want to keep him. He snored (heaven forbid!) and he only had five teeth. He didn't fit her idea of the perfect dog. She called the adoption group in Illinois, and they were willing to take him back, but she would have to deliver him. She couldn't be bothered. The one good thing she did was contact the local Cavalier rescue group. They contacted the Illinois group, and an agreement was made that Charlie would go into the Cavalier network. We agreed to pick him up in Pennsylvania immediately.

Charlie stayed with us for a few months, and we fell in love. He didn't snore (at least not as loudly as anyone else in the house) and he lost a tooth, so he was down to four. His x-rays showed he was extremely arthritic; his spine was fused in many places and his hind legs were awful. Half the time he scooted himself around instead of walking. He would wait at the top or bottom of the stairs to see if we were coming right back so he didn't waste a trip up or down. He was a grumpy old man with the other dogs at times, but he loved his girls (after all, he was a breeding male for a lot of years).

With Charlie, I had another chance to use my alternative treatments to help him. He took omega-3 fatty acids in large doses to reduce inflammation. He was on an herbal pain relief medicine and a tablet containing colostrum from hyper-immunized cows for his arthritis (Duralactin). He received laser therapy to decrease pain and inflammation in his back and legs. We put rubber "toe-grips" on his nails to help him slide less on the hardwood and tile floors.

In addition to arthritis, Charlie also had a disease called SM or syringomyelia. It's very common in Cavaliers and English Toy Spaniels, but other brachycephalic (short-nosed) breeds can be affected, such as the Brussels Griffon, Maltese, Yorkshire Terrier, Chihuahua, Boston Terrier, Pug, and Pitbull Terrier. With SM, part of the nervous tissue of the spinal cord is replaced by a fluid-filled cavity. The disease is commonly combined with Chiari malformation, a condition where the back of the skull compresses the brainstem and top of the spinal cord. A dog can have Chiari malformation without syringomyelia. The Chiari malformation is the most common cause of syringomyelia but not the only cause. Facial nerve paralysis often accompanies these diseases.

Symptoms vary; they usually include pain and scratching at the neck or "air-scratching", chewing along the spine, or scooting. Veterinarians unfamiliar with this disease will commonly treat these dogs with steroids and antihistamines for nonexistent allergies. Unfortunately, steroids sometimes help relieve symptoms, leading owners to believe their pet does have allergies when they are dealing with something much more significant. Charlie did not scratch much; instead, he had very strange seizures where he howled and screamed at the top of his lungs with his head thrown back. Many dogs will not allow petting of the head and neck, will shy away from touch, will not allow grooming or brushing, and may hide. Crying out when running, jumping, or being handled or picked up is common. Affected dogs may rub their faces incessantly.

Diagnosis is made with MRI. Radiographs are not very useful for diagnosis. Symptoms can occur at any time but tend to happen mostly in the middle of the night. Sometimes they can go days without symptoms, other times they will be miserable for days. Symptoms may progress over time, but it is impossible to predict progression.

Treatment for SM can include surgery on the spine, which is expensive, dangerous, and doesn't always decrease symptoms. We opted not to treat Charlie with surgery, so he took a combination of medications. I used gabapentin, because it has some pain relief properties to help arthritis pain and it also functions as an anti-seizure medicine (although newer studies show it may not be helpful in dogs). Pre-gabalin, or Lyrica, is another option if the gabapentin is not effective. He took furosemide, which is a diuretic to help decrease the fluid accumulation around his brainstem and spinal cord. He was on omeprazole which also helped decrease the fluid production in the spinal cord. The hyper-immunized cow's colostrum (Duralactin) that he took for his arthritis also helped decrease the inflammation in his spinal cord.

Charlie's protocol was a good combination of therapies to help him live a comfortable life and he was a very happy boy. However, as time went on, I became less comfortable with all the medications he was being given. Determined to give him a better quality of life, I did more research and came up with a plan to get him off all the medications: gabapentin, omeprazole, and furosemide. I'm happy to say I was successful!

Instead of medications, Charlie was treated with Duralactin, cold laser therapy, deer antler velvet, green lipped mussels, CBD oil, omega-3 oils, acupuncture, and PEA (palmatoylethanolamide). Since using PEA on Charlie I have been able to use this same protocol for all my dogs with CM and SM and have not had to resort to medications.

A pilot trial in the Netherlands gave PEA to 12 Cavalier King Charles Spaniels with confirmed cases of syringomyelia. After one week, the owners of all 12 dogs noticed improvements in pain-related behavior and inflammatory signs. PEA has worked wonders for our own dogs with syringomyelia, allowing us to discontinue the use of the drug Gabapentin. For more information on PEA, visit www.drjudymorgan.com

Current therapies used for SM and CM:

- Gabapentin or Pre-gabalin—These have many side effects including lethargy, drowsiness, stumbling, incoordination, depression, cognitive impairment, gastrointestinal upset, and behavior changes. The drug can also cause deficiencies in vitamin D, vitamin B1, and folate. Gabapentin should not be used in pets with kidney or liver disease.
- Tramadol—This is only effective in 20% of dogs. Side effects include constipation, lethargy, nausea, vomiting, loss of appetite, diarrhea, drowsiness, sedation, anxiety, and tremors.
- Furosemide or Spironolactone—Side effects include dehydration, kidney damage, electrolyte imbalances, low potassium levels.
- Prednisone or Dexamethasone—Side effects included weight gain, muscle loss, increased thirst and urination, gastrointestinal upset, stomach ulceration, high blood

pressure, pancreatitis, panting, and suppressed immune system.

- Nonsteroidal anti-inflammatory medications—Side effects include gastrointestinal upset, behavior changes, bowel ulceration or perforation, liver failure, and kidney failure.
- Apoquel (oclacitinib)—AVOID THIS ONE. Side effects include vomiting, diarrhea, anorexia, behavior changes, aggression, liver failure, bone marrow suppression, seizures, immune suppression, infections, poor wound healing, viral papillomas, demodex, and cancer.
- Duralactin—natural supplement with no side effects. Decreases pain and inflammation.
- Omeprazole—Side effects include allergic reaction with hives and swelling, vomiting, decreased appetite, gas, and diarrhea. It should be used with caution in pets with severe heart, kidney, and liver disease. Stomach cancer has been associated with long term use of this drug in people. This drug should not be used for more than eight weeks.
- Amitriptyline—Side effects include sedation, constipation, urinary retention, hyperexcitability, irregular heart rhythms, seizures, vomiting, diarrhea, decreased white blood cell counts, and endocrine problems. It should be used with caution in pets with thyroid disease, urinary retention, liver disorders, dry eye, glaucoma, heart arrhythmias, diabetes, or adrenal gland tumors.
- MSM—methyl sulfonyl methane—natural anti-inflammatory, give 15 mg per pound of body weight daily.
- PEA—palmitoylethanolamide—a natural anti-inflammatory and pain killer, treats nerve pain. PEA works by

supporting the healthy function of glial (nerve support) cells and mast (immune cells) in the body.

- CBD—natural anti-inflammatory available as oil or in treats. There are many, many companies selling CBD. Be sure to research the company before purchasing.
- Omega-3 fatty acids—Use fish, krill, algae, phytoplankton, or calamari oil which are high in EPA and DHA. Total EPA and DHA should supply 30 to 40 mg per pound of body weight once or twice daily.
- Cold Laser Therapy—stimulates circulation, cell regeneration, and decreases pain and inflammation.
- Surgery—This should only be performed if the quality of life is very poor, or the patient has not responded to medical therapy. The surgery has a very high failure rate; about half of the dogs treated surgically will decline by two years post-op or develop scar tissue necessitating more surgery.
- Removing affected dogs from breeding programs
- Food therapy add-ons that may help drain the fluid include Shiitake mushrooms, celery, lemon juice and lemon zest, dandelion greens or root, radishes, turnips, garlic, and barley. To get the fluid moving, foods that will resolve stagnation include carrots, parsley, radish, ginger, garlic, turmeric, and vinegar. I recommend a home-prepared or high-quality commercial raw or gently cooked food using whole-food ingredients. Do not feed starchy carbohydrates (potatoes, peas, lentils, pasta).

If you suspect your pet has SM or CM, you will need to work closely with your veterinarian to determine which therapies are the best for your pet. Not all dogs need all medications and not all dogs are candidates for surgery.

SAMPLE RECIPE FOR SYRINGOMYELIA

- ☐ 8 ounces boneless chicken thigh with skin
- ☐ 8 ounces boneless chicken breast with skin
- ☐ 3 ounces Shiitake mushrooms
- ☐ 4 ounces turnips
- ☐ 4 ounces carrots
- ☐ 4 ounces chicken liver
- ☐ 2 ounces fresh parsley
- ☐ 1 teaspoon grated fresh ginger root
- ☐ 1 teaspoon ground turmeric root
- ☐ 1 teaspoon eggshell or bonemeal powder
- ☐ 1/2 teaspoon kelp
- ☐ 1 ounce oyster or 1 zinc capsule 15 mg
- ☐ 1 ounce spirulina powder
- ☐ 500 IU vitamin D3
- ☐ 100 IU vitamin E

Provides 33 calories per ounce. May be fed raw or gently cooked. Follow feeding guidelines in Chapter 4.

10 Epilepsy and Seizures

Disorders of the nervous system of animals are varied, including congenital, infectious, traumatic, toxic, inflammatory, metabolic, nutritional, degenerative, and cancer. Many neurologic diseases have been well treated with traditional medications while others have had lackluster response. In acute situations like sudden paralysis or cluster seizures, Western medications can play a pivotal role in treatment. More chronic diseases are sometimes better suited to alternative forms of therapy. Patients with seizures, chronic back pain, inter-vertebral disc disease, degenerative myelopathy, and limb paresis or paralysis may find more long-term healing and relief when treated with acupuncture, chiropractic care, herbals, and nutritional therapy.

A seizure is a sudden, uncontrolled surge of electrical activity released by the cells in the brain. This causes small electrical signals to be sent through the nerves to the body's muscles, causing a change in how the body appears or acts for a short period of time. Seizures may produce physical shaking, minor physical signs like twitching, thought disturbances, lack of consciousness, or a combination of these. Temporary loss of vision, aggressive behavior, or inability to walk may occur.

It is estimated that 1% of the canine population has some form of seizure disorder. Any breed can develop seizures caused by infections, liver disease, kidney disease, low blood sugar, toxins, trauma, cancer, or other underlying conditions, but congenital or primary epilepsy is caused by genetic abnormalities. The incidence of idiopathic (inherited) epilepsy in certain breeds of dog can be as high as 15% to 20%, commonly affecting Belgian Tervuren, Shetland sheepdogs, beagles, Labrador retrievers, golden retrievers, keeshonds, vizslas, and German short haired pointers.

Seizures are rare in cats. Compared with dogs, cats more commonly exhibit partial seizures. These seizures only affect part of the body and are much more difficult to recognize. They may manifest as drooling, eyelid or facial twitching, excessive vocalization, growling, and abnormal head, neck, or limb movements. They may progress to generalized seizures and they may occur several times throughout the day (cluster seizure). Providing a video recording of the event to your veterinarian is helpful to ascertain if your cat is truly having an epileptic seizure. Although seizures in cats are believed to occur less commonly than in dogs, affected cats tend to experience high seizure frequency whatever the type and underlying cause.

Popular oral and topical flea and tick preventative products are commonly linked to seizures. Dogs and cats with a history of seizures should not be treated with isooxazoline products or products containing moxidectin. The federal Food and Drug Administration has issued a warning about isoxazoline-based flea and tick medications, cautioning that the products could lead to neurological issues such as seizures. Isoxazoline drugs affect GABA receptors in the brain, which can lead to seizures or tremors (and potentially death). I do not recommend using any neurotoxic chemicals on dogs and cats. Most flea and tick chemical products are neurotoxins. For natural flea prevention see chapter 5. Side effects of these products include:

- Aggression
- Personality changes
- Seizures
- Disorientation
- Wobbling or unstable gate
- Sensitivity to touch
- Abnormal vocalizations
- Urinary or fecal incontinence
- Death
- Liver failure
- Kidney failure
- Dry eye
- Clotting disorders
- Internal hemorrhage
- Skin disease and itching
- Vomiting
- Diarrhea
- Inappetence
- Drooling

Isoxazoline products include Nexgard, Simparica, Simparica Trio, Bravecto, Credelio, and Revolution Plus. If you have used isooxazoline-based flea and tick chemicals on your cat or dog, follow this detox protocol:

- Milk Thistle 50-100mg per 25lbs twice
- NAC (N-acetylcysteine) 500mg twice daily for 2 weeks then once daily for two weeks
- Chlorella 25mg twice daily for 3 weeks
- The Chinese Herb Di Tan Tang for seizures 0.5 gm per 20 pounds body weight twice daily until the pet has been free of seizures for at least three months.
- Liposomal Glutathione 100mg daily for a week

- Curcumin 100mg once daily for a week
- Broccoli Sprouts 100mg once daily for a week
- Gaba Aminobutyric Acid 100mg once daily for a week
- Add asparagus and dandelion greens or root to the diet. Dark leafy greens such as kale, beet tops, and spinach may be helpful.
- Epsom salt/baking soda baths to pull out toxins
- MCT oil (medium chain triglyceride) 1/2 teaspoon per 10 pounds or 1/2 tablespoon per 30 pounds of body weight. Start slowly.

Diagnostic testing to determine the cause of the seizures may include bloodwork (CBC, chemistry screen, thyroid testing, urinalysis), infectious disease testing (tick-borne diseases, toxoplasmosis, feline leukemia, feline immunodeficiency virus, feline infection peritonitis), blood pressure testing, imaging (MRI, CT scan), and cerebrospinal fluid testing. If tests fail to determine a cause, the disease is designated as idiopathic epilepsy (unknown cause).

Treatment for seizures using medication should not be started unless the pet is having frequent seizures (more often than once a month), is having clusters of seizures, or is not coming out of a seizure episode. Pets with seizures and epilepsy are commonly treated with phenobarbital, which is a wonderful drug and has saved many pets from a seizure-filled life. Unfortunately, the liver is the primary organ responsible for filtering and de-toxifying phenobarbital in the body. Pets receiving phenobarbital become thirsty, hungry, and sleepy for the first three weeks when taking the medication. The symptoms subside or diminish after three weeks because the liver makes a new enzyme-converting system that handles the drug. Unfortunately, most pets will develop cirrhosis of the liver with chronic phenobarbital usage. Many newer anti-epileptic drugs are replacing phenobarbital.

Any pet receiving anti-seizure medications should have liver enzyme values monitored frequently and should be fed with food and herbs that support the liver. Liver is the organ of spring which is associated with the color green. Dark green, leafy foods such as spinach, kale, mustard greens, spirulina, and chlorophyll will help keep the liver happy. Milk thistle (silymarin) and SAMe (s-adenylmethionine) help protect and regenerate liver cells.

Luckily, there are other methods available to deal with seizures, for those interested in using alternative medicine. I have successfully treated many pets with seizures using food therapy, herbs, and acupuncture. There is no "one-size-fits-all" herbal remedy for seizures. Clients often purchase online products to treat seizures which can be harmful. Seizures can be associated with Internal Wind, Liver Stagnation with Phlegm-Fire, Blood Stagnation, Liver Yin and/or Blood Deficiency, or Kidney Jing Deficiency (different Chinese medicine patterns). Without the help of a veterinarian trained in Traditional Chinese Medicine it would be impossible to choose the correct formula of herbs. Please do not be misled by online testimonials claiming one product will cure all pets with seizures. In addition, if you don't straighten out the diet being fed, the herbs will have no effect. I do not vaccinate pets with epilepsy or other seizure disorders.

One of my patients, Breeze, was a Border Collie who had a very active life as a search and rescue dog. He searched for people that were lost or killed (a cadaver dog). He developed a seizure disorder that could have ended his career. Search and rescue dogs go through years of training, and it would have been a shame to lose such a valued member of a team. His owner was very concerned about medicating with phenobarbital, as that could affect his tracking abilities, so she sought out alternative therapy for his treatments. His diet was changed from dry food to a high quality commercial frozen and freeze-dried raw product.

Instead of vaccinating, titers were run to test immunity level to Distemper and Parvovirus. He received dry needle acupuncture treatments to drain his liver excess and stop internal wind. He took a combination of herbal medications including Di Tan Tang, Long Dan Xie Gan Wan, and Epimedium. This combination kept him seizure-free for over a year. Before treatment he had seizures every two to three weeks. Unfortunately, the work he performed required vaccination against Rabies once every three years, so he had to be vaccinated. His heartworm preventative was changed from ivermectin to low dose milbemycin. Ivermectin, moxidectin, and selamectin may lower the seizure threshold and may increase seizure frequency when given; therefore, I do not recommend using products containing these ingredients in pets with known seizure history.

Current recommendations for pets with seizures include:

- Judicious use of anti-seizure medications including phenobarbital, potassium bromide, leviteracetam, felbamate, or zonisamide.
- Monitor liver and kidney function every few months.
- Feed a healthy, species-appropriate diet free from dyes, preservatives, or chemicals. Feed diets with high quality proteins that are low in carbohydrates.
- Feed liver-supporting foods including dark leafy greens such as spinach, dandelion greens, and kale.
- Add herbs to support the liver including milk thistle at 5 to 10 mg per pound and SAMe at 90 mg for cats and small dogs, 225 mg for medium dogs, and 400 mg for large dogs once daily.
- Limit use of vaccinations.
- Chinese herbals based on tongue and pulse diagnostics by a veterinarian trained in Traditional Chinese Veterinary

Medicine; check www.tcvm.com to locate a veterinarian in your area.

- Use acupuncture to repair imbalances, drain liver fire or stagnation, and de-crease internal wind.
- Limit or eliminate (preferably) the use of topical and systemic parasiticides.
- Use milbemycin for heartworm prevention (Sentinel, not Trifexis, as spinosad in Trifexis can contribute to seizure occurrence); avoid ivermectin, moxidectin, and selamectin products.

SAMPLE DIET FOR SEIZURES IN DOGS

- ☐ 1 pound pork 85% lean
- ☐ 4 ounces crab
- ☐ 2 ounces beef liver
- ☐ 4 ounces Shiitake mushrooms
- ☐ 3 ounces beet greens
- ☐ 4 ounces yellow squash
- ☐ 2 tablespoons honey
- ☐ 1/2 teaspoon ground turmeric powder
- ☐ 2 teaspoons hempseed oil
- ☐ 1/2 teaspoon kelp
- ☐ 1.5 teaspoons eggshell or bonemeal powder

Provide 30 calories per ounce. May be fed raw or gently cooked. Follow feeding guidelines in chapter 4.

SAMPLE DIET FOR SEIZURES IN CATS

- ☐ 1 pound pork tenderloin
- ☐ 4 ounces crab
- ☐ 4 ounces beef liver
- ☐ 2 ounces Shiitake mushrooms
- ☐ 2 ounces beet greens
- ☐ 2 ounces yellow squash
- ☐ 1 teaspoon ground turmeric
- ☐ 3 teaspoons hempseed oil
- ☐ 1/2 teaspoon kelp
- ☐ 1 teaspoon eggshell or bonemeal powder
- ☐ 1.5 ounces oyster or 1 zinc 15 mg capsule
- ☐ 500 mg taurine
- ☐ 1 ounce (2 tablespoons) spirulina powder

Provides 35 calories per ounce. May be fed raw or gently cooked. Follow feeding guidelines in chapter 4.

11 Heart Disease

Over the years we have owned quite a few dogs and cats with heart disease. While a diagnosis of heart disease can be devastating, that does not mean there is no hope. Our Cavalier King Charles Spaniel, Delilah, lived a year past her predicted expiration date when she was diagnosed with mitral valve disease. Our Cavalier, Stewie, lived two years past his predicted expiration date. One of our cats was given three to six months to live at age three and lived to age eighteen! Many times, our cardiologist has been shocked when we returned with a pet for a recheck exam when he was sure they would have passed by then. Feeding a diet that supports heart health and providing supplements that support the heart, liver, and kidneys can help keep your pet going strong, even in the face of grim news.

Many breeds of dogs and cats are prone to heart disease. While there are no proven methods to decrease the risk of heart disease in a breed genetically prone to its development, a pet owner has many nutritional, herbal, and therapeutic options to support healthy heart function.

Heart Disease in Cats

Heart disease is a silent killer of cats, causing 62% of sudden death cases in cats. Radiographs rarely show heart enlargement, even when significant heart disease is present. Cats often do not have a heart murmur even with advanced heart disease. My cat P.S. died suddenly at age 12. On autopsy I discovered he had hypertrophic cardiomyopathy, yet he had never shown any symptoms of heart disease.

Cardiomyopathy is the name given to any disease affecting the heart muscle. This is the most common form of heart disease seen in cats; it is the most common cause of heart failure. Unlike dogs and humans, disease of the heart valves is not very common in cats.

Most feline cardiomyopathies are primary diseases, meaning they are the result of genetics or unknown causes. Three types of heart disease account for nearly all the primary cardiomyopathies:

- *Hypertrophic cardiomyopathy* is diagnosed in 85 to 90 percent of primary cardiomyopathy cases. Many times, there is no explanation other than the strong likelihood of genetic influence. This cardiomyopathy is characterized by a thickening of the muscle tissue associated with the left ventricle (lower chamber of the heart).
- *Restrictive cardiomyopathy* accounts for approximately 10 percent of the primary heart muscle diseases; it is caused by the excessive buildup of scar tissue on the inner lining and muscle of a ventricle. This prevents the heart muscle from relaxing completely which does not allow blood to flow normally between chambers. Most often affecting older cats, this disorder is also characterized by severely enlarged atria (upper heart chambers) and reduced cardiac filling and pumping efficiency.
- *Dilated cardiomyopathy* is comparatively rare, probably accounting for only one or two percent of primary cardiomyopathy cases. It is characterized by an enlarged left ventricle with a thin muscle wall. The weak muscle does

not pump blood forward through the heart very effectively. The heart will appear enlarged on radiographs. This disease has been associated with taurine deficiencies in the diet. Taurine is an amino acid that is found in meat; it must be supplied in the cat's diet.

Causes of secondary cardiomyopathy in cats may include:

- Hyperthyroidism—tumors of the thyroid gland produce excess thyroid hormone which causes metabolism to speed up. The heart beats faster, leading to enlargement of the heart muscle and hypertrophic cardiomyopathy. These cats commonly also have hypertension and kidney disease.
- Hypertension—high blood pressure can be seen with hyperthyroidism or kidney disease which can lead to hypertrophic cardiomyopathy. High blood pressure affects one in eight cats over age nine.
- Anemia—lack of red blood cells carrying oxygen causes the heart to work harder.
- Acromegaly—increased growth hormone production (usually from a pituitary gland tumor) causes heart enlargement and heart failure.
- Toxins—may damage the heart muscle or cause inflammation of the heart muscle. Some chemotherapy drugs and anti-viral drugs can damage the heart muscle.
- Cancers—lymphoma and other cancers can infiltrate the heart muscle.
- Viral infections—FIV (Feline Immunodeficiency Virus) has been associated with viral myocarditis (inflammation of the heart muscle).

Maine Coon cats, Persians, and Ragdolls have a genetic predisposition to develop hypertrophic cardiomyopathy. Genetic tests may help identify whether your cat has an increased risk of HCM, but this does not guarantee the cat will develop the disease. Males are much more likely than females to have heart disease. Older cats are more likely to have heart disease than younger cats, although predisposed breeds may show disease at a young age.

Symptoms can vary from none to sudden death. Early warning signs that might be noticed can include:

- Heart murmur heard during veterinary exam—not all cats will have a murmur.
- Abnormally high heart rate.
- Skipped beats or abnormal rhythm noticed on auscultation (listening to the heart).
- Panting or open mouth breathing.
- Exaggerated respiratory effort.
- Increased respiratory rate.
- Cold legs and feet due to poor circulation.
- Pale mucous membranes due to poor circulation.
- Exercise intolerance.
- Lethargy.
- Inability to move the hind legs which may be accompanied by severe pain—this means a blood clot has lodged in the arteries supplying the hind legs.
- Loss of appetite.
- Gagging—Coughing is rarely a sign of heart disease in cats—this is more likely to be associated with airway disease.
- Collapse

If cardiomyopathy is suspected based on symptoms and physical examination, blood will be drawn to check for kidney disease, hyperthyroidism, and anemia. Blood pressure should be measured to check for hypertension. Radiographs are not generally diagnostic, unless the cat has dilated cardiomyopathy which can be seen on x-rays. An electrocardiogram will show if there are abnormalities in the rate or rhythm of the heartbeat. Ultimately, an echocardiogram or ultrasound of the heart will be needed to diagnose the condition.

Although there is no known cure, a specialized care plan can help manage clinical signs of the condition in your cat. Treatment goals include controlling the heart rate, eliminating fluid buildup in the lungs from congestive heart failure, and preventing the formation of blood clots.

Any underlying conditions such as hypertension, hyperthyroidism, and kidney disease must also be treated.

Medication can help manage cardiomyopathy and can be administered orally to stable patients or by injection in more serious situations. The cardiologist will determine which medications are appropriate for each individual pet.

Unfortunately, no therapy has been shown to prevent the progression of cardiomyopathy, even when started before clinical signs are observed.

The prognosis for cats with heart disease is extremely variable. Some cats with no symptoms can remain stable and survive for years. Cardiomyopathy is generally a progressive disease with a worse prognosis once the cat develops heart failure. Cats with severe disease can sometimes go months or years without symptoms, while others will deteriorate very quickly.

Heart Disease in Dogs

There are two main types of heart disease in dogs.

Mitral Valve Disease is the cause of 75% of heart disease in dogs. Small breed dogs that weigh less than 20 pounds are more prone to mitral valve disease (MVD), however the disease can develop in any breed. Breeds most affected include Cavalier King

Charles Spaniels, English Toy Spaniels, Dachshunds, Pekingese, Pugs, Chihuahuas, Maltese, Yorkies, Papillons, Bichons, and small poodles and terriers. MVD, a degenerative valve disease, is an inflammatory condition, as evidenced by studies showing increased circulating inflammatory markers in dogs suffering with this disease. The risk of MVD increases with age. A heart murmur is a leak, or "turbulence" in the blood flow. Murmurs are graded according to severity from low (1) to high (6). The grade has nothing to do with the strength of the heart—the heart muscle may be working normally. But over time with MVD, the heart will enlarge, and the condition will eventually lead to heart failure. Symptoms of MVD include:

- Rapid shallow breathing at rest
- Depressed attitude
- Restlessness (due to fluid build-up in the chest)
- Syncope (fainting)
- Coughing/gagging sounds

Dilated Cardiomyopathy or DCM is mostly a large-breed disease. Breeds affected include Dobermans, Boxers, Great Danes, Greyhounds, Irish Wolfhounds, Afghan Hounds, and Saint Bernards. Boxers may have a carnitine-responsive cardiomyopathy while Cocker Spaniels and Golden Retrievers may have taurine-responsive disease. DCM is a primary disease of the heart muscle. Over time, the muscle becomes thin, stretched, and weak, losing its ability to pump blood through the system. Symptoms of DCM include:

- Sudden death
- Respiratory distress
- Syncope (fainting)
- Weakness
- Ataxia (wobbly gait)

- Loss of appetite
- Gagging, coughing
- Swollen stomach

Risk factors associated with worsening heart disease include:

- Breed predisposition
- Age
- High blood pressure
- Dental disease
- Bacterial, rickettsial, and viral infections
- Heartworms

In the past few years, concerns have been raised by veterinary cardiologists and nutritionists that more cases of DCM have been diagnosed. Questions were raised regarding the relationship of diets such as grain-free diets, legume-filled diets, novel protein diets, and diets produced by small manufacturers with the uptick in cases of DCM. Although there was no proof that these diets cause cardiomyopathy, some individuals (mostly funded by large pet food companies) were very outspoken about the need to move away from these diets and return to feeding grain-filled kibble manufactured by major pet food corporations.

"Dr. Freeman has received research support from, given sponsored lectures for, or provided professional services to Aratana Therapeutics, Hill's Pet Nutrition Nestlé Purina PetCare, and Royal Canin. Dr. Heinze has done consulting for Lafeber and WellPet, given sponsored talks for Nestlé Purina PetCare and the Pet Food Institute; and provided professional services to Balance IT.com and Mark Morris Institute. Dr. Linder has received speaker fees or research funding from Hill's Pet Nutrition, Nestlé Purina PetCare, and Royal Canin, and has provided professional services for Mark Morris Institute." –Tufts Petfoodology

A review of veterinary teaching hospital records showed an incidence of DCM of 0.4% of the dogs seen. Based on an estimated population of 77,000,000 dogs in the United States, we would expect over 300,000 dogs to be diagnosed with DCM at this incidence rate. Yet the FDA released a public statement incriminating pet food based on a mere 560 cases. There was no science or research to back their statement.

We do know that diets low in protein, taurine, and sulfur-containing amino acids methionine and cysteine (such as diets designed to manage urate stones) have been associated with taurine-deficient DCM. When these diets are supplemented with taurine and L-carnitine, DCM clinical signs can be reversed.

Dogs can make taurine from amino-acid precursors, whereas cats do not perform this metabolism very efficiently. Because of this, feline diets have been supplemented with taurine for decades. Prior to the addition of taurine to cat food, many cats were diagnosed with dilated cardiomyopathy secondary to taurine deficiency.

The number of Golden Retrievers with DCM has been increasing, raising the question of a genetic propensity toward disease. Recent studies have noted Golden Retrievers may be at risk for developing DCM but have failed to identify a definitive causal relationship between diet, taurine, and cardiac function. Differences in measuring taurine concentration also play a role: the relationship between whole blood taurine, plasma taurine, and cardiac muscle taurine concentrations remains unknown.

Many nutrients other than taurine are important for ideal heart health, including carnitine, thiamin, copper, vitamin E, selenium, magnesium, choline, and potassium. A review of the current literature reveals faults within DCM studies in dogs, including sampling bias, inconsistencies in sampling parameters, too many variables, and lack of complete data for case studies on DCM and known genetic predisposition in certain dog breeds. Small sample sizes and overrepresentation of breeds are commonplace in recent DCM studies. Studies involving multiple breeds and larger sample groups are warranted to better understand if relationships exist between potential etiologies (such as diet) and the development of DCM for the overall dog population.

On June 27, 2019, FDA released an updated list of dogs affected by DCM. Of the 305 dogs listed, 73% were breeds with known genetic predisposition for DCM. Also, 61% of the dogs included had other diseases which may have contributed to cardiac disease, including hypothyroidism, Lyme disease, and mitral valve degeneration. It is impossible to implicate specific types of dog food as being a causative factor when the data is already skewed.

Boutique diets, defined as produced by a small manufacturer, have been implicated in association with DCM. However, when the FDA report is broken down into which pet food manufacturers made the called-out diets, 49% of the brands listed were made by one of the six largest pet food manufacturers in North America. Given that almost half of the brands listed on the FDA report on June 27, 2019, are not manufactured by boutique pet food companies, it is unlikely that an association can be made to DCM. This did not stop veterinarians or the FDA from incriminating smaller pet food manufacturers, resulting in huge losses in revenue and jobs for many of those companies. 76% of the proteins listed in the FDA report included chicken, beef, pork, lamb, salmon, turkey, and whitefish, which are NOT exotic proteins that FDA labeled as problematic.

A study performed at the University of Illinois in which dogs were fed a diet with 45% legumes (peas, lentils) showed no differences in plasma amino acids (taurine, carnitine) from dogs fed diets without legumes. Although FDA has called-out grain-free diets and implicated legumes as causative agents of DCM, this study shows no relation.

Many pet owners have been made to feel guilty for feeding what they considered to be higher-quality diets. Unfortunately, there is no basis for this. The pet food and veterinary communities rushed to a conclusion that has no support. Our pets need meat in their diets to maintain good health. Balanced diets are important in ensuring that all nutrients are provided for optimum health and longevity.

In December 2022, the FDA ended their "study" on DCM related to grain-free diets. The agency stated based on the reports of DCM cases received, "they do not supply sufficient data to establish a causal relationship with reported product(s)" and they do not intend to release any further information about the issue "until there is meaningful new scientific information to share". In other words, the FDA does not believe grain-free pet foods are/were the cause of DCM in dogs. Sadly, many veterinarians have jumped on the DCM bandwagon, insisting that pets be fed dry kibble formulated with grains which is exactly the opposite of what our pets should be eating.

Any pet suffering from degenerative heart disease of any type should be under the care of a veterinary cardiologist. An ultrasound, called an echocardiogram, is the best method to determine the stage of heart disease and heart function. Medications are available that will increase longevity and help keep pets comfortable. A diagnosis of heart disease is not an immediate death sentence. Many pets will live for years after diagnosis when given a high-quality diet and supplements. If you have a breed that is predisposed to heart disease, it is best to place your dog under the care of a cardiologist early in life.

Clinical signs vary among different breeds in dogs. This may result in a delay in proper diagnosis or a misdiagnosis. Veterinarians need to know the different signs and symptoms between the breeds. Research your breed and be sure your veterinarian is familiar with your breed.

When diagnosing heart disease, your veterinarian should listen for a murmur, which is detected by a stethoscope. Heart enlargement can be seen on a chest x-ray. Blood pressure should be measured. A human blood pressure wrist cuff can be used on larger dogs; pediatric cuffs will work on smaller dogs and cats. Work with your veterinarian to determine the best placement of the cuff on your pet's leg. An EKG, or electrocardiogram, can detect abnormal beats or rhythm of the heart. An EKG should always be performed prior to any anesthetic procedure.

My mother's first Doberman had the cardiac form of Lyme disease. It was early in my veterinary career and Lyme disease was new to the veterinary world. I wanted to sedate the dog for a dental cleaning. During the pre-operative workup, I performed an EKG, which revealed an abnormal heartbeat. Lab work revealed she was positive for Lyme disease, even though she had no other symptoms. I treated her with Doxycycline for a month and her arrhythmia cleared. Her dental was performed with no complications.

Tests to be performed include urinalysis, CBC (complete blood count), and a complete chemistry panel. These tests will detect other organ damage caused by heart disease. Special blood tests, such as the NT-proBNP test evaluates the pressure of the heart based on the stretching of the heart muscle. This test involves a very special blood draw and procedure. A cTnl blood test checks for elevated serum concentration of cardiac troponin and is a highly sensitive and specific marker of heart damage.

Mitral Valve heart disease is graded in stages A through D:

- Stage A—No symptoms, but the breed is prone to MVD
- Stage B1—Murmur, no need for meds, no symptoms
- Stage B2—Murmur, weakness in heart muscle, a few symptoms. The decision to start medication will depend on the individual patient. It is up to the cardiologist to suggest a treatment plan.

- Stage C—Clinical signs with heart enlargement. Medication will be prescribed. Medication can place the disease in a "holding pattern", often for long periods of time.
- Stage D—heart enlargement with heart failure that is refractory to traditional medications. Medications may be changed, often adding a more powerful diuretic (torsemide). Cardiologists will often give a prognosis of 2-3 months of remaining life, although many pets will outlive that prognosis by months to years. Animals in Stage D failure may benefit from supplemental oxygen which can be delivered at home with an oxygen concentrator and home oxygen cage. Be sure to place a cooling mat inside the cage when in use and monitor the pet closely for any distress.

Dilated Cardiomyopathy is graded in stages 1 through 3:

- Stage 1: Affected dogs show no clinical signs of DCM.

- Stage 2: Presence of the heart disease slowly becomes evident as abnormal heartbeats and heart dilation occur. However, clinical signs remain absent. This stage can last up to 2–4 years.
- Stage 3: Clinical signs of heart failure in affected canines begin to manifest during the final stages of DCM in dogs.

Complications that can be associated with heart disease include:

- Tumors in the heart
- Hypertension (high blood pressure)
- Pulmonary hypertension (high pressure in the lungs)
- PLE—protein losing enteropathy
- Ascites—fluid leaking into the abdomen

- Arrhythmias (abnormal heart rhythms)
- Syncope (fainting)

You can proactively support younger dogs and cats that are prone to heart disease, even though a murmur may not yet be detected. No good studies have been performed to prove this; however, I recommend proactive care early in life which may delay the onset of heart disease. Typical supplements I recommend for my dog and cat patients include:

- CoQ10—Studies have shown CoQ10 causes a reduction of cardiac troponin levels in dogs with heart disease. Systolic function increased significantly because CoQ10 is a factor required during energy production in muscle cells. Thus, CoQ10 supplementation may improve energy availability for cardiac muscle contraction. CoQ10 may protect heart muscle cells from injury through its antioxidant action. CoQ10 was also found to decrease vascular resistance, therefore allowing blood flow from the heart to move forward more easily. Recommended doses of 1 mg per pound of body weight are not high enough to produce these beneficial effects. I dose my dogs and patients much higher, at around 5 mg per pound twice daily.
- Herbal support can be used to nourish heart health, including hawthorn, dandelion, cactus grandifloras, motherwort, red clover, cayenne, and ginger. There are many tinctures available on the market specifically made for dogs and cats.
- L-carnitine—500 mg for small dogs and cats up to 2,000 mg for large dogs twice daily. Nutritional sources with high levels of carnitine include red meat (beef) and heart muscle meat of any source.
- Taurine—250 to 750 mg twice daily for dogs and cats

(some dogs with DCM may require up to 5,000 mg daily). Nutritional sources with high levels of taurine include shellfish such as mussels, scallops, and clams, dark meat poultry, and goat milk.

- Hawthorn—increases cardiac muscle contraction strength, found in many herbal formulations of differing strengths. One teaspoon of ground hawthorn berry powder or 1/4 to 1/2 teaspoon of hawthorn tincture can be added per pound of food fed. Combination formulas often contain this herb, however these formulas often do not have high enough doses of all ingredients I want to include so I use single ingredient products and layer them in. This may be more of an inconvenience, but it allows me to tailor the protocol based on my pet's condition.

- Gingko—dilates blood vessels and improves circulation.

- Yarrow—dilates blood vessels and improves circulation.

- Dandelion leaf—diuretic action to move fluid out of the lungs to be eliminated through the kidneys.

- Omega 3 fatty acids decrease cardiac inflammation, decrease triglycerides, and decrease muscle wasting. If the pet cannot tolerate fish oil, use krill oil, algae oil, or phytoplankton. Fish oils should not be stored in a plastic bottle or exposed to air, as this can result in oxidation and rancidity. Give 30 mg of EPA and DHA per pound of body weight daily, along with 1 to 2 IU of vitamin E per pound of body weight.

- Calcium—the diet needs to have adequate calcium, particularly when formulating home prepared diets.

- Pets with heart disease often have low vitamin D levels. Vitamin D levels should be tested before beginning vitamin D supplementation. Toxicity and kidney failure from high levels of vitamin D can result. Do not use human vitamin D supplements as they are much stronger than needed for dogs and cats.

- Vitamin E—important for heart muscle function, acts as an antioxidant to protect heart cells from oxidative damage. Supply 400 to 800 IU daily depending on the size of the pet.
- Selenium—trace mineral that supports cardiac function—found in fish, chicken, beef, and pork. The diet should supply 0.5 mg per ten pounds body weight per day.
- Chromium—trace mineral that supports cardiac function—found in broccoli and mushrooms.
- D-Ribose—D-Ribose is a natural sugar. It has been shown in several human studies to increase cardiac contractility and prolong survival from heart failure. It is very inexpensive, and no side effects have been reported. Give 500 mg of powder twice daily to dogs or cats.
- PEA (palmitoylethanolamide)—natural anti-inflammatory that works on the endocannabinoid system. Particularly helpful for inflammatory heart disease. Dose is 400 mg to 2,000 mg per day depending on the size of the pet.
- CBD oil—It possesses anti-inflammatory and anti-anxiety effects; the recommended dose is 1 mg per 10 pounds body weight 2 to 3 times daily. This is particularly helpful for inflammatory heart disease or anxiety associated with heart failure and respiratory distress.
- Acupuncture can be helpful to increase energy flow to the heart and stabilize blood pressure.

Nutritional additions for my pets and patients include:

- Fermented raw goat milk—high in taurine, medium chain triglycerides, and vitamins essential for cardiac function; helps decrease inflammation. Goat milk also contains GABA (⊠-aminobutyric acid), a neurotransmitter, with diverse physiologic effects, such as modulation of blood pressure, immune function, insulin sensitivity and stress.

- Species-appropriate meat-based diet, preferably raw or gently cooked, that includes heart muscle meat. From a Traditional Chinese Medicine perspective, heart failure and heart enlargement are related to Heart Qi Deficiency and Blood Stagnation. When designing a diet to support optimum heart function, I include Qi tonics (energy) and ingredients to resolve stagnation (blood pooling) that keep the blood moving.

- Qi (energy) tonic foods—beef, dark meat poultry, rabbit, tripe, pumpkin, squash, sweet potato, Golden Paste, and Shiitake mushrooms. An herbal formulation for Heart Qi deficiency is Stasis in the Mansion of the Blood.

- Foods to help eliminate fluid build-up—celery, watermelon, dandelion greens and roots, barley, mushrooms, garlic, and parsley.

- Blood tonic foods—egg yolks, sardines, dark leafy greens, liver, beef. Heart Blood deficiency can be treated with the herbal formulation Si Wu Tang (Four Substances) for anemia or Heart Blood deficiency with Shen disturbance (behavior changes, vocalizing at night, fear of loud noises) with the herbal formulation Tian Wang Bu Xin Wan (Emperor's Tea pills).

I am NOT a fan of the prescription heart diet foods. Most are made with inferior ingredients that have been highly processed, with synthetic chemical additives. Omega-3 fatty acids are added but become rancid in the heating process of making kibble. Additional synthetic vitamins and minerals that support heart health are being added; however, the immune system of some animals sees the synthetic vitamins as "foreign" to the system resulting in gastrointestinal problems (Leaky gut, IBD) and allergies.

Dogs and cats have no need for carbohydrates in the form of grains. Our pets have zero requirements for grains in food. Feed a meat-based diet. Dry kibble does not supply the amount of meat needed to support the heart.

The best way to support your pet's heart is to feed real, whole foods, free of synthetic ingredients. Supplements should also be derived from real food rather than synthetic ingredients. My patients have performed much better when fed real foods that contain the necessary ingredients for optimum heart health.

Treats to support heart health include freeze-dried hearts, freeze-dried lung, and fish-based treats high in omega-3 fatty acids. You can also make your own dehydrated treats at home.

SAMPLE DIET FOR HEART DISEASE IN DOGS

- ☐ 16 ounces ground beef 90% lean
- ☐ 16 ounces beef heart
- ☐ 4 ounces beef liver
- ☐ 4 ounces salmon
- ☐ 4 eggs with shells or use 1 tsp. eggshell or bone-meal powder
- ☐ 4 ounces asparagus
- ☐ 4 ounces kale
- ☐ 6 ounces butternut squash
- ☐ 1/2 cup cranberries chopped or ground

- ☐ 4 ounces Shiitake mushrooms
- ☐ 1 ounce mussels
- ☐ 1 Tbsp wheat germ oil
- ☐ 1 Tbsp ground sunflower seeds
- ☐ 1/2 tsp seaweed or kelp powder

Provides 42 calories per ounce. Chop or grind all vegetables, heart, liver, and salmon. Place all ingredients in a slow cooker set on low for 6 to 8 hours. Can also be served raw or baked in a pan in the oven at 325 degrees for 45 minutes—do not overcook. Follow feeding guidelines in Chapter 4.

SAMPLE DIET TO DRAIN FLUID FOR HEART FAILURE IN DOGS

- ☐ 1 pound venison
- ☐ 11 ounces turkey gizzards
- ☐ 5 ounces turkey liver
- ☐ 2 ounces cabbage
- ☐ 2 ounces turnips
- ☐ 2 ounces fresh basil
- ☐ 4 ounces Shiitake mushrooms
- ☐ 3 ounces celery
- ☐ 3 ounces sardines

- [ ] 2 tablespoons flaxseed oil
- [ ] 1 teaspoon ground eggshell powder or bonemeal
- [ ] 1/2 teaspoon kelp
- [ ] 2 teaspoons wheatgrass powder

Provides 34 calories per ounce. May be served raw or gently cooked. See feeding directions in chapter 4.

SAMPLE DIET FOR HEART DISEASE IN CATS

- [ ] 6 ounces ground beef 90% lean
- [ ] 6 ounces beef heart
- [ ] 3 ounces salmon, boneless
- [ ] 2 ounces beef liver
- [ ] 1/2 teaspoon wheat germ oil
- [ ] 1 large egg
- [ ] 1 teaspoon ground eggshell or bonemeal powder
- [ ] 2 ounces (pre-cooked weight) pureed kale
- [ ] 2 ounces (pre-cooked weight) pureed asparagus
- [ ] 3 ounces baked butternut squash
- [ ] 1 teaspoon Rx Vitamins Feline Essentials

Supplies 40 calories per ounce. Steam or sauté green vegetables. Mix all ingredients in a food processor. Feed 8 to 10 ounces per day for a 10 to 12 -pound cat.

12 Urinary Tract Disease

My fourth cat, LMNO, suffered from urinary tract disease. Okay, I know, what kind of name is LMNO for a cat? My first cat was Mr. P (short for Puff), then came P.S. (you know, an afterthought), and my son named his first cat Q, after the bad guy on Star Trek, which was his favorite television show when he was four years old. My husband told me we were not going to have 26 cats, so I had to start combining letters of the alphabet. Right after we decided on the name LMNO for the new cat, there was a skit on Saturday Night Live about the "metric alphabet" and they combined LMNO into one letter: "Please LMNOpen the door". So, I guess it was an okay name.

Anyway, back to his urinary problems. I adopted LMNO off the streets when he was about six months old. I fed all our cats dry cat food at that time because that was what I was taught in veterinary school, and I didn't know any better. LMNO developed urinary problems by the time he was two years old. He had bloody urine and strained to urinate most of the time. He had urinary obstructions several times and had to be catheterized. Eventually, his problems became so bad, he had to have a surgical procedure called a perineal urethrostomy to remove his penis and make him into a her so he could urinate. It was traumatic, to say the least.

It is said in Chinese Medicine that the kidneys are responsible for life and death. They store the "essence" or "Jing" that we have at birth. When the kidneys deteriorate so does health. Kidneys are responsible for reproduction, production of marrow to fill the brain, production of blood, and manifest as hair on the head. Pets and people who suffer from early graying of their hair may have a kidney deficiency. The kidneys are connected to the ears, just as the liver is connected to the eyes. Ability to detect sound diminishes with age as kidney function declines. The kidneys also rule the bones and chronic inflammation of the kidneys goes hand in hand with arthritis. They also rule the teeth, so many dental problems are related to declining kidney function. The kidneys are the organ of the Water Element and they like moisture.

Chronic feeding of diets devoid of moisture causes chronic stress to the kidneys. Pets fed dry kibble will drink much more than their counterparts consuming a high moisture diet. (Imagine how you would feel if your diet consisted solely of dry cereal and crackers.) Urine of pets consuming dry food will be highly concentrated with an increase in crystal and stone formation. For years we have treated cats for Feline Lower Urinary Tract Disease (FLUTD) using antibiotics, urine acidifiers (dl-methionine in pet foods), anti-depressant and anti-inflammatory medications, and magnesium-restricted dry diets, with little success. In worst case scenarios, male cats have their penis removed to allow the stones and crystals to pass through a larger, female type of opening. When did our society become so barbaric? And why is it not obvious to traditional veterinarians that we are torturing cats by feeding dry kibble to carnivores?

The first and most obvious, in my opinion, change to make for these poor beasts is an increase in moisture in the diet! There is no reason to feed a dry prescription diet to a cat (or a dog). The addition of chemicals to the diet encourages the pet to drink more (adding salt) and acidifiers (dl-methionine) in the diet change the pH of the urine. This can have detrimental effects on other organ systems. Pets can make two kinds of crystals, one in high pH and one in low pH urine. By altering the urine to avoid one type of crystal the opposite crystal may show up instead. This is not a solution to the problem.

The pets at highest risk for disease are those that refuse to switch to a high moisture diet. Cats are picky and you cannot starve them into a diet change. Don't ever believe they'll eat if they get hungry enough. Cats will die by developing hepatic lipidosis (fatty liver syndrome) while holding out for the food they want. My recommendation is to keep trying to get them to switch by gradually decreasing the amount of dry food offered while offering varied flavors and textures of canned or raw foods. Dehydrated raw meat seems to be a favorite of many cats and sprinkling this on top of the dry kibble may be a way to gradually get them to change. Once they like the meat you can start adding small amounts of water and gradually increase until you are feeding a high moisture diet.

For cats in crisis treatment will be required. A cat with urinary crystals or urinary obstruction needs to be treated immediately. Most obstructions are sterile, meaning there is no urinary tract infection, therefore antibiotic therapy is not necessary. The long-term solution resides in the addition of moisture to keep the kidneys happy.

Urinary Tract Infections

Bacterial urinary tract infections are uncommon in cats, however, older cats or cats suffering from an underlying endocrine disease such as hyperthyroidism or diabetes mellitus are more prone to infection. UTIs are more common in female dogs because they have a wider opening and shorter urethra than males. In males they are usually related to prostate disease, kidney disease, inability to empty the bladder completely, or stones.

Causes of urinary tract infection can include:

- Bacteria—Most commonly, a UTI occurs when bacteria (such as E. coli) travel up the urethra and into the bladder. Severe dental disease can contribute to urinary tract infections as the blood flow passes around the dental infection, picking up bacteria that will be filtered through the kidneys. Urine in the bladder is supposed to be sterile, but once bacteria find their way there, they can grow and reproduce, causing a UTI.
- Abnormal pH levels—Dogs and cats are carnivores and should be eating a species-appropriate diet high in meat protein and low in starches. For a healthy dog or cat eating such a diet, the pH of the urine will be on the slightly acidic side of neutral (between 6.0 and 7.5). When the urine pH goes below or above this range, crystals and even bladder stones can form.
- Dry food/kibble diet—Ultra-processed kibble is higher in carbohydrates and starches. This type of diet will raise pH levels in the urine which will predispose your pet to bacterial infections and crystal formation. Furthermore, many over-the-counter diets are too high in magnesium, ammonium, and phosphate, which is what makes up the common struvite crystal.
- Congenital abnormalities—Some female puppies can have an inverted vulva, which allows urine to pool in the folds. This makes it easier for bacteria to ascend the urethra and cause an infection in the bladder. If you have a puppy with this issue, it is best to have them go through a heat cycle before spaying them to allow the vulva to fully develop. (Early spaying is not recommended for a variety of reasons.) Hormones produced during the heat

cycle will cause the vulva to swell and can help resolve the problem. Dogs with this condition may need surgical repair with a procedure called a vulvoplasty to avoid chronic infections. Spinal cord issues and ectopic ureters can also trigger urinary tract problems.

- Medications and comorbidities—UTI infections are more common if there are concurrent conditions that lower your pet's immunity, such as diabetes, Cushing's disease, cancer, or other chronic inflammatory diseases. Diabetes can put sugar into the urine and that sugar feeds on bacteria. Immunosuppressive drugs like steroids, cyclosporine, and Apoquel also lower immunity.
- Incontinence due to excessive water consumption, a weak bladder sphincter, early spay, congenital anomalies, or neurologic damage can lead to infection.
- Emotional or environmental stressors—This is more common in cats than dogs. There may not be bacterial infection; symptoms may be caused by stress-related sterile cystitis instead.
- Injury, polyp, or tumor in the urinary tract.

Signs of urinary tract infection include:

- Bloody urine
- Straining to urinate
- Lethargy
- Incontinence
- Dribbling urine
- Urinating in strange places
- Frequent urination
- Malodorous urine
- Vomiting

Most dogs do not develop a fever with a UTI that is restricted to the bladder. Infection in the kidneys is more serious and pets will usually present with vomiting and fever.

Diagnosis of a urinary tract infection requires testing of the urine microscopically, looking for bacteria, red blood cells, white blood cells, crystals, or cancer cells. Treating with antibiotics without performing a microscopic analysis is bad medicine. If a UTI is diagnosed, a culture and sensitivity should be performed to determine the type of bacteria present and the appropriate antibiotic for treatment. For pets that have received multiple courses of antibiotics, the culture is essential.

Treatment with antibiotics usually requires ten to fourteen days to clear the infection. It is important to retest urine after treatment to be sure the infection has cleared. Probiotics, including *Saccharomyces boulardii*, should be given along with the antibiotics and for an additional two weeks to repopulate the bowel with a healthy microbiome. Prevention of recurrent urinary tract infections lies in determining the underlying cause of infection.

Most pets less than one year of age will not have infections; when they do it may signal an underlying deficiency in the immune system or congenital abnormality. Pets with repeat infections may have bladder stones that serve as a chronic source of infection. Radiographs or abdominal ultrasound should be performed to rule out stones. Tumors of the bladder are being seen with increased frequency and should be ruled out with ultrasound. Pets with weakened immune systems from poor breeding, early spay, poor diet, and over-vaccination will also be more prone to infection.

As discussed, treatment may include a course of antibiotics and probiotics, although a good holistic veterinarian may be able to clear the infection without the use of antibiotics. Increased moisture in the diet will promote urination and flushing of the bladder. In addition, there are many natural substances that can be used to help treat or prevent infection as well:

- Cranberry—contains proanthocyanidins which prevent bacterial attachment to the bladder wall. Fresh cranberries can be ground and added to the diet 1/2 teaspoon to 1/4 cup twice daily depending on the size of the pet. Many cranberry extracts and powders are also available.
- Uva Ursi—decreases bleeding and inflammation, promotes urination to flush the bladder, helps dissolve bladder stones. Give 2.5 to 5 mg per pound of body weight every 8 to 12 hours.
- Grapefruit seed extract—antiviral, antifungal, antibacterial, boosts immune system. Give 1 drop per pound of body weight three times daily.
- Juniper berry—increases kidney filtration and helps flush the bacteria from the urinary tract. They are antibacterial, antifungal, and helpful in dissolving urinary stones. Do not use it for pets with kidney failure or those who are pregnant. 2 to 3 mg per pound of body weight once or twice daily should be safe.
- Marshmallow root—stimulates the immune system, acts as a diuretic to increase urine flow, and soothes bladder inflammation by producing a film that covers the bladder wall. Add 1/4 to 1 teaspoon to food twice daily.
- Parsley leaf—Antimicrobial, antioxidant, anti-inflammatory, and its diuretic action helps flush the urinary tract. Do not use it in pregnant pets or pets with kidney failure. Add 1 teaspoon of dried or fresh chopped leaves per 20 pounds of body weight per day.
- Glucosamine and Chondroitin—15 mg per pound of body weight, strengthens the protective lining layer of the bladder to decrease invasion by bacteria.

● Chinese herbal combinations—can decrease infection, soothe the bladder, and decrease bleeding. There are many combinations. Work with a TCVM practitioner to choose the right formula for your pet.

SAMPLE DIET FOR URINARY TRACT INFECTIONS IN DOGS (LOW OXALATE)

- ☐ 10 ounces cod
- ☐ 8 ounces lean pork tenderloin
- ☐ 2 ounces beef liver
- ☐ 4 ounces canned pumpkin
- ☐ 4 ounces cranberries
- ☐ 2 ounces crab
- ☐ 2 ounces clams
- ☐ 1 ounce oyster
- ☐ 2 ounces asparagus
- ☐ 2 ounces carrot
- ☐ 2 ounces cabbage
- ☐ 4.5 teaspoons flaxseed oil
- ☐ 3 teaspoons bonemeal powder
- ☐ 2 teaspoons turmeric
- ☐ 1/2 teaspoon sea salt

Provide 26 calories per ounce. May be fed raw or gently cooked. See feeding directions in chapter 4.

SAMPLE DIET FOR URINARY TRACT INFECTIONS IN CATS (LOW OXALATE)

- ☐ 11 ounces cod
- ☐ 4 ounces pork tenderloin
- ☐ 2 ounces beef liver
- ☐ 2 ounces crab
- ☐ 2 ounces oyster
- ☐ 2 ounces cranberries
- ☐ 1 ounce asparagus
- ☐ 1 ounce carrot
- ☐ 3 teaspoons bonemeal powder
- ☐ 2.5 teaspoons flaxseed oil
- ☐ 2 teaspoons turmeric powder
- ☐ 1/2 teaspoon kelp powder
- ☐ 3 teaspoons spirulina powder

Provides 27 calories per ounce. May be fed raw or gently cooked. See feeding directions in Chapter 4.

Bladder and Kidney Stones

I often receive inquiries from pet owners regarding treatment of crystals in their pet's urine. Crystals are the precursors to stones. The presence of crystals does not indicate a need for antibiotics or prescription diets. In general, diet manipulation can be used to eliminate crystal formation in the urine. Diets high in moisture result in fewer crystals in the urine, mostly due to dilution factor. The more fluid that enters the bladder, the more diluted the urine will be, and the more often the bladder is flushed. Dogs and cats that take in very little moisture, eat dry diets, and urinate infrequently will be more prone to urine crystal formation. Cats are desert animals and do not usually drink large volumes, making them particularly susceptible to crystal formation when fed dry kibble.

In recent years I have noticed a big increase in the number of pets suffering from bladder stones. Bladder stones occur in two main types: struvite, which are secondary to highly concentrated urine and bacterial infection, and oxalate, which are related to high levels of calcium, genetic disorders, overuse of antibiotics causing a decrease in intestinal flora that feed on oxalate, and poor diet. Once stones are diagnosed, they are usually removed surgically. Small stones may pass, but particularly in males, the stones may lodge in the urethra causing obstruction and death if not treated.

One way to avoid stone formation is to feed a high moisture diet, thereby decreasing the concentration of the urine. More moisture going into the pet results in more urine coming out of the pet, helping to flush the kidneys and bladder. Most pets diagnosed with bladder stones will be started on a prescription diet once the stones are removed. Commonly these are dry formulations which makes no sense because we need to flush the bladder with moisture from the diet. The diets are usually high in salt to encourage the pet to drink more. I do not use prescription diets.

I love to diagnose struvite stones because they are always caused by bacterial infection, and they are the easiest to treat. Struvite stones form in urine with a high pH above 7.5. The Ideal urine pH is 6.5 to 7.0, but 6.0 to 7.5 is acceptable. Stones can be surgically removed or dissolved using diet and herbs. A urine culture and sensitivity must be performed to determine which bacterial infection caused the problem. Antibiotics should be given until the urine culture is negative. Antimicrobial herbs may help clear infection. The pet should be fed a high moisture diet (canned, home-prepared, or raw) and a complete urinalysis should be monitored at least every three months for signs of infection.

Monitoring urine pH at home with pH strips can signal early signs of trouble if the pH consistently stays above 7.5. Dogs that return repeatedly with struvite stones requiring multiple surgeries are dogs that have non-compliant or non-informed owners, or the underlying cause of the repeat infections has not been determined and dealt with. Tucked vulva in female dogs is a common cause of repeat infections. Struvite stones are rare in cats.

A good immune system is paramount to controlling infection, so these pets need a healthy diet and a healthy gut, including the addition of good probiotics. Cranberry supplements may be helpful in preventing infection by not allowing bacteria to attach to the bladder wall. Do not feed cranberry juice with high fructose corn syrup or sweeteners. Repeated use of antibiotics, medications, and over-vaccination will be detrimental; a healthy immune system is the key.

Oxalate stones are more difficult to treat. They are common in certain breeds like the Bichon Frise, Miniature Schnauzer, Lhasa Apso, Yorkie, and Shih Tzu but I have seen them in large breed dogs as well. These breeds may have a genetic predisposition. Cats usually make oxalate stones. Oxalate stones form in urine with low pH 6.0 or less. Oxalate stones occur commonly in pets with Cushing's Disease, parathyroid tumors, and diseases associated with high calcium levels in the blood. Over-supplementation with calcium or Vitamin C and certain foods like soy and wheat are common culprits.

Soy and wheat have been two major additions to the pet food industry in the past few decades, which may be contributing to the increase in oxalate stone formation we are seeing in pets. Other foods that are high in oxalates include spinach, sardines, sweet potatoes, white potatoes, beets, mustard greens, figs, almonds, and peanuts. Meat, on the other hand, is low in oxalates. It stands to reason these pets could be fed a low oxalate diet that is meat-based, and their life could improve dramatically.

Unfortunately, prescription diets for oxalate stones are based on providing a low protein diet and do not include much meat. The ingredient list for one of the commonly used prescription products includes egg product, corn starch, chicken fat, pork liver, sucrose, (Sugar!) rice, soybean oil, soy fiber, and a whole bunch of chemicals, vitamins, and minerals. I find this to be an oxymoronic diet since soy is high in oxalates and there is no meat included.

Oxalate stones are very difficult to dissolve and usually need to be removed. They are usually sharp and rough causing pain in the bladder or urethra. If they cause obstruction, they must be removed. Male dogs may need to have a new opening made behind the penis (perineal urethrostomy) to allow small stones to pass as in over 50% of dogs, the stones will reoccur. Potassium citrate is commonly prescribed to raise the urine pH and decrease chances of reoccurrence; I prefer to provide a fresh diet that will decrease chances of recurrence.

Drugs such as steroids and furosemide can increase risk of developing oxalate stones and should be avoided whenever possible. Again, providing a species-appropriate diet with added probiotics, decreased vaccinations and medications, and a healthy immune system are the answer.

Less common forms of stones include urate, seen mostly in Dalmations, and cystine stones, seen mostly in Bulldogs, Newfoundlands, Irish Setters, Bassett Hounds, Dachshunds, Chihuahuas, and Yorkies. These are less likely to be diet related and are seen more commonly due to genetic dysfunction. However, they do require specialized diets to prevent further formation of crystals and stones.

SAMPLE LOW PURINE DIET FOR
URATE STONES IN DOGS

- ☐ 20 ounces ground beef (85% lean, 15% fat)
- ☐ 8 whole chicken eggs
- ☐ 4 ounces blueberries
- ☐ 4 ounces kale
- ☐ 4 teaspoons hulled hempseed
- ☐ 1 tablespoon bonemeal powder
- ☐ 1 teaspoon wheat grass powder
- ☐ 1 teaspoon dried kelp powder
- ☐ 1/2 teaspoon sea salt

Provides 41 calories per ounce. May be served raw or gently cooked. Follow feeding guidelines in chapter 4.

SAMPLE DIET FOR DOGS WITH CYSTINE STONES
Ingredients Daily Amount

Proteins (choose 1)

- ☐ 2 hard-boiled eggs
- ☐ 7.5 ounces drained firm tofu
- ☐ 14 ounces baked sweet potato

Vegetables (choose 2)

- ☐ 4.5 ounces of celery, cucumber, or zucchini
- ☐ 2.8 ounces of cabbage

- ☐ 2.3 ounces of strawberries or green beans
- ☐ 2.1 ounces of watermelon
- ☐ 1.5 ounces of broccoli, carrots, butternut squash, or apples
- ☐ 1.25 ounces of blueberries

Supplements (use all)

- ☐ 1 cup egg whites
- ☐ 3 teaspoons organic sunflower oil
- ☐ 1/8th teaspoon Now Taurine powder
- ☐ 1/8th teaspoon Now L-Carnitine powder
- ☐ 2 1/2 scoops Rx Vitamins Canine Minerals
- ☐ 2 scoops Rx Vitamins Canine Essentials
- ☐ 1 pump Iceland Pure Sardine/Anchovy oil

Measure all ingredients raw.

- ☐ Scramble eggs whites in a medium saucepan (preferable stainless). Prepare eggs for hard boiling by first washing them and then placing clean eggs in a pot and cover with cold water. Bring pot to a rapid boil. Once pot begins to boil, remove from heat and let stand for 10 mins. Drain and peel the eggs after cooling.
- ☐ Remove Tofu from packaging and thoroughly drain as much water as possible. Cut tofu into 1/2 inch strips and lightly sear over medium heat or bake at 350.
- ☐ Sweet Potato can be baked or microwaved until a fork is able to easily pierce all the way through.

- [ ] Vegetables should be chopped finely. All cruciferous vegetables should be boiled or steamed first. We suggest rotating vegetables every week if possible.

- [ ] Combine protein, vegetables, and egg whites in a large bowl and mix (mixture can be further processed through a blender or grinder if desired)

- [ ] Add all supplements and oil at the time of feeding. Do not combine prior to cooking as heat will degrade the nutrient profile and cooked oil will oxidize.

This recipe will feed a 50-pound dog for a day.

Bladder Cancer

Cancer can occur anywhere in the urinary system, but bladder cancer, most commonly Transitional Cell Carcinoma (TCC), has been diagnosed more frequently in recent years. Scottish Terriers are 20 times more likely to develop TCC but, Beagles, Wire Hair Fox Terriers, West Highland White Terriers, and Shetland Sheepdogs are also predisposed. Bladder cancer is more common in middle-aged and older female dogs. Other tumors that occur less often in the bladder include leiomyosarcomas, which account for 12% of all bladder cancer cases in dogs, and fibrosarcomas, which are rare and very aggressive.

OXALATES in FOOD

LOW OXALATES:
Beef, Chicken, Turkey, Lamb, Liver (all), Organ Meats (all), Clams, Cod, White Fish, Oysters, Salmon, Tuna, Butter, Cottage Cheese, Eggs, Goat Milk, Vegetable Oils, Oat bran, White Rice, Apples, Pears, Watermelon, Cranberries, Coconut, Banana, Apricot, Lemon, Pineapple, String Beans, Asparagus, Broccoli, Brussels Sprouts, Cabbage, Cauliflower, Cucumber, Parsley, Peppermint, Sage, Thyme, Ginger, Garlic, Basil, Dill, Lettuce, Mushrooms, Peppers, Pumpkin Squash

MODERATE OXALATES:
Walnuts, Black Pepper, Cloves, Pasta, Oatmeal, Tofu, Brown Rice, Rye Flower, Blueberries, Lemon Peel, Mandarin Oranges, Mango, Orange & Peel, Prunes, Kidney Beans, Pinto Beans, Carrots, Celery, Adzuki Beans, White Potatoes, Summer Squash, Tomatoes, Winter Squash

HIGH OXALATES:
Peanuts, Lentils, Turmeric, Soy Milk, Soybeans, Barley, Cornmeal, Wheat Flour, Rice Flour, Whole-wheat Pasta, Wheat Bran, Apricots, Figs, Okra, Collard Greens, Mustard Greens, Sweet Potatoes, Black Beans, White Beans, Chili Beans, Navy Beans, Pink Beans

VERY HIGH OXALATES to AVOID:
Almonds, Buckwheat, Beets, Sesame Seeds, Spinach, Swiss Chard

The number one cause of this cancer in humans is smoking. Many pets are subjected to second-hand smoke and have no say in the matter. This is unfair. If you smoke, go outside. Second-hand smoke lingers on furniture and carpets, chronically exposing your pets. Obesity, pesticides, lawn herbicides, topical flea and tick products, and chronic bladder infection and inflammation have been incriminated as well. Current treatments for TCC include surgical removal, if possible, radiation and chemotherapy, and use of the drug Piroxicam, an NSAID.

Symptoms include:

- Blood in the urine
- Frequent urination in small amounts
- Incontinence
- Straining to urinate
- Inability to urinate

Diagnosis is made using abdominal ultrasound imaging and a specialized urine test called the CADET BRAF Mutation Detection Assay to detect a common genetic mutation in dogs with transitional cell carcinoma.

Traditional options for treatment include chemotherapy, radiation, and the use of NSAIDs. Treatment is rarely curative and is focused on maintaining comfort and a good quality of life. Surgical tumor removal is rarely successful in removing the entire tumor; tumors may extend into the urethra. For tumors that are causing an obstruction of the urinary tract, stents can be placed to help keep urine flowing.

Complementary or alternative therapies can include the use of herbs, food therapy, acupuncture, and vitamin therapy. Feed a nutritious meat-based diet that is raw or gently cooked and low in carbohydrates. Give filtered water to eliminate contaminants found in tap water. Astragalus, selenium, and echinacea can help boost the immune system, stimulate the appetite, and reduce fatigue. Milk thistle, ashwagandha, garlic, green tea, ginger, and medicinal mushrooms can all be beneficial for detoxification and immune support. Burdock root, slippery elm, sorrel, and turkey rhubarb root help treat the cancer. Intravenous vitamin C therapy and injections of mistletoe may be available through a holistic veterinarian.

The feeding of fresh vegetables has some protective effect against this cancer. Avoid the use of herbicides, pesticides, and topical insecticides.

Kidney Disease or Kidney Failure

In 2007, one of the largest pet food recalls in history was announced when melamine, a chemical used to manufacture plastics, was added illegally to pet food ingredients including wheat gluten and rice protein sourced from China. Over 13,000 American pets died. A similar outbreak in Asia in 2004 resulted in the deaths of over 6,000 animals. Melamine causes kidney failure and formation of stones in the kidneys and bladder. When I visited China in 2008 all dairy products were recalled because melamine had been added to infant formula and milk, resulting in the death of infants. This happened again in 2011 and 2013. Melamine has also been added to feed products fed to chickens and swine; it is unknown what effect this will have on pets or people consuming the meat. Studies have shown the people who eat hot food off dishes made of melamine will excrete melamine in their urine.

Kidney disease, one of the most common ailments in cats and dogs, may go unnoticed in its early stages. By the time symptoms are noticed kidney disease is usually advanced. Kidney disease is a broad term that applies to any disease process that leaves the kidneys unable to effectively filter toxins out of the blood and maintain water balance in the body. Kidney (renal) disease is also called kidney (or renal) failure and renal insufficiency. All bodily systems are affected when the kidneys aren't working well. Diagnosis and treatment of kidney disease should include monitoring of other organs such as the heart, liver, and pancreas.

The function of the kidneys is to filter the blood, conserve water and electrolytes in the body, keep the pH balanced and send waste products out through the urine. Kidney function should be checked during your regular visits to the veterinarian. Your veterinarian should palpate your pets' kidneys during their physical examination. Palpation is an examination of the shape, contour, and size of the kidneys. Lab tests, such as urinalysis, complete blood count (CBC), and chemistry screens are critically important in catching kidney disease in its early stages.

Once damaged, kidney tissue (nephrons) will not regenerate. There is no cure for kidney disease. However, the kidneys have a great deal of reserve capacity to function, even when disease has damaged them to some degree. At least two thirds of the kidney must be dysfunctional before any clinical signs appear. Animals can survive with only one kidney. The goal of treating kidney disease is to optimize and support the kidney function still present. Kidney disease is common in older dogs and cats and is considered the "wearing out" of kidney tissue. For smaller dogs and cats, kidney disease occurs on average between 12 to 14 years of age. For larger dogs, kidney disease can be diagnosed as early as 7 years of age.

Kidney disease can occur over weeks, months, and years (called chronic kidney disease or CKD) or suddenly within days (acute kidney injury or AKD). For AKD, early treatment is crucial. CKD is the result of degenerative changes in the kidney and can be subtle to diagnose in its early stages.

Common causes of kidney disease include:

- *Toxins* can damage your pet's kidneys. The primary culprits are antifreeze, rat poison containing cholecalciferol, foods such as grapes, raisins and certain commercial jerky treats, excess vitamin D, common over-the-counter medications (OTCs) such as aspirin and other nonsteroidals (NSAIDS such as ibuprofen and naproxen), prescribed medications, pesticides, heavy metals, and venoms.

- *Diuretics* such as furosemide are generally considered a safe medication when given as directed; however, overdoses that remain untreated can lead to dehydration, electrolyte imbalances, and kidney malfunctions. Stronger medications, such as torsemide, can result in diuretic toxicity and need to be monitored carefully by your veterinarian.

- *Trauma such as a* kidney contusion, often called a kidney bruise, occurs following blunt trauma or direct impact to the lower back. This trauma leads to bleeding inside of the kidney. Acute kidney injury (AKI) is a sudden episode of kidney failure or kidney damage that happens within a few hours or a few days. AKI causes a build-up of waste products in the blood and makes it hard for the kidneys to keep the right balance of fluid in the body.

- *Infections* of the kidney tissues can occur in dogs and cats. Severe urinary tract infections can move from the bladder up to the kidneys. When a severe urinary tract infection is diagnosed, an ultrasound of the kidneys and bladder can be performed to determine the status of the kidneys. A urinalysis and a culture and sensitivity test will verify the presence and type of bacteria so that proper treatment can be prescribed.

- In cats, diseases such as *feline infectious peritonitis (FIP), feline immunodeficiency virus (FIV), and feline leukemia* can result in kidney failure to varying degrees.

- *Glomerular disease* is a condition affecting the kidney filtration mechanism in both dogs and cats and can be caused by infections (i.e. Lyme disease, Leptospirosis, e-coli), cancer, and high blood pressure. Lyme nephritis (inflammation of the kidneys) is seen in less than 1 to 2% of Lyme positive dogs; predisposition for retriever breeds may suggest a genetic relationship. For Lyme positive dogs with rapidly progressing kidney disease, treatment with doxycycline, fluid therapy, and the immune suppressing drug mycophenolate is currently recommended.

- *Urinary tract obstruction by k*idney stones can be caused by a chronic bacterial infection, genetics, and other diseases that alter blood and urine. Most stones in the kidney are oxalate stones and are usually not removed if small. The stones don't often seem to cause a dog or cat pain, unless they cause a blockage within the kidney or kidney ducts. When a blockage occurs, urine cannot exit the kidneys easily, and as the urine backs up, the kidneys will swell and can become damaged.

- The *genetics* of certain dog and cat breeds can play a role in kidney disease. Polycystic kidney disease is a genetic marker for several purebred dog and cat breeds.

Chronic kidney failure progression is like a series of dominoes each falling one after the other. When the kidney's filtration process becomes inefficient, less toxins are eliminated in the urine. This inefficiency increases blood flow to the kidneys to remove the toxins, resulting in increased urine production. The increased urine production results in fluid loss (and possible dehydration); thirst and water consumption increases. This process creates the earliest clinical signs of kidney disease known as *compensated renal failure*. This process can play out over months and years.

Symptoms of AKD and CKD are similar; the difference is how quickly the symptoms appear. Early indicators of kidney disease include increased thirst and urination, lethargy, decreased or loss of appetite, nausea, vomiting, diarrhea, and weight loss (especially in CKD and in cats). As the disease progresses, toxins built up in the body will increase and the symptoms will worsen. Signs of advancing kidney disease include:

- Dehydration—severe dehydration can be painful cause a "grimace" in cats. Signs of pain include "squinty" eyes, wrinkled forehead, flattened ears, and drooping whiskers.
- Increased water consumption and urination
- Lethargy
- High blood pressure
- Ulceration of the mouth or the digestive tract—these conditions can cause bad breath and dark, tarry stools.
- Further loss of appetite and/or anorexia/weight loss
- Diarrhea
- Blood in the urine
- Inability to regulate body temperature results in the animal becoming cold.
- Failure to groom (in cats)
- Pale gums due to secondary anemia
- Seizures due to high ammonia levels in the blood

Several tests are recommended to accurately diagnose kidney disease and its associated stage.

- A *urinalysis* assesses whether the kidneys are producing concentrated or diluted urine. Good kidney function will result in good urine concentration. A urinalysis will also indicate the level of protein in the urine. Some conditions can produce falsely elevated levels of protein in the urine; secondary tests called *microalbumin* and *urine protein creatinine ratio (UPC)* can be performed to confirm the presence of protein in the urine.
- A *urine culture* involves growing bacteria from a urine

sample in a lab to diagnose urinary tract infections and other infections.

- ☙ A *complete blood count (CBC)* will indicate red cell count decreases in chronic or late-stage kidney disease.
- ☙ A full *blood chemistry panel* assesses the function of various internal organs, and it is important to look at several values when diagnosing kidney disease. These include:
  - *Blood urea nitrogen (BUN) and blood creatinine (CREA)* testing measures the level of these two waste products in the blood.
  - *Electrolytes* (sodium, chloride, and potassium) levels can drastically increase or decrease. Levels can drop when an animal is drinking and urinating to the point of diluting the electrolytes out of the blood stream. Severe kidney disease can also result in elevated potassium levels which can affect heart function.
  - *Amylase* is an enzyme produced by the pancreas and is filtered by the kidneys. Sometimes kidney disease can be mistaken for pancreatitis if amylase levels are increasing. Diagnosis for both kidney disease and pancreatitis should include an assessment of more than just amylase levels.
  - *SDMA* is a blood test that is used to determine the stage of kidney disease. SDMA is a naturally occurring biological indicator for kidney function. SDMA concentrations above the normal range can diagnose kidney disease at an earlier stage (25% loss of function). SDMA can be falsely elevated if your pet is dehydrated or suffering from another illness.
  - *Thyroid levels,* particularly in cats, should also be assessed. Hyperthyroidism is cats can result in

high blood pressure which in turn produces kidney disease.

- *Elevated blood phosphorus* is a problem for animals with kidney disease; maintaining normal levels is essential in managing kidney disease.
- A *diagnostic ultrasound* can provide further clues to problems by examining an image of the kidneys.
- *Blood pressure* should be checked, as high levels can indicate kidney disease and cause disease to progress more rapidly.

A diagnosis of kidney disease is based on an evaluation of all available clinical and diagnostic information in a stable patient. The staging of kidney disease is based on the IRIS (International Renal Interest Society) parameters. In addition to the parameters, IRIS also recommends treatment protocols for each disease stage. However, the parameters and protocols should be treated as *guidelines*, since no one dog or cat is the same. Holistic veterinarians will often recommend treatment protocols not listed in the IRIS guidelines.

There are four stages of chronic kidney disease in dogs and cats. Each stage in the IRIS guidelines is based on SDMA and creatinine results. Again, all available clinical and diagnostic information should be used in evaluating the patient. For example, one high SDMA test result may not indicate kidney failure. The SDMA test should be rerun when the animal is well-hydrated.

Once a treatment protocol has been started, it is important to continue to monitor treatment progress with urinalysis and blood work.

- *Fluid therapy* is the cornerstone of both conventional and holistic treatment. Fluid therapy replaces various electrolytes, flushes toxins from the body, and reverses dehydration. If BUN is elevated or the animal is not eating, it is recommended to start IV fluids in a hospital setting for about 2-3 days. The biggest problem with IV fluid administration is managing animals that have co-morbidities, such as heart disease. In these instances, your veterinarian may be uncomfortable treating your pet with IV fluids. Never hesitate to ask your veterinarian about this, as you may need to seek out a specialist to administer treatment. Once the animal is stabilized, your veterinarian may recommend maintenance levels of fluids to be administered at home under the skin (subcutaneously).

- *Medications:* To stabilize *high blood pressure,* conventional treatment would include medications such as enalapril or lisinopril. Holistic treatment might include herbs and/or supplements that lower blood pressure. To help with *nausea, vomiting, or anorexia,* conventional treatment might include medications such as Cerenia or ondansetron. Herbal supplements, ginger tea, or a ginger cookie would also help to settle the stomach. For *stomach ulcerations,* medication to reduce acid (such as omeprazole) might be prescribed. Magic Mouth Wash (a mixture of lidocaine, diphenhydramine, and magnesium or aluminum hydroxide) can be used to reduce pain from *ulcerations in the mouth.* Ace inhibitors can help with *protein loss.* Calcitriol may be needed if vitamin D levels are low (always test before treating). Potassium supplementation may be needed if potassium is low.

- *Avoid nephro-toxic medications (medications that damage the kidneys).* When a medication is prescribed for any reason, always check the side effects of the drug. All medications have side effects. This is particularly important if your pet has co-morbidities.

- *Phosphorus binders* are used when the phosphorus levels in the blood are elevated. The body will automatically try to keep phosphorus and calcium in balance. If an animal has low calcium levels, the body will take it from the bones and teeth resulting in osteoporosis, brittle bones and tooth and jawbone loss.
- A hormone produced by the kidneys called *erythropoietin* stimulates the bone marrow to make red blood cells. With advanced kidney disease, the hormone is no longer produced. *Epogen or Procrit is a human replacement hormone* that can be given by injection to stimulate the bone marrow to produce red blood cells. It is not approved for use in dogs and cats by the FDA but is prescribed legally be veterinarians as an extra-label drug. Unfortunately, the drug may not be used long term because the immune system recognizes the drug as "foreign" and may make antibodies against it.
- **Acupuncture** can be very beneficial to improve appetite, decrease nausea, and slow the progression of disease.

Many veterinarians will immediately recommend a protein-restricted diet for pets with any stage of kidney disease. Protein should not be restricted in early stages of kidney disease, as this will result in muscle wasting and weakness. When the kidneys are inflamed and failing, they lose protein in the urine. The animal's body will draw protein from the body muscles, resulting in loss of muscle and energy. Rather than restricting protein to ultra-low levels it is more important to address the quality of the proteins eaten.

It is important to be somewhat restrictive with phosphorous levels in the diet once the phosphorous levels start to increase on lab tests. No restriction is needed prior to phosphorus levels rising in the blood. Many grains are higher in phosphorous than meats, so if you are making home-prepared diets you might want to check phosphorous levels in the ingredients you plan to use. Processed foods commonly have phosphates added and should be avoided. If phosphorous levels in the blood begin to rise the body will draw calcium from the bones to keep the calcium to phosphorous ratio in balance. Once a pet is in the late stages of kidney disease, it is imperative to work closely with the veterinarian to monitor the calcium, phosphorous, and potassium levels. Phosphate binders may need to be added to the treatment regimen to decrease absorption of phosphate from the intestines.

Sodium restriction is not a huge concern in pets, as most pet foods do not contain high levels of salt (be careful with processed treats, however). The ideal diet for pets with kidney disease should contain abundant moisture (no dry kibble, even if it is prescription diet).

Diets for pets with kidney disease should include a lot of "baby" foods; things like eggs, sprouts, walnuts, almonds, black sesame seeds, berries, royal jelly, shiitake mushrooms, tofu, root vegetables, and beans. These foods help replace the kidney "Jing" that has been lost over time. If the pet is seeking warmth, energetically warm foods like sweet potatoes, turnips, oats, and chicken can be added to the diet. If the pet is panting, hot, and dry, energetically cooling foods like fish, rabbit, millet, tomatoes, string beans, and barley are good additions.

One of the biggest problems with pets in advanced stages of kidney disease is anorexia. They become nauseous and refuse to eat. Rotation in the diet can be important to keep them eating. Try new foods like a bowl of warm oatmeal or mashed sweet potatoes with cinnamon. Grated parmesan cheese, garlic powder (not salt), or sugar-free tomato sauce can be used on top of the meal. Do not hide medications in the meal as this can make them turn away from their food. Offer small meals every few hours. Do not give a second helping if they like a meal. If they feel nauseous after eating, they will not eat that food again. Wait a day or two before offering the favored food again, as this will keep them more interested.

Nutritional supplements have helped immensely for pets with kidney disease. Some of these include:

- Aminavast—combination of naturally occurring peptides and amino acids that decreases symptoms and makes pets feel better, which helps improve the appetite. Dosage is on the bottle.
- Bentonite clay is a natural phosphate binder that is safe to use in kidney disease. Give 1/4 to 1/2 teaspoon mixed with water a teaspoon of water to form a paste. Do not give herbs, food, or medications within two hours after dosing.
- Omega 3 fatty acids—Derived from fish oil, algae oil, calamari oil, phytoplankton, or krill. Give 20 to 30 mg of EPA and DHA per pound of body weight daily.
- CoQ10—Give 5 mg per pound twice daily to help decrease inflammation.
- Probiotics—to support the immune system and digestion. Soil-based probiotics with fulvic and humic acid provide good support of the microbiome. The good bacteria in the bowel help decrease protein waste products that are absorbed into the blood stream and produce short chain fatty acids that support the immune system.
- Vitamin B12 –weekly injections to help digestion and appetite as well as supporting formation of red blood cells. Give 250 micrograms (1/4 ml) to cats and small dogs, 500 micrograms (1/2 ml) to medium and large dogs. Your veterinarian can supply this.
- Soluble fiber—added to the diet from sources like

non-starchy, dark, leafy green vegetables can help absorb toxins from the bowel.

- PEA—palmitoyethanolamide—anti-inflammatory; protects the kidneys from hypertensive injury. Give 400 to 2,000 mg daily depending on the size of the pet.
- Rehmannia 8 increases renal blood flow to help return blood values to normal.
- Cordyceps mushrooms can help protect against CKD and improve kidney function. Give 10 mg of extract per pound of body weight per day.
- Dandelion greens have diuretic function and help to move fluid through the kidneys. Feed 1 teaspoon per 20 pounds body weight per day.

There are many herbal and homeopathic support formulas available to treat kidney disease, but they should be prescribed after evaluation by an alternative therapy practitioner. Many owners will buy herbal combinations online that are not helpful and may be detrimental to the health of the pet. There is no "one-size-fits-all" herbal formula to support kidney failure. As in diet, the supplement may need to warm the body, cool the body, or support the kidney Jing.

SAMPLE DIET FOR KIDNEY FAILURE IN DOGS

- ☐ 16 ounces Cod
- ☐ 2 ounces beef liver
- ☐ 1 ounce oysters
- ☐ 2 ounces dry millet
- ☐ 4 ounces sweet potato
- ☐ 4 ounces green beans
- ☐ 4 ounces spinach or kale (raw weight)

- ☐ 1 egg
- ☐ 1/2 can sardines in oil
- ☐ 1 tsp seaweed or kelp
- ☐ 1 tsp ground eggshell powder
- ☐ 1 1/4 tsp wheat germ oil

Provides 25 calories per ounce. Cook all ingredients in a slow cooker (4 hours on high or 8 hours on low). Mix cooked ingredients in a food processor when cooled. Feed according to chapter 4. May be stored 3 to 5 days in the refrigerator.

SAMPLE DIET FOR KIDNEY FAILURE IN CATS

- ☐ 12 ounces dark meat chicken without skin
- ☐ 6 ounces chicken liver
- ☐ 3 whole eggs
- ☐ 4 ounces baked sweet potato, no skin
- ☐ 4 ounces vegetable medley (cabbage, zucchini, kale, carrots, green
- ☐ beans, red peppers)
- ☐ 3 ounces cooked salmon
- ☐ 2 ounces oysters
- ☐ 4 teaspoons ground flaxseed
- ☐ 2 teaspoons ground turmeric

☐ 1 teaspoon bonemeal powder

☐ 1/2 teaspoon wheat germ oil

☐ 1/2 teaspoon dried kelp powder

Provides 32 calories per ounce. May be fed raw or gently cooked (vegetables should be cooked or finely ground). Feed according to directions in chapter 4.

Urinary Incontinence

Urinary incontinence can be a huge issue for pet owners, sometimes resulting in euthanasia when pet owners are disgusted by pets leaving puddles of urine around the house. Urinary incontinence can be seen at any age, depending on the cause.

Common causes of urinary incontinence can include:

- Low estrogen levels (may be associated with early spay)
- Weak urethral sphincter (the muscle that closes to stop urinary outflow)
- Spinal cord disease
- Metabolic diseases causing increased water consumption (diabetes, hypothyroidism, cancer, autoimmune disease, kidney failure)
- Drugs (steroids, some antibiotics)
- Urinary tract infection
- Bladder stones
- Enlarged prostate
- Birth defects (ectopic ureter, persistent urachal diverticulum).

Obviously, with so many causes, diagnosis is the key to treatment.

Symptoms may include foul odor from urine saturation of the hindquarters, urine scalding of the skin with secondary skin infection, urine saturation of hair around the urethral openings, and puddles left where pets sit or lie down.

Diagnostic tests that should be performed may include urinalysis, urine culture and sensitivity, bladder and kidney x-ray +/- bladder and kidney ultrasound, blood serum chemistry, rectal exam (males), and possibly dye studies for pets with suspected birth defects. Once a diagnosis has confirmed the source of the problem, proper treatment can be initiated.

From a TCVM (Chinese Medicine) perspective, urine leakage can be associated with Bladder Damp Heat (infection or stones), Kidney Qi Deficiency (kidney failure and leakage), or Kidney Yang Deficiency (old, cold pets). Acupuncture, including moxa therapy (heat therapy) and electro-acupuncture, can be very helpful for these pets, along with herbal therapies. There are multiple herbal formulas available for urinary leakage, with some of the more common remedies including Suo Quan Wan, Hindquarter Weakness, Si Maio San, Bu Yang Yuan Wan, and Wu Bi Shan Yao Wan. Consultation with a TCVM holistic practitioner can help determine which formula would be most beneficial. Homeopathic products may also be helpful.

Food therapy that may help old, cold pets (Kidney Yang and Qi Deficiency) include Qi tonics such as beef, chicken, lamb, oats, brown rice, pumpkin, sweet potato, figs, and Shiitake mushrooms. Yang tonics to warm the pet include venison, lamb, kidney, dried ginger and cinnamon, garlic, dill seed, fennel seed, basil, and thyme.

Proin, or phenylpropanolamine, is commonly used to increase urethral sphincter tone. This drug can cause extreme elevations in blood pressure and should not be used in pets with any heart disease, high blood pressure, kidney disease, or glaucoma. Blood pressure should be monitored frequently if this drug is used. Other side effects include elevated heart rate, excitement, restlessness, panting, aggression, vomiting, diarrhea, anorexia, hypersalivation, seizures, abnormal gait, tremors, coma, hemorrhagic stroke, elevated liver enzymes, and kidney failure.

Estrogen hormone replacement therapy is also commonly used. Estrogen can be very beneficial in low doses, but side effects can include bone marrow red blood cell suppression, leading to fatal anemia. Red blood cell counts should be monitored closely in pets that receive estrogen therapy.

Cold laser therapy, acupuncture, chiropractic care, and herbal formulas can be used effectively for pets with spinal disorders contributing to urinary incontinence.

The most important treatment the pet owner can offer for pets with urinary incontinence is vigilance and cleanliness. If the pet continues to leak urine once all diagnostics have been performed and therapy instituted, it is imperative to keep the pet clean and odor free. Diapers can be a huge help, but daily bathing and inspection for skin infection and urine scalding must be performed. Every summer we see multiple cases of pets infested with maggots secondary to urine incontinence.

13 Eye Diseases

Eye care is an integral part of your dog or cat's wellness regimen. A proactive approach to your pet's vision care can save you and your pet a great deal of pain and possibly a trip to the emergency room or veterinary ophthalmologist. The steps you take to keep your pet's eyes healthy and safe will help to preserve eye health and vision long into their senior years.

The first step in proactively caring for your pet's vision is feeding them a high moisture, meat-based, species-appropriate diet rich in naturally occurring antioxidants. Carotenoids are antioxidants that lower inflammation in the body. Foods high in carotenoids can help protect the cells in the eye. These foods include blueberries, broccoli, eggs, carrots, cold water fish (haddock, sardines, cod, tuna, and salmon), kale, pumpkin, sweet potato, tomato, and bilberry. In addition to feeding naturally occurring antioxidants, eye-supporting supplements can be added. Supplemental omega-3 essential fatty acids, like those found in krill, sardine, anchovy, or squid oils, will cross the blood-brain barrier to nourish the eyes. Other vitamins and antioxidants that support eye health include Vitamin E and C, lutein, and zeaxanthin (or astaxanthin). Turmeric is a powerful antioxidant; its anti-inflammatory properties help prevent oxidative damage and delay the development of cataracts.

The next step is a daily check of your dog or cat's eyes. When observing, look for any changes, such as squinting or holding the eye(s) closed, tearing, redness, discharge, and rubbing or pawing at the eye(s). There should not be any build-up of discharge that requires regular cleaning. The following symptoms may signal a problem and a visit to the veterinarian.

- *Red eyes* signify inflammation. Engorged blood vessels tell you that blood is being rushed to the eye to bring oxygen and nutrients to help fight disease. Red eyes can signal such problems as Keratoconjunctivitis sicca (KCS, or dry eye), "cherry" eye (a visible tear gland), glaucoma, entropion (eyelids rolled in, rubbing on the cornea), ectropion (droopy eye lids), inflammation of the liver, or lymphoma.
- *Rubbing, squinting and light sensitivity* can be caused by itchy eyes, painful eyes, foreign bodies, tumors, increased pressure in the eye, or an eye injury stemming from a corneal ulcer/abrasion or blunt trauma, entropion (eyelids turn in causing eye lashes or hair to cause irritation to the eye), or eyelashes growing in the wrong direction (Distichiasis and Trichiasis).
- *Bulging eye(s)* is a serious condition that needs immediate attention. Bulging eye(s) is a sign of high pressure within the globe of the eye. The high pressure can be caused by glaucoma or a tumor behind the eye or on the surface of the eye or eyelid. Bulging eyes can also signal an injury. If not treated quickly, these conditions can quickly cause blindness.
- *Excessive tearing* can occur from allergies, pain from corneal ulcers, foreign bodies, or increased pressure. Blocked tear ducts may also result in excess tears spilling over onto the face.
- *Cloudy eyes* indicate swelling in the cornea. Swelling in the cells of the cornea shows there has been damage to the cornea. Cataracts appear as a white opaque filling of

the lens in the center of the eye. They block transmission of light and cause blindness. Cataracts are generally seen as an old age disease but can be congenital or secondary to diabetes mellitus. Surgery for cataract removal may be an option. Degeneration of the lens, called nuclear or lenticular sclerosis, is a normal aging process that causes clouding of the lens.

- *Green, yellow, or mucoid discharge* indicates an infection. Mucous will be produced when there are not enough tears, or the eye is dry.

- *Dilated or unequal pupils* can be diagnosed by placing a bright light in front of your pet. If the pupils do not constrict in bright light, this is an indication that vision is being lost. This can be secondary to hypertension (heart or kidney disease, hyperthyroidism in cats) or inflammation like SARDS (Sudden Acquired Retinal Degeneration Syndrome) or PRA (Progressive Retinal Atrophy). Unequal pupil sizes can be an indication of an eye problem or a neurologic problem and should be checked as soon as possible.

- *Confusion, or bumping into things* shows that your pet is having trouble finding its way around and should have the eyes checked. Sudden blindness can be an indication of a more serious disease, like lymphoma.

- An *elevated (or visible) third eyelid* indicates inflammation where the eye is trying to protect itself. This can also be seen in animals that are very thin and have lost the fat that pushes the eye forward in the socket. This is particularly noticed in old, thin cats with chronic kidney disease or untreated hyperthyroidism. Horner's syndrome, which is a disease of the nerves supplying the face, can also result in an elevated third eyelid.

While waiting for an appointment with your veterinarian or the local emergency service, use a gentle drop or gel to moisten and soothe the eye. Look for water-based products rather than petroleum-based. Drops containing hyaluronic acid are especially good for eye disease. Eye problems should not wait days to be seen. Insist on an immediate appointment or take your pet to an emergency clinic.

Different breeds are prone to different eye problems. In dog breeds for example, English Springer Spaniels are prone to developing glaucoma and cataracts. Collie breeds can develop a range of severities of Collie Eye Anomaly (CEA) which is an incurable condition that affects the retina, choroid and sclera. Boston Terriers and other short-nosed (brachycephalic) breeds are prone to "cherry" eye, as well as excessive tearing. Progressive Retinal Atrophy (PRA) is an inherited condition in Abyssinian and Persian cats, Bedlington Terriers, Cavalier King Charles Spaniels, Labrador and Golden Retrievers, Rottweilers, American Cocker Spaniels, English Springer Spaniels, Old English Mastiffs, Bullmastiffs, Siberian Huskies, and the Samoyed. Himalayan and Burmese cats can inherit eye defects such as entropion and corneal sequestrum (dark areas of dead tissue in the cornea). These examples are by no means exhaustive. The point is to understand the symptoms of the disease so that it can be diagnosed, monitored, and treated in its early stages.

Paying attention to your pet's eye health can prevent eye diseases from becoming a serious problem. The sooner you notice an issue and act, the better chance there is to treat it with more resources and possibly reverse the problem. If in doubt, do not wait to take your pet to a veterinarian. Your pet's vision depends on it!

The eyes are the windows into the body, commonly showing inflammation and disease when there is a systemic problem. In Chinese Medicine, the eyes are linked to the liver, so anytime there is a problem with the eyes the liver should be examined as well. When treating eye disease with acupuncture and herbs the liver should always be treated.

Glaucoma

Glaucoma, or elevated pressure within the eye, is a common problem, particularly in certain breeds. There is a genetic predisposition in Cocker Spaniels, Shar Pei, Chows, Labradors, Basset Hounds, and Australian Shepherds. Secondary glaucoma can occur secondary to high blood pressure, cataracts, inflammation in the eye, or trauma.

One of our rescue spaniels, Lora Lu, developed secondary glaucoma while spending the day at a local town festival. We took five dogs with us to walk through town and visit friends and local businesses. While chatting with a friend in front of the local music store, we did not realize a band had formed and was about to start playing. Lora happened to be sitting right next to a speaker and jumped three feet in the air with the first, extremely loud, strum of the bass guitar. When I looked down, she was trembling, and her eyes were bright red and bulging out of their sockets. We quickly left the area, but the damage was already done. Her blood pressure had sky-rocketed, along with the pressure in her eyes.

Symptoms of glaucoma include:

- Cloudy eye
- Bulging eye
- Red eye
- Dilated pupil
- Squinting
- Excessive tear production
- Pain
- Hiding or avoiding interaction

- Sudden aggression
- Sleeping more than normal
- Pawing or rubbing the face
- Blindness

Causes of glaucoma include:

- Chronic inflammation in the eye
- Infectious diseases (feline leukemia, feline infectious peritonitis, feline immunodeficiency virus, toxoplasmosis)
- Cancer (lymphoma or melanoma)
- Lens luxation (dislocation)
- Cataracts causing inflammation
- Genetic predisposition
- Trauma
- Fungal diseases
- High blood pressure

If not caught early and treated immediately, blindness is irreversible. Glaucoma is diagnosed by measuring the pressure within the eyes with a tonometer. Intravenous mannitol can be administered to help lower the pressure quickly, along with medications for pain relief. Whenever your pet has any symptoms of eye disease you should request a pressure measurement be taken to make sure glaucoma is not brewing. If the pressure in the eye is elevated, a blood pressure measurement should also be performed.

Supplements can be given to help prevent glaucoma in breeds prone to this disease, as well as any pet suffering from the disease. These include CoQ10, Lutein, beta-carotene, and vitamins A, C, and E. Ocu-Glo, which contains all these ingredients, is currently the best eye supplement on the market and is available online direct to consumers.

Avoid choke collars or anything that will put pressure around the neck as these can cause increased pressure in the eyes. Breeds at risk should have blood pressure and eye pressure measured at least twice annually to detect any early increases that can be addressed prior to development of full-blown glaucoma.

Once glaucoma develops, acupuncture can be utilized to help decrease blood pressure and drain liver heat and stagnation (the eyes are connected to the Liver in TCVM). Topical eye drops, including Dorzolamide, Timolol, and Latanoprost, and oral medications, such as Methazolamide, may be used to lower the pressure as well. If normal pressure is not attainable the eye will remain painful and blind. Treatment will be life-long and require regular monitoring of eye pressure.

Once the pet is blind, an injection of a caustic antibiotic, gentamycin, can be placed inside the eye to decrease fluid production and thereby, decrease pain. This will also guarantee no return to vision. One study showed 39.5% of dogs undergoing this procedure had tumors in the eyes at the time of enucleation or death. Rather than subject my pet to this procedure, I would have the eye removed if it was completely blind and had no hope of regaining vision.

Fortunately, Lora Lu did recover from the initial incident of glaucoma. She was treated with oral medication (Amlodipine) to lower her blood pressure and drops (Dorzolamide and Latanoprost) in her eyes three times daily to lower her eye pressure. Unfortunately, three years later her glaucoma became uncontrollable, and she had both eyes removed within a three-month span of time. While it took me some time to adjust to the thought of having a dog with no eyes, Lora Lu adjusted rather quickly. She no longer had the painful eyes causing her to be anxious and she was much calmer immediately after surgery. She did, however, get a bit annoyed with me when I did the house cleaning and moved the furniture around!

Corneal Ulceration

Corneal ulceration (a scratched eye) can occur due to fighting (particularly cats), rough play, foreign bodies, chemical irritation or burns (shampoos, cleaning products), bacterial or viral infections, dry eyes, facial paralysis, entropion, distichiasis, trichiasis, or endocrine disease (hypothyroidism, Cushing's disease, diabetes mellitus). Any time a corneal ulceration occurs the tear production should be tested to be sure the eye is producing enough tears. Treating the ulcer and not treating the dry eye will result in reoccurrence of the ulcers.

In cats, corneal ulceration is commonly seen secondary to viral respiratory infections. For this reason, steroids should rarely be used to treat eye problems in cats. Even if the virus is not currently active, the dosing of steroids may suppress the immune system, allowing the virus to activate, which will cause more damage.

Symptoms of corneal abrasion or ulceration include:

- Blinking more often
- Excessive tearing
- Redness of the eye
- Swelling of the eyelid or skin around the eye
- Pawing or rubbing the face
- Elevated third eyelid
- Hiding in dark spaces (they are very light-sensitive)
- Holding the eye shut
- Yellow, green, or bloody eye discharge
- Hole in the outer layer of the eye
- Rupture of the eye
- Blindness
- Decreased appetite
- Lethargy

Scratches on the cornea are always worthy of a visit to the veterinarian; an infection can cause the eye to perforate, causing permanent damage and blindness. The veterinarian will use a dye called fluorescein to stain the eye; ulcers will stain bright green. If the ulcer is deep, a culture and sensitivity may be warranted to determine whether there is infection with bacteria. Corneal scratches can be extremely painful, and many pets will require medication to help with pain. Do not allow your pet to rub the eye; use an Elizabethan collar if necessary.

Superficial abrasions generally heal within three to five days. An antibiotic drop or ointment is prescribed and may be accompanied by drops to relieve pain and spasm in the eye. Steroids will delay healing and suppress immune function which can lead to worsening infection; they should not be used. I prefer to use drops, as ointments are usually petroleum based. Deep or nonhealing ulcers may require further treatment such as a corneal graft or grid keratectomy. Any underlying medical conditions or congenital abnormalities must be diagnosed and correctly treated to avoid chronic eye ulcers or frequent development of corneal ulcers in the future.

Cataracts

Recently, we adopted a Cocker Spaniel that was blind with cataracts in both eyes. Charlie was found as a stray and was estimated to be at least thirteen years old because of the cataracts. Once we saw him, we realized he was a young dog with congenital cataracts, not a senior citizen with age-related cataracts. That was great news because it meant that surgical cataract removal might be an option to restore vision. Unfortunately, one eye had too much damage that would prevent return of sight even with cataract removal. The other eye seemed to be a good candidate for return of vision, so the cataract was surgically removed. While his vision was not great after surgery, there was at least a partial return of sight which improved his quality of life.

Cataracts are a whitening of the lens of the eye. The lens is made of water and proteins. Cataracts form when the proteins begin to clump together, forming the cloudy appearance which blocks light from reaching the retina. Cataracts can form slowly or very quickly.

Cataracts can be congenital (present at birth) or can develop later in life as part of the aging process. Hereditary cataracts are common in American Cocker spaniels, Labrador and Golden retrievers, French poodles, Boston terriers, Siberian huskies, miniature schnauzers, and Welsh Springer Spaniels. They are commonly seen secondary to diabetes mellitus and hypertension. Sometimes these are the first thing the owner notices in a diabetic dog. Cataracts can also develop from toxins introduced into the dog's system, like vaccines, drugs, radiation, UV lights, cancer therapy treatments, and pollution. The liver filters all toxins and the eyes will be affected if the liver is burdened.

Cataracts can rupture, leaking lens contents into the eye, which is highly inflammatory and painful. Mature cataracts may need to be removed before reaching this point. Currently, there are new eye medications undergoing investigation to prevent maturation of cataracts, particularly in diabetic dogs. Some owners have reported good results using Cineraria Eye Drops for cataracts. Topical anti-inflammatory drops may be prescribed to decrease inflammation secondary to cataracts.

Congenital Conditions

Trichiasis, distichiasis, and ectopic cilia are eyelash disorders that are found in dogs but rarely found in cats. The more commonly affected breeds include American Cocker Spaniel, Cavalier King Charles Spaniel, Shih Tzu, Lhasa Apso, Dachshund, Shetland

Sheepdog, Golden Retriever, Chesapeake Retriever, Bulldog, Boston Terrier, Pug, Boxer Dog, and Pekingese. Trichiasis is the ingrowth of the eyelashes; distichiasis is an eyelash that grows from an abnormal spot on the eyelid; and ectopic cilia are single or multiple hairs that grow through the inside of the eyelid. In all these conditions, the eyelash hair can come into contact with and damage the cornea or conjunctiva of the eye.

The signs will vary with the severity of the condition, including the number of extra eyelashes, their size, and their stiffness. In some cases, when the extra eyelashes are very soft, the patient does not show any symptoms. In other cases, the distichiae irritate the eye and cause inflammation, eye discharges, and pain; left untreated the cornea may become ulcerated. Ophthalmic lubricants may relief irritation or surgery may be required to remove the offending lashes.

Entropion is an abnormality of the eyelids in which the eyelid rolls inward. This inward rolling often causes the hair on the surface of the eyelid to rub against the cornea resulting in pain, corneal ulcers, perforations, or pigment developing on the cornea which can interfere with vision. In most cases both eyes will be affected. Entropion is primarily an inherited disorder seen often in many breeds of dogs. In cats it is more often a disease of old age in thin cats with eyes that are sunken back in the sockets from loss of fat. Brachycephalic (flat-faced) dog and cat breeds are prone to this condition. Entropion is most often treated with eyelid surgery with a very good success rate.

Ectropion is an abnormality of the eyelids in which the lower eyelid 'rolls' outward or is everted. This causes the lower eyelids to appear droopy. This results in **conjunctivitis**. The **cornea** may also dry out, resulting in **keratitis** (corneal inflammation). All these conditions are painful. Corneal damage can also result in corneal scarring, that can impair or obstruct vision. In most cases, both eyes are affected. Ectropion is usually diagnosed in dogs less than one year of age; it is rarely seen in cats. Breeds with a higher incidence of ectropion include Cocker spaniel, Saint Bernard, Bloodhound, Basset hound, Mastiff, Newfoundland, Bulldog, Chow, English springer spaniel, and American and English cocker spaniels.

Ectropion can also be caused by facial nerve paralysis, hypothyroidism, chronic inflammation, and neuromuscular disease. Treatment usually requires surgical correction which is very successful.

Cherry eye in pets is a disfiguring but not painful condition. The third eyelid, or nictitating membrane, which contains a tear gland that produces a significant portion of the eye's tear film, prolapses (pops out), and causes a red bulge in the inner corner of the eye. A cherry eye appears as a red, swollen mass on the lower eyelid near the nose or muzzle, resembling a cherry.

The third eyelid gland is normally anchored to the lower inner rim of the eye by a fibrous attachment. This attachment is thought to be weak in certain dog breeds, allowing the gland to prolapse easily. The breeds most affected include the Cocker Spaniel, English Bulldog, French Bulldog, Boston Terrier, Beagle, Bloodhound, Lhasa Apso, Shih Tzu, Pug, and other brachycephalic (flat-faced) breeds. Burmese and Persian cats can also be affected by a cherry eye.

Preferred treatment involves surgical replacement of the third eyelid gland. Removal of the gland is not recommended. This is critical because the third eyelid gland produces up to 50% of the watery portion of the tear film. Without adequate tear production, the pet is much more likely to develop dry eyes, which can seriously impair vision. Approximately 5 to 20% of patients may experience a re-prolapse and require additional surgery.

Progressive Retinal Atrophy

Progressive Retinal Atrophy (PRA) is an inherited disease that causes slow degeneration of the retina leading to blindness. It is most seen in Poodles, Bedlington terriers, Cavalier King Charles spaniels, Rottweilers, Mastiffs, Cocker Spaniels, Siamese, Persian, and Abyssinian cats but different forms of the disease have been seen in many breeds. While the pet may suddenly appear blind, the degeneration occurs over a long period of time, usually one to two years. There is no therapy to treat this disease. Genetic testing and selective breeding may be the best method to avoid this disease.

Suddenly Acquired Retinal Degeneration

Suddenly Acquired Retinal Degeneration (SARDS) and Immune Mediated Retinitis (IMR) are two diseases that can cause sudden blindness in dogs. It is seen mostly in female mixed breed dogs, although Dachshunds, miniature Schnauzers, and Pugs seem to be overrepresented. Average age of onset is 7 to 10 years. The cause is unknown.

These inflammatory conditions are often indicators of a much more serious systemic disease. They have been associated with auto-immune disease, Cushing's disease, cancer, and stresses on the immune system. SARDS patients do not respond to traditional immunosuppressive therapy used to control other autoimmune diseases. Many patients lose their sense of smell, indicating a neuroendocrine disorder may be involved. From a Chinese Medicine viewpoint this makes perfect sense. If we keep stressing the liver with vaccinations, toxins, chemicals, and poor diet, the eyes are going to suffer.

I have only seen this disease in patients that have been over-vaccinated, are suffering from concurrent disease like cancer, or have other immune system dysfunction. One of my clients had two Pugs, Parker and Hudson, who were both afflicted with this condition. One of them had been undergoing treatment for Mast Cell tumors and they both had been over-vaccinated and over-medicated, causing severe immune system dysfunction. Both were able to maintain at least a little vision for a few years by changing to a better diet, using topical drops like Dorzolamide and Latanoprost, and oral supplements like Ocu-Glo, SAMe, and milk thistle.

Traditional treatment consists of high doses of steroids and immunosuppressive drugs along with topical eye medications but these are minimally effective. Ultimately the underlying problem needs to be addressed. These pets should no longer receive vaccinations of any kind and need to be fed a healthy diet including probiotics to get the gut immune system functioning at a higher level.

In summary, for any pet with eye disease:

- Feed a healthy diet with plenty of leafy green vegetables like spinach and kale to support the liver.
- Minimize toxins and stress on the liver; minimize vaccinations.
- Supplement with antioxidants like CoQ10 at 5 mg per pound of body weight twice daily.
- Ocu-Glo vitamins may be beneficial for dogs. It is not available for cats.
- Milk thistle (silymarin) at 5 to 10 mg per pound of body weight daily.
- SAMe (s-adenosylmethionine) at 90 mg for small dogs and cats, 225 mg for medium dogs, and 400 mg for large dogs once daily on an empty stomach.

Keratoconjunctivitis Sicca or Dry Eye

KCS is a condition where the eyes do not have enough fluids to make tears, so they produce mucous or phlegm to coat and protect the cornea. It doesn't protect the eyes very well because many dogs with this condition end up with corneal ulcers and erosions. Many dogs become blind with time. It is uncommon in cats.

Causes of KCS include:

- Immune-mediated diseases that damage the tear producing glands. This is the most common cause of KCS and is poorly understood. The body's immune system attacks the cells that produce a portion of the tear film resulting in decreased production. This is thought to be an inherited disorder.
- Systemic diseases such as canine distemper virus or feline herpes infections.
- Bacterial infections, such as chlamydia.
- Facial paralysis.
- Medications such as certain sulphonamides (sulfa drugs).
- Anesthesia.
- Hypothyroidism.
- Nervous system effects of an inner ear infection (neurogenic KCS).
- Genetic predisposition: American cocker spaniel, bloodhound, Boston terrier, Cavalier King Charles spaniel, English bulldog, English springer spaniel, Lhasa Apso, miniature Schnauzer, Pekingese, pug, Samoyed, Shih Tzu, West Highland white terrier, Yorkshire terrier

Symptoms include:

- Excessive blinking.
- Squinting due to pain and discomfort.
- Discharge from the eyes—usually cloudy white, yellow, or green.
- Redness of the outer layer of the eye due to inflammation of the blood vessels.
- Swelling of the conjunctiva, the tissue that lines the surface of the eye and the inner eyelids.

- Elevation of the third eyelid.
- Scarring or cloudiness of the cornea.
- Dull appearance to the eyes.
- Impaired vision or blindness (in severe cases where scarring is extensive)

Diagnosis is made by measuring tear production using a non-invasive test called the Schirmer tear test which can be performed in any veterinary office. The test uses a special wicking paper to measure the amount of tear film produced in one minute. Additional tests may include staining of the cornea to look for abrasion or ulceration, measurement of pressure within the eye to check for glaucoma, and examination of the tear ducts to check for blockage.

Cyclosporine, Tacrolimus, and artificial tears are traditionally used to treat KCS. Cyclosporine and tacrolimus decrease inflammation and stimulate tear production. I prefer tacrolimus in MCT oil. Pilocarpine may be used to stimulate tear production if the cause is neurogenic KCS due to nerve damage. Daily, gentle cleaning of discharge from around the eyes using a warm, wet cloth must be maintained to prevent secondary infection. Application of lubricating drops containing hyaluronic acid may be necessary multiple times per day. Avoid petroleum-based drops or ointments. Surgical treatment may include repositioning a salivary gland duct to secrete saliva into the eyes. There is a significant risk of complication with this surgery.

There are many foods that help moisten and drain phlegm including clams (canned, minced, rinsed and drained), pears (canned, in their own juice), almond milk or ground almonds, and fresh peppermint. Eggs, carrots, and sardines are also beneficial. Omega-3 fatty acids decrease inflammation and probiotics help the immune system.

Our English Toy Spaniel came to us with severe dry eye disease. I started him on home-prepared food to address phlegm and moisture deficiency. Within a few weeks I was able to decrease the medication for George's eyes to once daily treatment. Within a few months, his eyes looked great, and he no longer needed any medications. His coat had grown thick and shiny, and he was the picture of health.

George's diet is now a staple in my treatment regimen and has been used to treat many dogs with dry eye. This was a perfect example of using food therapy to treat a disease that had been described as incurable and requiring lifelong drug therapy.

This disease can be easy to treat if the owners will agree to discontinue dry food and increase the moisture in the diet, although some dogs will require lifelong medication.

SAMPLE DRY EYE DIET (GOOD FOR ALL EYE DISEASES) FOR DOGS

- ☐ 1 pound ground beef (90% lean, 10% fat)
- ☐ 3 ounces beef liver
- ☐ 4 ounces beef heart
- ☐ 6 ounces spinach
- ☐ 3 ounces carrot
- ☐ 3 whole eggs
- ☐ 2 teaspoons ground eggshell or bonemeal powder
- ☐ 2 ounces clams rinsed well to remove salt
- ☐ 1 pear
- ☐ 3 teaspoons finely ground almonds
- ☐ 3 teaspoons chopped fresh peppermint

- ☐ 2 ounces fresh sardines or canned in water
- ☐ 1 teaspoon dried kelp powder

Provides 31 calories per ounce. This diet can be ground and mixed together, cooking at 325° F. for 30 to 45 minutes in a loaf or square baking pan, cooked on low for 4 to 6 hours in a slow cooker, or fed raw. Follow feeding guidelines in chapter 4.

SAMPLE EYE SUPPORT DIET FOR CATS

- ☐ 8 ounces chicken hearts
- ☐ 2 ounces beef liver
- ☐ 1 ounce kale
- ☐ 1 ounce canned pumpkin
- ☐ 1 egg
- ☐ 1 ounce canned sardine in water
- ☐ 1/2 teaspoon eggshell or bonemeal powder
- ☐ 1/2 teaspoon kelp powder
- ☐ 2.5 teaspoons spirulina powder

Provides 35 calories per ounce. This diet can be ground and mixed, cooking at 325° F. for 30 to 45 minutes in a loaf or square baking pan, cooked on low for 4 to 6 hours in a slow cooker, or fed raw. Follow feeding guidelines in chapter 4.

14 Respiratory Diseases

Influenza

Vaccine companies and veterinarians would like to scare every dog owner into believing their pets will surely die if they do not receive the influenza vaccine. Once flu season arrives, television news shows, newspapers articles, and veterinary emails start bombarding pet owners with forecasts of epidemics and significant loss of life if all dogs aren't immediately rushed in to be injected with the vaccine that is supposed to prevent influenza.

Just like human influenza, canine influenza comes in multiple strains. The H3N8 strain of influenza mutated from infecting horses to infecting Greyhounds at racetracks in Florida in 2004. From there, the infection spread throughout the United States, making many dogs sick. Vaccine companies worked quickly to develop an influenza vaccine to protect pets, aggressively marketing it to veterinarians and pet owners. Unfortunately, many pets were vaccinated that had no risk of encountering the disease.

In 2007, a new strain of canine influenza appeared initially in South Korea, the H3N2 virus, which originated in birds. It was first detected in the United States in 2015. Veterinarians and vaccine companies recommended vaccinating every dog with the H3N8 vaccine, even though it would not protect against the H3N2 virus.

But the vaccine companies came to the rescue and developed a second influenza vaccine. Now some veterinarians and vaccine companies are recommending giving dogs both vaccines. We don't tell people they should get multiple flu vaccines every year; why would we do this to our pets?

Some dogs (and people) get sick when given the vaccines, with symptoms ranging from vomiting and diarrhea, to muscle aches and pain, and respiratory distress. According to the AVMA "The canine influenza vaccine is a "lifestyle" vaccine and is not recommended for every dog. In general, the vaccine is intended for the protection of dogs at risk for exposure to the canine influenza virus". Dogs at high risk for the disease include dogs that go to competitions, training, boarding, or daycare with large groups of dogs *in an endemic area and those that are immunocompromised.*

Vaccines require active participation by the immune system of the animal. Over-vaccination can cause immune distress. Vaccines should only be given to healthy dogs, which rules out a large portion of the population suffering from chronic disease and inflammation.

While the media, the vaccine companies, and many veterinarians would like to scare you into vaccinating your dogs, remember that not all dogs will become ill when exposed to the influenza virus. Of those infected, most will have minor symptoms, such as an annoying cough, runny nose, fever, lethargy, eye discharge, and reduced appetite for two to four weeks. Those with the severe form develop pneumonia and high fever. Cats can be infected with the H3N2 virus, showing signs of upper respiratory illness such as runny nose, congestion, lethargy, and excessive salivation.

According to the CDC, "The percentage of dogs infected with this disease that die is very small. Some dogs have asymptomatic infections (no signs of illness), while some have severe infections. Severe illness is characterized by the onset of pneumonia." From Iowa State University's Center for Food Security and Public Health:

"informal reports suggest that most cases have been characterized by relatively mild upper respiratory signs, with few deaths".

Testing to confirm H3N8 and H3N2 canine influenza virus infection in dogs is available. Treatment largely consists of supportive care to keep the dog hydrated and comfortable while the immune system does its job fighting viral infection.

Kennel Cough or Infectious Tracheobronchitis

Also known as infectious tracheobronchitis, kennel cough can have many causes. It can affect both dogs and cats and spread between species. The most common is a bacterium, *Bordetella bronchiseptica*, but many other organisms such as parainfluenza, adenovirus, feline upper respiratory viruses, and mycoplasma may be the culprit or occur in conjunction. Kennel cough is spread through the air when bacterial and viral particles are sneezed or coughed from infected animals. Crowded conditions, such as those found in shelters, kennels, daycare, grooming, dog and cat shows, or veterinary hospitals, along with poor ventilation, cold air, and cigarette smoke, may contribute to the spread of disease. It is possible, however, for your pet to come down with kennel cough in your own back yard if your neighbor's dog happens to be carrying the disease or was recently vaccinated.

The airways in the nasal passages and lungs are lined with small hairs that filter out pathogens as they enter the respiratory tract. When pathogens invade, the cells lining the airways secrete liquid and mucous to wash the pathogens out of the body. A healthy immune system will attack the invaders and destroy them. Under conditions of stress or weakened immune system, the animal will fall victim to the disease. Clinical signs of coughing, sneezing, runny eyes, conjunctivitis, lethargy, and inappetence may appear three to four days after exposure and may last for seven to 21 days.

Many kennels, daycare, and boarding facilities require kennel cough vaccination before an animal is allowed to visit. There are multiple vaccination types available, including intraoral (given in the mouth), intranasal (given up the nose), and injectable (given under the skin). The oral and nasal vaccinations may produce a slightly quicker response to vaccination. The injectable vaccine requires two doses be given two to four weeks apart initially, followed by annual or semi-annual revaccination (the time interval is up for debate). I do not ever recommend the injectable form of kennel cough vaccination. Only healthy pets that are not currently suffering from airway disease should be considered for vaccination.

Many pets will develop symptoms of kennel cough after being vaccinated. Brachycephalic dogs and dogs with collapsing trachea are poor candidates for intranasal or intraoral vaccination. Pets undergoing surgery or any anesthetic procedure should not be vaccinated within four weeks of the hospital stay. Do not ever allow your pet to be vaccinated the same day as a procedure.

When pets are vaccinated, they will shed the Bordetella organism for up to seven weeks and the parainfluenza organism for up to one week. The vaccine insert states "**Contraindications, warnings:** *Particularly in very young susceptible puppies, mild discharges from the eyes and nose can occur from the day after vaccination, sometimes accompanied by sneezing and coughing. Signs are generally transient, but in occasional cases may persist for up to four weeks. In animals, which show more severe signs, appropriate antibiotic treatment may be indicated.*" Based on this, most dogs coming into daycare, boarding, or grooming facilities are constantly being exposed to the most common organisms that cause kennel cough. They will be getting "vaccinated" naturally or they will come down with kennel cough. Anaphylactic (shock) reactions may occur when the vaccine is given. Vaccines have the potential to cause harm and should not be taken lightly.

The kennel cough vaccine does not prevent the disease; it may decrease severity of symptoms if your pet is exposed. Remember

that kennel cough is rarely severe and never fatal, unless complicated by secondary bacterial or viral pneumonia. It's comparable to
your kids coming down with a cold. In my opinion, this is a useless
(at best) and dangerous (at worst) vaccination and should not be
required. I recommend finding facilities for training, boarding,
and grooming that do not require this vaccine. Stand up to these
facilities, offer to sign a waiver, or find another facility.

Most cases of kennel cough will resolve on their own without
treatment, although the cough can certainly be annoying to all
concerned. Best home remedies include:

- Steam treatment with a humidifier or bathroom steam
- A teaspoon of honey or lemon tea with honey to stop the
  cough.
- Coconut oil (two teaspoons per day) can be effective at
  quelling the cough.
- Probiotics will help the immune system function more
  optimally.
- Ceylon cinnamon sprinkled on the food has antiviral
  effects.
- Homeopathic remedies can help resolve symptoms.
- Foods that help drain phlegm if there is nasal discharge or
  a productive cough include clams, ground almonds, citrus
  peel, thyme, olive leaf, Shiitake mushrooms, tea, and peppermint. Any of these can be added to the meals in small
  amounts.
- Essential oils that are pet-safe can be sprayed or diffused.
  Peppermint, eucalyptus, and cinnamon might be considered. Extra care should be taken when used around cats.
  Research the oils before using.
- Bone broth to support the immune system and prevent
  dehydration.

Collapsing Trachea

Other than allergies and IBD, collapsing trachea is at the top of the list for questions in my inbox. While small dogs such as Maltese, Pomeranians, Pugs, and Yorkies commonly suffer from this problem, it can affect any breed of dog. It is rare in cats.

The trachea or "windpipe" is the semi-rigid tube that connects the nasal passages to the bronchi in the lungs. It is formed of C-shaped cartilage rings with muscular connective tissue running along the top of the rings. With age, the muscular layer can weaken, causing it to collapse downward into the airway, resulting in difficulty moving air through the trachea.

Symptoms of tracheal collapse include a distinctive "goose-honk" cough, heavy panting, open-mouth breathing, fainting, and cyanosis (blue tongue and gums). Symptoms are worse with obesity, excitement, exercise, extreme heat and humidity, excessive dryness, tracheal irritants such as perfumes and smoke, and are sometimes set off just by eating and drinking.

Symptoms can be seen at any age, although most dogs and cats are diagnosed after age seven. A surprisingly high number of dogs with tracheal collapse also suffer with obesity, heart disease, liver disease, brachycephalic airway disease, and other respiratory conditions. Diagnosis is made using x-rays of the neck and chest, fluoroscopy, or bronchoscopy (which requires sedation).

Treatment for collapsing trachea may include many facets. Traditional veterinarians commonly use these drugs:

- Cough suppressants—hydrocodone is commonly used. It also has a sedative effect for most dogs, decreasing anxiety associated with respiratory distress.
- Bronchodilators—theophylline, terbutaline, albuterol. These drugs help open airways but have side effects and may have limited use in dogs with concomitant heart disease.

- Sedatives—butorphanol, acepromazine. Sedatives help alleviate distress associated with the anxiety of being unable to get good airflow. They may also be useful at times when dogs may undergo stress or excitement.
- Antibiotics—commonly these dogs will develop respiratory tract infections secondary to poor airway flow. These should be used very judiciously!
- Anabolic steroids—stanozolol—This derivative of testosterone has some anti-inflammatory activity and can help strengthen the muscle along the top of the trachea.
- Surgical repair. This is a technically difficult surgery that is only performed by specialists. Results are variable.

From a holistic point of view, herbs, diet, and acupuncture may be helpful for these pets. Some therapies worth trying:

- First and foremost, if the pet is overweight, change the diet to get the pet to an appropriate weight.
- Strengthen the airways with foods that support the lung system, including white fish, white mushrooms, white meats, radishes, eggs, and barley.
- Pears, apples, peppermint, ginger, and clams will help decrease phlegm production.
- Support the muscle in the trachea by nourishing digestive function. This may include using gently cooked foods and digestive enzymes.
- Strengthen cartilage by feeding bone broth.
- Supplement with natural sources of glucosamine, chondroitin, and hyaluronic acid to support cartilage such as green-lipped mussels and deer antler velvet.
- Honey is a great cough suppressant and helps the immune system. A dab of honey given with meals and when coughing fits occur can be helpful.

- Acupuncture can help strengthen the immune system, decrease phlegm, and increase strength of the cartilage rings and muscle in the trachea.
- Use a harness instead of a collar. Do not apply pressure to the throat area.
- Vaporize the air. Lungs and airways dislike dryness, particularly in winter.
- Avoid exercise in high heat and humidity.
- Use HEPA air filters in your home to clean the air.
- No smoking. No scented candles or artificial scent diffusers. No heavy perfumes.
- Keep dust to a minimum.
- Weight management—do not allow your pet to become overweight.
- Keep stress to a minimum. Keep the animal calm using flower essences, CBD oil, homeopathy, essential oils, or pheromone diffusers.
- Herbal formulations specifically made for cough and tracheal support are available through natural pet care companies.

While tracheal collapse can be a frightening disease, it can usually be managed, and the pet can live a good quality life. By combining traditional and alternative therapies, you can use all the tools in your toolbox to keep your dog comfortable.

Pulmonary Fibrosis

Pulmonary fibrosis is a chronic, progressive lung disease of dogs and cats in which the lungs become scarred, stiff, and thickened, resulting in respiratory distress. Pneumonia, chronic bronchitis, congestive heart failure, and environmental pollutants cause irreversible damage to the lung tissue. In idiopathic pulmonary fibrosis, the cause is unknown. Terriers, especially West Highland white terriers, are at risk for developing this disorder.

Symptoms include exercise intolerance, respiratory distress, decreased appetite, syncope (fainting), and cough. The symptoms do not improve with conventional treatments. Pulmonary fibrosis is an incurable condition. Medications including steroids, bronchodilators, sedatives, and cough suppressants may provide some relief, but do not decrease the progression of the disease. Sildenafil (Viagra) may be used to treat pulmonary hypertension that develops in the late stages of the condition. The average life expectancy is 12 to 18 months from diagnosis.

Natural cough suppressants include honey, coconut oil, marshmallow root, and hyssop. Ultra-micronized palmitoylethanolamide (PEA) at 3 to 10 mg per kg of body weight has been studied for treatment of pulmonary fibrosis in humans with good results showing reduced lung inflammation, reduced pulmonary damage, and decreased fibrosis in mouse studies. This novel product is available for pets at www.drjudymorgan.com

Brachycephalic Airway Syndrome

Brachycephalic airway syndrome refers to a particular set of upper airway abnormalities that affect brachycephalic dogs and cats, including bulldogs, boxers, Boston terriers, Pekingese, Chinese Shar-Pei, pugs, Cavalier King Charles spaniel, English toy spaniel, Lhasa apsos, shih tzus, bull mastiffs, Persians, Himalayans, and Burmese cats. This syndrome is also called brachycephalic respiratory syndrome, brachycephalic syndrome, or congenital obstructive upper airway disease. The upper airway abnormalities that occur in this syndrome include:

- Stenotic nares. Pets with stenotic nares have abnormally narrowed, small nostrils; the narrowing restricts the amount of air that can flow into the nose.

- Elongated soft palate. A cat or dog with an elongated soft palate (the soft part of the roof of the mouth) has a soft palate that is too long for the length of the mouth; the excess length partially blocks the entrance to the trachea (windpipe) at the back of the throat. This, as well as stenotic nares, are the most seen abnormalities in brachycephalic pets.
- Hypoplastic trachea. This means that the trachea has a smaller diameter than normal.
- Everted laryngeal saccules. Laryngeal saccules are small pouches that are located just inside the larynx (voice box); these saccules are sucked into the airway by the pressure associated with the increased respiratory effort caused by the stenotic nares and/or the elongated soft palate. Everted laryngeal saccules will further obstruct airway flow.
- **Laryngeal collapse.** Laryngeal collapse is caused by the chronic stress placed on the cartilage of the larynx by other features of brachycephalic airway syndrome. Eventually, the larynx is not able to open as wide as normal, causing further restriction in airflow.

Clinical signs of brachycephalic airway syndrome include:

- Increased respiratory effort
- Open mouth breathing
- Noisy breathing
- Snoring
- Exercise intolerance
- Snorting
- Coughing
- Gagging

- 🐾 Retching
- 🐾 Vomiting
- 🐾 Overheating

Signs are often worse in hot or humid weather when exercise should be limited. Avoid stress, allergens, smoke, strong perfumes, and artificial scents. Obesity worsens the symptoms; weight control is critical. Steroids, NSAIDs, and oxygen therapy may be administered for short-term relief of airway inflammation or respiratory distress, but medical management does not correct the underlying anatomical abnormalities. Surgical reconstruction of the airway is commonly recommended. A harness that does not put pressure on the neck area should be used rather than a collar for walking. Natural calming supplements may help decrease anxiety during episodes of stress including CBD oil, flower essences, or calming herbs.

Asthma

Asthma is a disease of the lower airways of the lungs. It is caused by an inflammatory allergic reaction to inhaled allergens resulting in irritation, swelling, and reactive constriction of the airways. Mucous may accumulate in the airway passages. In cats, asthma is usually diagnosed between 4 and 5 years of age, affecting 1 to 5% of cats. Asthma-like symptoms in dogs are more often associated with allergic bronchitis which causes more low-grade, constant, or chronic symptoms, rather than true asthma.

Causes include dust, cigarette smoke, mold, pollen, cat litter dust, perfumes, and dust mites.

Symptoms include:

- 🐾 Open mouth breathing
- 🐾 Coughing

- Wheezing
- Respiratory distress
- Rapid shallow respiration
- Increased respiratory effort
- Hunched body with neck extended forward

Radiographs will usually provide the diagnosis, but CT and bronchoscopy may also be utilized. Lungworms and heartworms should be ruled out.

Treatment options include:

- Avoid inhaled allergens.
- Change to dust-free litter for cats.
- Do not use perfumes, scented candles, or artificial fragrances.
- Do not smoke.
- Add air purifiers and HEPA filters.
- Steroids are the most used treatment.
- Immunosuppressive drugs (cyclosporine) have been used when steroids cannot.
- Inhaler or nebulizer; bronchodilators may be prescribed.
- Oxygen therapy with an ICU cage or face mask can be used at home.
- Allergy desensitization injections after allergy testing.
- Stem cell therapy is showing promising results.
- Omega-3 fatty acids: fish oil, krill oil, calamari oil, algae oil, or phytoplankton. Supply 30 mg of EPA and DHA per pound of body weight once or twice daily.
- Palmitoylethanolamide (PEA) 400 to 2,000 mg per day depending on the size of the pet decreases lung inflammation.
- Feed a high moisture diet.
- The Chinese herbal preparation Bu Fei San can be given at 0.5 grams per ten to 20 pounds of body weight twice daily.
- Acupuncture may help.

Sinus Infections

Signs of sinus infections may include:

- Intermittent sneezing
- Nasal discharge (clear, gray, white, yellow, green, or bloody)
- Swelling on the side of the face under the eye
- Poor appetite
- Lethargy
- Head pain
- Bad breath
- Noisy or congested breathing
- Open mouth breathing or heavy panting
- Fever

Causes of sinus infections may include:

- Trauma to the nose or face
- Nasal or sinus tumor
- Bacterial, viral, or fungal infection
- Tooth root abscesses
- Parasites
- Allergies
- Sensitivity to perfumes, smoke, and fragrances

Diagnosis is made with radiographs, CT scan, or MRI along with laboratory testing including culture and sensitivity of the nasal discharge. A biopsy may be required to obtain the diagnosis.

Treatment will depend on the underlying cause. Home therapies may include:

- Use a nasal aspirator to suck out mucus like you would for a stuffy child.
- Keep the nostrils clean and open using a warm wet cloth.
- Use steam to loosen nasal secretions: humidifiers or shower steam.

- Apply warm compresses over the sinus area.
- Quercetin stabilizes the cells that stimulate mucus secretion in the sinuses. Give 5 to 10 mg per pound of body weight twice daily.
- Licorice root, cayenne pepper (capsicum), nettles, and thyme are herbs that can be sprinkled on the food.
- Do not give antihistamines as they will dry the nasal passages making the discharge thicker and harder to remove.
- Eliminate smoke, perfumes, and fragrances from the home.
- Treat the underlying cause.
- Huey's formula from Jing Tang herbs (prescription required) dosed at 0.5 grams per 10 to 20 pounds body weight twice daily.
- Peppermint or spearmint—Give 1 teaspoon of fresh, minced leaves per 20 pounds body weight twice daily.
- Thyme—Give 1 teaspoon of fresh, minced leaves per 20 pounds body weight twice daily.

SAMPLE DIET FOR DOGS WITH MUCUS NASAL DISCHARGE OR COUGH

- ☐ 16 ounces of beef 90% lean OR 8 ounces skinless boneless chicken breast and 8 ounces boneless chicken thigh with skin (if using beef, add 1 teaspoon flaxseed oil to the recipe)
- ☐ 4 ounces chicken liver
- ☐ 4 ounces butternut squash
- ☐ 3 ounces clams
- ☐ 2 ounces turnip
- ☐ 3 ounces apple with skin

- 2 ounces asparagus
- 1 ounce Daikon radish
- 1 teaspoon fresh thyme
- 2 teaspoons grated fresh ginger root
- 1/2 teaspoon kelp powder
- 1 teaspoon ground eggshell or bonemeal powder
- 1/4 teaspoon wheat grass
- 300 IU vitamin D3

Provides 35 calories per ounce. May be fed raw or gently cooked. Follow feeding guidelines in chapter 4.

SAMPLE DIET FOR DOGS TO SUPPORT LUNGS

- 1 pound pork tenderloin
- 4 ounces beef kidney
- 3 ounces beef liver
- 6 ounces mashed cooked sweet potato
- 3 ounces kale
- 2 tablespoons honey
- 1 tablespoon ground peppermint
- 1 pear
- 2 teaspoons hempseed oil
- 300 IU vitamin D#
- 2 teaspoons Rx Vitamins Canine Minerals

☐ 1/2 ounce oyster

☐ 1/2 teaspoon kelp

Provides 32.5 calories per ounce. May be fed raw or gently cooked. Follow feeding guidelines in chapter 4.

SAMPLE DIET FOR CATS TO SUPPORT LUNGS

☐ 8 ounces boneless chicken thigh with skin

☐ 2.5 ounces beef liver

☐ 2 ounces beef kidney

☐ 4 ounces beef heart

☐ 1 ounce cabbage

☐ 1 ounce sweet potato

☐ 1 tablespoon honey

☐ 2 ounces pear

☐ 1.5 teaspoons hempseed oil

☐ 1 ounce or 1 tablespoon spirulina powder

☐ 1/2 teaspoon sea salt

☐ 1/2 teaspoon kelp

☐ 1 teaspoon turmeric

☐ 1.5 teaspoons eggshell or bonemeal powder

☐ 1 ounce oyster

Provides 42.5 calories per ounce. May be fed raw or gently cooked. Follow feeding guidelines in chapter 4.

15 Liver Disease

The liver performs over five hundred functions in the body. It helps breakdown nutrients, produces bile acids necessary to digest fats, detoxifies the blood, makes proteins that help with blood clotting, excretes bilirubin produced as a by-product of red blood cell breakdown, and helps break down carbohydrates to regulate blood sugar. The liver stores nutrients including iron, copper, and vitamins B12, A, D, E, and K. Liver disease develops when any of these functions are disrupted. The liver has a large capacity to regenerate.

Common symptoms of liver disease are gastrointestinal and neurologic signs including:

- Decreased appetite
- Vomiting
- Diarrhea
- Weight loss
- Increased thirst
- Increased urination
- Changes in stool color
- Ascites—fluid in the abdomen
- Jaundice—yellow tint to skin, mucous membranes, and eyes
- Bruising or bleeding
- Lethargy

- Head pressing
- Coma
- Seizures

Liver disease is diagnosed through blood tests, radiographs, abdominal ultrasound, CT scan, MRI, fine needle aspiration, and liver biopsy. Laboratory testing may include ALT, AST, ALP or SAP, bilirubin, GGT, bile acids, BUN, cholesterol, and albumin levels.

- ALT: alanine transaminase. This enzyme helps convert proteins into energy for the liver cells. When the liver is damaged, ALT is released from cells. This enzyme is also found in kidneys, muscle cells, and red blood cells in small amounts. May be elevated secondary to medications being administered.
- AST: aspartate transaminase. This enzyme helps metabolize amino acids. It is found in red blood cells, heart, muscle, pancreas, and bile. An increase in AST may indicate damage to liver cells or muscle cells; it is not only liver specific. May be elevated secondary to medications being administered.
- SAP or ALP: alkaline phosphatase. This enzyme is found in the liver, bones, intestines, and uterus and helps break down proteins. High levels may indicate liver cell damage, liver cell swelling, blocked bile ducts, bone disease (osteomyelitis, osteosarcoma), or uterine disease. ALP may also be elevated in young animals with active bone growth. This is commonly elevated in pets with endocrine diseases including hyperadrenocorticism (Cushing's disease), hypothyroidism, hepatic lipidosis, and diabetes mellitus due to vacuolar hepatopathy. Will also be elevated if the pet is being medicated with steroids or phenobarbital.

- ALB: albumin. Albumin is a protein made by the liver. It helps fight infection. Damage to the liver results in decreased production and low albumin levels. This is commonly low with portosystemic shunts.
- GGT: gamma-glutamyltransferase. Elevations of this enzyme indicate liver or bile duct damage. This enzyme is not always included on chemistry panels but is the most sensitive for liver disease.
- TBil: total bilirubin. Bilirubin is a substance produced during the normal breakdown of red blood cells. It passes through the liver and is excreted in stool. Elevated levels may indicate liver damage or autoimmune hemolytic anemia.
- Bile acids. Will be increased with portosystemic shunt, microvascular dysplasia, liver disease, or bile duct obstruction.
- BUN: blood urea nitrogen (may be shown as SUN or serum urea nitrogen). BUN is normally used to diagnose kidney disease or intestinal hemorrhage when elevated. Low BUN may signal severe liver damage, cirrhosis, or portosystemic shunt with decreased production of protein.
- Cholesterol. Low cholesterol signifies decreased production by the liver, seen with portosystemic shunts, liver cell destruction, starvation, and hypoadrenocorticism (Addison's disease). Cholesterol may be elevated in animals with hypothyroidism, hyperadrenocorticism (Cushing's disease), and after consuming a meal.

Infectious Hepatitis

The liver can be infected by bacteria, viruses, rickettsia, protozoa, parasites, or fungi. These include adenovirus, Leptospirosis, tularemia, coccidioidomycosis, and histoplasmosis.

Bowel disease, immunosuppression, and altered gut motility result in altered blood flow to the liver resulting in unchecked pathogen access resulting in hepatitis or cholangiohepatitis (gall bladder and liver inflammation or infection). Common bacterial infection includes *E. coli, Enterococcus, Bacteroides, Streptococcus,* and *Clostridium* species.

Leptospirosis transmission occurs via contact with infected urine from rats, raccoons, skunks, or dogs and contaminated water sources. Chronic hepatitis has been seen after pets are infected with leptospirosis. Diagnosis is made with blood testing titers and PCR (polymerase chain reaction). Antibiotics are the treatment of choice.

Tularemia bacteria can be spread by ticks, flies, fleas, ingestion of wild rabbit, and contaminated water sources. Death may occur in a few hours or days. Symptoms include swollen lymph nodes, pneumonia, and fever. Antibiotics are the treatment of choice.

Fungal infections (*Coocidioides, Blastomyces, Aspergillosis, Cryptococcus,* and *Sporothrix*) are associated with diarrhea with blood and mucus. Treatment includes the use of anti-fungal medications, usually itraconazole, fluconazole, or amphotericin. Relapses are common after treatment.

Leishmania is transmitted by the sandfly. Clinical disease is more common in animals that are immunocompromised. Infection can be associated with chronic hepatitis.

Toxoplasmosis in cats and Neosporosis in dogs are protozoal diseases associated with hepatitis. Transmission can occur trans placentally or through ingestion of cysts. Toxoplasmosis is treated with clindamycin. Neosporosis usually affects young puppies, resulting in progressive paralysis; antibiotics are the treatment of choice.

Viral infections include canine adenovirus, canine herpesvirus, feline leukemia virus, and feline infectious peritonitis. Treatment involves supportive care. Prognosis is guarded.

Liver fluke parasites can occur in dogs and cats. Intermediate hosts include snails, lizards, fish, and toads. Praziquantel is the treatment of choice.

Vacuolar Hepatopathy

Vacuolar hepatopathy causes liver cells to undergo reversible vacuolar changes due to glycogen (the storage form of glucose) accumulation in liver cells due to overmedication with steroids, overproduction of steroids in the body, an endocrine disorder (hyperadrenocorticism or Cushing's disease, atypical adrenal hyperplasia or atypical Cushing's disease), benign nodular hyperplasia of senior dogs, chronic infections, or cancer. This is rare in cats but may be seen with hepatic lipidosis.

ALP levels are sometimes significantly elevated with this condition. Administration of steroids will cause elevation of ALP within three days. ALP will remain high for weeks to months after discontinuation of the medication. Symptoms are based on the underlying cause rather than signs of liver disease. Treatment lies with addressing the underlying cause.

Diet should be low-glycemic and contain high-quality proteins. See the recipes under endocrine diseases in chapter 6.

Portosystemic Shunts

The portal vein is a large vein that collects blood from the gastrointestinal system, pancreas, and spleen and carries it into the liver, where toxins and other byproducts are removed. A liver shunt occurs when an abnormal connection persists or forms between the portal vein or one of its branches, and another vein, allowing blood to bypass, or shunt, around the liver. In most cases, a liver shunt is caused by a birth defect called a congenital portosystemic shunt. Certain breeds such as Yorkshire Terriers, Old English Sheepdogs, Irish Wolfhounds, Cairn Terriers, and Beagles have an increased incidence of portosystemic shunts. This disease is rare in cats.

Decreased levels of BUN, total protein, albumin, cholesterol, and glucose may be seen on laboratory testing. Diagnosis is confirmed with radiography, ultrasound, or CT scan. The most common clinical signs with congenital shunts include stunted growth, poor muscle development, abnormal behaviors such as disorientation, staring into space, circling or head pressing, and seizures. Behavioral clinical signs may only occur after eating high protein meals.

Less common symptoms include drinking or urinating too much, vomiting, and diarrhea. Dogs with a liver shunt often take a long time recovering from anesthesia because the liver is not able to process and break down the drugs. Some dogs do not show signs until they are older, when they develop urinary problems such as recurrent kidney or bladder infections or presence of urate crystals or stones.

To prevent urate crystals and stones, feed low and medium purine foods such as kale, broccoli, eggs, dairy products, muscle meat from chicken, turkey, lamb, pork, and beef, oats, and fruits. Avoid high purine foods including organs (brain, heart, liver, kidneys), game meat, duck, goose, nutritional yeast, mackerel, herring, sardines, mussels, scallops, spinach, cauliflower, mushrooms, and legumes (peas, beans, lentils, chickpeas).

LOW PURINE DIET FOR
ADULT DOGS WITH LIVER SHUNT

☐ 5 eggs

☐ 4 ounces blueberries

☐ 4 ounces kale

☐ 4 ounces cottage cheese

☐ 4 teaspoons ground hulled hempseed

- ☐ 1.5 teaspoons bonemeal powder
- ☐ 1/2 teaspoon kelp powder
- ☐ 1/2 teaspoon sea salt
- ☐ 4 teaspoons spirulina powder
- ☐ 1 zinc capsule 15 mg

Provides 30 calories per ounce. Eggs, fruit, and vegetables may be served raw or gently cooked. Feed according to directions in chapter 4.

LOW PURINE RECIPE #2
FOR ADULT DOGS WITH LIVER SHUNT

(This recipe may be too high in protein for dogs with significant shunts.)

- ☐ 20 ounces 85% lean ground beef
- ☐ 8 chicken eggs
- ☐ 4 ounces blueberries
- ☐ 4 ounces kale
- ☐ 4 teaspoons ground hulled hempseed
- ☐ 3 teaspoons bonemeal powder
- ☐ 1 teaspoon wheat grass powder
- ☐ 1 teaspoon kelp powder
- ☐ 1/2 teaspoon sea salt

Provides 41 calories per ounce. May be served raw or gently cooked. Feed according to directions in chapter 4.

In some cases, multiple small shunts form because of severe liver disease such as cirrhosis. These are referred to as acquired portosystemic shunts.

Bile acids are elevated in pets with liver shunts because the liver does not get a chance to remove them from the blood.

Treatment involves specialized diets and sometimes medication or surgery. The diet should consist of high quality, highly digestible proteins. Lactulose can be administered to decrease absorption of ammonia into the bloodstream. Antibiotics are used to alter the bacterial population in the intestines (use with caution).

Liver Cancers

Cats tend to develop more benign tumors than dogs. Bile duct adenomas account for more than half of all liver tumors in cats yet are uncommon in dogs. Bile duct carcinomas are the most common malignant liver tumor in cats and the second most common liver tumor in dogs, with hepatocellular carcinoma being the most common. Metastatic cancer is associated with pancreatic cancer, lymphoma, intestinal carcinoma, thyroid cancer, fibrosarcoma, osteosarcoma, mast cell tumors, hemangiosarcoma, mammary carcinoma, pheochromocytoma, and transition cell sarcoma.

Warning signs of liver cancer are nonspecific and include lethargy, decreased appetite, weight loss, vomiting, increased thirst and urination, ascites (fluid in the abdomen), and seizures. Some dogs and cats will become jaundiced (yellow discoloration of skin, gums, and eyes).

Cancer is diagnosed with lab work, radiographs, abdominal ultrasound, and advanced imaging such as CT scan or MRI. Many liver tumors can be successfully surgically removed, particularly if the tumor is confined to one liver lobe. Survival times commonly exceed three years and metastasis (spread) is seen in less than 5 percent of pets with hepatocellular carcinoma. Bile duct carcinomas have worse prognosis due to metastasis and regrowth of the tumor. Sarcomas have a poor prognosis, as the majority of these have already metastasized at the time of diagnosis.

Copper Storage Disease

Copper storage hepatopathy is a condition caused by an abnormal accumulation of copper in the animal's liver, which leads to progressive damage and scarring of the liver (cirrhosis). This condition may be secondary to a primary disease or the result of genetic-based abnormal copper metabolism. It can affect both dogs, and less commonly, cats.

Bedlington terriers, Doberman pinschers, West Highland white terriers, Skye terriers, Keeshond, American cocker spaniel, and Labrador retrievers are dog breeds known to be susceptible to this disease. Copper storage hepatopathy is more prevalent in females than in males.

According to Dr. Sharon Center, internal medicine professor at Cornell University's College of Veterinary Medicine "the excess amount of the essential trace mineral copper in commercial dog food can cause a serious, potentially lethal illness called dietary-induced copper-associated hepatopathy (CAH). The incidence of CAH is increasing at a rate that's causing alarm among veterinarians and dog owners, with one study showing that 30% of canine liver biopsies have evidence of CAH."

While pet food regulations call for a minimum of 7.3 milligrams of copper per kilogram of food for adult dogs and 5 mg/kg for adult cats, there is no maximum limit for copper in pet food. Supplementation may be 25 to 50% over the minimum recommended level in most commercial diets with added copper. One popular dry pet food contains 44 milligrams of copper per kilogram of food! If you are feeding a commercial diet, request a complete nutrient breakdown from the company to determine whether the food is appropriate for continued feeding.

Avoid pet foods that have added copper supplements such as copper sulfate, copper proteinate, or copper complexed with an amino acid. Natural sources of copper include liver (especially beef liver), fish and seafood, chickpeas, sweet potatoes, sunflower seeds, and kale.

Pets can be affected at any age. Genetics is the main contributing factor in Bedlington terriers while dietary supplementation is the most likely culprit in most animals. Diagnosis is usually made through liver biopsy. Repeat biopsy is the only definitive way to determine how the pet is responding to therapy, but most are monitored with lab work rather than invasive surgery.

Treatment includes dietary modification to a low copper diet. Most commercially available diets contain high amounts of copper. Those that are formulated with low copper often also have low protein, which is not appropriate in all cases. Avoid giving mineral supplements containing copper. If you have copper pipes in your home or your water has high levels of metals, bottled water is advised. The drug penicillamine and supplementation with zinc can help eliminate copper from the body.

SAMPLE LOW COPPER RECIPE FOR ADULT DOGS

☐ 10 ounces turkey wings with bone and skin (must be very finely ground if feeding gently cooked, otherwise can be fed raw or ground for raw food)

- ☐ 10 ounces chicken gizzards
- ☐ 16 ounces boneless chicken thigh with skin
- ☐ 3 ounces celery
- ☐ 3 ounces carrots
- ☐ 2 ounces cucumber
- ☐ 2 ounces kale
- ☐ 2 ounces cabbage
- ☐ 2 ounces apple with skin
- ☐ 1 ounce fresh basil
- ☐ 2 teaspoons ground turmeric
- ☐ 1/2 teaspoon kelp
- ☐ 1/2 teaspoon wheat grass
- ☐ 1/2 teaspoon cod liver oil

Provides 34 calories per ounce. Follow feeding guidelines in chapter 4.

Idiopathic Chronic Hepatitis

Idiopathic means no underlying cause has been found for the inflammation in the liver. The cause may be autoimmune disease or secondary to chronic drug, vaccine, and toxin exposure. These pets have chronically elevated liver enzymes on laboratory testing with no known underlying cause. Diagnosis is made by ruling out infectious diseases, copper storage disease, cancer, endocrine disease, and dietary toxins such as aflatoxin.

Immunosuppressive drugs, steroids, antibiotics, and antioxidants are commonly prescribed. Most often, the immunosuppressive drugs, steroids, and antibiotics cause more harm than help. Side effects from the drugs can include bone marrow suppression, vacuolar hepatopathy, diabetes, pancreatitis, immune suppression with predisposition to secondary infections, Cushing's disease, gastroenteritis, and cancer.

These drugs should only be considered if a definitive diagnosis of immune-mediated hepatitis (autoimmune disease where the immune system is attacking the liver) can be definitively proven. Treatment should be aimed at finding and eliminating the underlying cause of inflammation and supporting liver function.

These dogs should not receive vaccinations.

Liver Failure and Cirrhosis

Cirrhosis is chronic, end-stage liver disease in which normal liver tissue has been replaced by fibrous scar tissue. Your pet needs approximately 20% of normal liver function to survive. When cirrhosis occurs, scar tissue replaces functioning liver cells. If normal liver function falls below 20%, the disease becomes terminal. Cirrhosis can occur in pets of any age but is most common in middle-aged or older animals. Cirrhosis occurs because of damage to the liver by many diseases, drugs, or toxins.

Treatment is supportive. Finding the underlying cause of the damage to the liver to stop the progression of the damage.

Hepatic Lipidosis

Hepatic lipidosis is a type of liver disease where the liver tissue is flooded with fat that has been rapidly mobilized from the fat stores. The fat, along with metabolic byproducts of its processing, prevent the liver from functioning normally, leading to liver failure.

It's a disease that most often affects obese cats that have recently lost weight or cats that stop eating or are eating significantly less for more than a few days. It usually affects middle-aged and older cats but can happen at any age. Other concurrent illnesses such as kidney disease, diabetes mellitus, hyperthyroidism, pancreatitis, inflammatory bowel disease, and gall bladder disease may be contributing factors.

Clinical signs include:

- inappetence or anorexia
- weight loss with muscle wasting
- lethargy and dullness
- weakness, unable to exercise and jump
- vomiting and diarrhea
- drooling
- jaundice, with yellowing of the gums and the whites of the eyes
- behavioral changes

Treatment involves general liver support and nutritional support. Medications and supplements commonly include the use of ursodeoxycholic acid (Ursodiol), SAMe, L-carnitine, omega-3 fatty acids, taurine, vitamin B12 (cobalamin), vitamin K, and appetite stimulants. Feeding tubes are often placed to deliver nutrients. Around 90% of cats make a full recovery, depending on severity at the time of diagnosis.

Cholangiohepatitis and Portal Triad Disease

Portal triad disease of cats involves inflammation of the liver, pancreas, and intestines. Cholangiohepatitis involves inflammation of the liver and gall bladder and is seen in dogs and cats. Symptoms are like all cases of liver disease. Diagnosis is made through laboratory testing, abdominal imaging with radiographs, ultrasound, CT scan, and MRI, and biopsy.

Treatment is like other liver diseases, along with supportive nutritional care.

Toxins

Xylitol, aflatoxins (mold toxins found in grains in pet food), environmental toxins, herbicides, pesticides, rodenticides, blue-green algae, heavy metals, medications (NSAIDs, antifungals, anti-seizure, antibiotics, parasite preventatives, acetaminophen, methimazole), and Sago palms can all be toxic to the liver. The best prevention is avoidance.

Hepatic Encephalopathy

Hepatic encephalopathy is a neurologic condition that develops secondary to liver disease. It is most associated with a portosystemic shunt (PSS), hepatic lipidosis in cats, and severe liver disease such as cirrhosis.

The clinical signs are varied and may appear shortly after eating, as the protein from the meal breaks down into ammonia which affects the brain. Pets may seem dull, have an unsteady gait, drool heavily, and seizures may occur. Some pets will cry or whine, experience muscle tremors and/or sudden blindness, or might press their heads into objects. The underlying liver disease may cause weight loss, decreased appetite, jaundice, vomiting, diarrhea, and increased thirst and urination.

Treatment is aimed at lowering ammonia levels in the blood. If in crisis, intravenous mannitol or hypertonic saline may be used to decrease swelling in the brain. Enemas may be used to flush protein metabolites of the colon. Low protein diets will be prescribed to reduce ammonia levels in the blood. Making your own food rather than using prescription diets will provide more rapid recovery. Zinc supplementation and probiotics can also help. Further treatment should be aimed at treating the underlying cause of liver disease.

Supplements to Support and Detoxify the Liver

- Ursodiol—bile acid used to treat the symptoms of gallbladder disease or bile sludge in the liver causing inflammation. Side effects are uncommon but may include diarrhea, vomiting, lack of appetite, or jaundice (which may be due to the underlying disease). This is a prescription medication. Use cautiously with gallstones or pancreatitis.
- Glutathione—potent antioxidant, detoxifies the body, helps build DNA, helps regenerate other antioxidants such as Vitamins E and C. Breaks down in the digestive tract; best supplementation is through intravenous or liposomal delivery via paste or injection. Foods that boost glutathione include beef, fish, poultry, eggs, beef liver, cruciferous vegetables, and mushrooms.
- NAC—N-acetyl-cysteine—helps boost glutathione production in the body and remove toxins from the liver. Give 30 mg per pound three times daily on an empty stomach.
- SAMe—S-adenosyl-L-methionine—helps boost glutathione production in the body. Detoxifies, helps metabolize fat, and is an antioxidant. It should be given on an empty stomach. Give 9 -10 mg per pound of body weight. Tablets cannot be split; use the dose closest to the calculated dose.
- Milk thistle or silymarin—protects the liver and supports regeneration of liver cells (do not use in pregnant or lactating animals). It is antioxidant, anti-inflammatory, and

increases glutathione levels. The recommended dose is 7 to 10 mg per pound of body weight twice daily but can be as high as 20 mg per pound.

- Dandelion root and dandelion greens—these can be added through whole plant or supplements. Diuretic, anti-inflammatory, antioxidant, liver tonic, rich source of potassium, vitamins A, B, C, D, and K, suppresses fat accumulation in the liver, and stimulates bile production and circulation through the liver. 1 teaspoon of dried leaves or root for each 20 pounds body weight can be used daily. Dandelion tea can be given at 1/3 cup tea per 20 pounds body weight up to three times daily.

- CBD oil—cannabidiol—anti-inflammatory, protects the liver by preventing overreaction of the endocannabinoid system. Lowers seizure threshold for animals suffering with seizures. Dose is usually 1 mg per 10 pounds body weight 2 to 3 times daily.

- Turmeric—can be given as Golden Paste. It stimulates bile output and is anti-inflammatory. It improves digestion by stimulating enzyme secretion.

- Artichoke leaf extract—decreases liver enzymes, antioxidant, decreases liver damage, promotes bile flow, helps remove toxins and fat from the liver.

- DMG—dimethylglycine—an amino acid that helps rebuild liver cells and encourages the elimination of toxins from the body.

- Vitamin E—antioxidant, anti-inflammatory, anti-fibrotic, protects the liver from copper accumulation. Plant oils are high in vitamin E. Give 150 to 600 IU per day depending on the size of the pet.

- Phosphatidylcholine—helps prevent fibrosis and protects liver cell membranes. Clear dose in dogs and cats is unknown. Empirical dosing is 150 to 600 mg per day depending on the size of the pet.

- Zinc—inhibits collagen synthesis and decreases hepatic fibrosis, is an antioxidant, and impairs copper absorption. Give 7 mg per pound of body weight per day. GI upset is common; zinc should be given on an empty stomach.

- Bentonite clay—helps restore liver function, especially in cases of aflatoxin (from moldy grain) toxicity.

- Probiotics—beneficial bacteria can help remove urea nitrogen waste products from the bowel and stimulate the immune system to decrease inflammation.

- L-Carnitine—a nutritional supplement that assists with fat transport in the body. Supply 250 to 500 mg daily.

- Essential fatty acid supplementation may be recommended. Omega-3 fatty acids EPA and DHA can be given at 30 to 40 mg per pound of body weight once or twice daily.

- Taurine—this is an essential amino acid that's usually deficient in anorexic cats. It makes sense to give cats a supplement of this until they are eating normally again. Give 500 mg daily for cats up to 4,000 mg for large dogs.

- Vitamin B12 (cobalamin)—a vitamin that is used by every cell in the body and supports liver function, amino acid metabolism, intestinal cell function, central nervous system maintenance, and blood production. Daily oral supplementation with 250 to 1000 micrograms depending on the size of the pet is advised.

- Vitamin K—many cats with hepatic lipidosis have inadequate blood clotting ability because the liver is not able to continue to maintain normal levels of blood clotting factors. The veterinarian should determine if this is recommended.

- Blueberries are a powerful antioxidant. Add blueberries to the diet.

- Dark leafy greens and sprouts support the liver.
- Antibiotics are often recommended to deal with secondary bacterial infections.
- Appetite stimulants, to encourage the pet to start eating again may be prescribed.

First and foremost, if your pet is experiencing elevations in liver enzymes, eliminate as many toxins as possible. Do not give vaccinations, use chemicals for parasite prevention, or chemicals in your household and environment. Change the diet from commercially prepared food using grains that may have aflatoxins or rendered ingredients that may contain contaminants such as euthanasia solution. Feed only human-grade, USDA inspected and passed meats and vegetables. Use organic products whenever possible. Some commercial pet food companies make GMO-free, organic, human-grade raw or gently cooked food if you do not want to make your own.

Your pet gets exposed to toxins from vaccinations, drugs, parasite preventative chemicals, poor quality foods, cleaning products, fertilizers, and pollution. The liver works constantly to filter and remove those toxins from the body. Behavioral issues, digestive problems, dry coat and nails, and discharge from the eyes can all be signs of toxin buildup. Performing a liver cleanse twice a year can help remove toxins from the body. Liver cleanse can be as simple as adding milk thistle, dandelion, sprouts, and organic dark leafy greens or sprouts to the diet for four to six weeks.

LIVER SUPPORTING DETOX RECIPE FOR DOGS

- ☐ 10 ounces boneless chicken or turkey thigh with skin
- ☐ 6 ounces chicken or turkey gizzards
- ☐ 4 ounces chicken or turkey liver

- ☐ 4 ounces broccoli
- ☐ 5 ounces dandelion greens
- ☐ 1 ounce alfalfa sprouts
- ☐ 1 teaspoon hempseed oil
- ☐ 1 teaspoon eggshell powder
- ☐ 1/2 teaspoon kelp

Provides 27 calories per ounce. May be served raw or gently cooked. See feeding guidelines in chapter 4.

LIVER SUPPORTING DETOX RECIPE FOR CATS

- ☐ 4 ounces boneless turkey thigh with skin
- ☐ 2 ounces turkey gizzard
- ☐ 2.5 ounces turkey liver
- ☐ 1 ounce dandelion greens
- ☐ 1/2 ounce alfalfa sprouts
- ☐ 1/2 teaspoon hempseed oil
- ☐ 2 teaspoons spirulina powder
- ☐ 1/2 teaspoon eggshell powder
- ☐ 1/2 teaspoon kelp powder
- ☐ 1 capsule zinc 15 mg

Provides 34 calories per ounce. May be served raw or gently cooked. See feeding guidelines in chapter 4.

16 Gastrointestinal Diseases

Digestive issues include intestinal parasites, viral or bacterial infections, diarrhea, vomiting, constipation, foreign bodies, vomiting hairballs (cats), inflammatory bowel disease, food intolerance, cancer, bloat, obstruction, intussusception, ulceration, hemorrhagic gastroenteritis, exocrine pancreatic insufficiency, malabsorption, protein losing enteropathy, lymphangiectasia, and more.

Intestinal Parasites

Intestinal worms can be a serious problem in young puppies and kittens. In adult dogs, intestinal parasites are only occasionally life-threatening. Debilitated animals or those that have a weakened immune system are more likely to experience severe intestinal parasitism and show clinical signs due to their worms; they are also likely to be infected with multiple parasites at the same time. Healthy animals are less likely to be plagued by these invaders. Regular testing to determine whether parasites are living inside your pet should be performed at least once per year, preferably twice.

Diarrhea is the most common symptom and may include stools containing blood or mucous. Severe infestations may result in loss of appetite and weight loss. Take a fresh stool sample to your veterinarian to be checked for parasites at least twice per year or any time your pet has loose stools for more than a day. If parasites are detected, be sure to take a stool sample after completing treatment to be sure the parasites have been cleared. Multi-drug-resistance is becoming more common which means multiple treatments may be required. All pets in the home should be tested, as they may easily transmit parasites to each other.

Tapeworms—Tapeworms are transmitted through ingestion of fleas or small rodents (mice, rabbits). They are flat, segmented worms that attach to the intestinal wall. As the adult worms mature, individual segments of the worm break off and are passed in the stool intermittently. The segments may be seen around the anus or on the feces that is passed. They are about half an inch long and look like grains of rice or cucumber seeds. Because the segments pass intermittently, they may not be found on routine laboratory testing and are more often found by seeing segments on the pet or in the stool. Tapeworms cannot be passed directly from pet to pet or pet to person; they must go through the intermediate host—the flea or mouse. Treatment consists of oral or injectable medication; one dose is sufficient, unless the dog or cat has continued exposure to fleas or hunts small prey.

Roundworms—These are very common in puppies and kittens. A typical pot-bellied appearance occurs in young animals with severe infestation. Adult worms are four to six inches long, round, and white. They can be passed in feces or vomit. The adult roundworms mate in the intestines; the female worm lays thousands of eggs per day which are shed in the feces into the environment. The eggs become infective in two to four weeks in the environment. When the eggs are ingested, they hatch in the intestine, penetrate the intestinal wall, and travel via the blood to the liver and then to the lungs. From the lungs, the larvae can ascend the trachea and travel to the intestine to mature into adults or into the blood vessels where they travel to muscles and organs, a condition known as larva migrans.

Humans can also become infected with roundworms and develop larva migrans. This condition in humans is typically associated with the eye. Infection commonly occurs when children eat dirt containing infectious eggs. It is important to keep children's sandboxes covered to keep cats and wildlife from defecating in the sand.

Puppies and kittens can be infected with roundworms through the milk of their infected mother or through the umbilical vein (dogs only) to the liver and lungs of the newborn. At the time of birth, when the lungs inflate, the larvae burst out and travel to the intestines where they mature in three weeks.

Roundworm eggs are extremely resistant to common disinfectants, including bleach, and environmental changes (heat and cold). Eggs can survive for years in the environment.

Treatment consists of oral medication repeated in two weeks.

Hookworms—These worms are shaped like a hook and are about half an inch in length. Hookworms have three sets of teeth which enable them to attach to the wall of the small intestine where the parasite drinks blood from the host animal. Hookworm infestation may result in anemia (low red blood cell count). Adult hookworms mate in the intestine where the females lay large numbers of eggs which are passed in the feces into the environment. Within ten days, the eggs will develop into infective larvae that can infect a new host through ingestion or skin penetration. Hookworms that enter through the skin migrate to the lungs, enter the trachea, and are swallowed into the intestines. They also can migrate into muscles and organs throughout the body and become encased in a cyst. Puppies can become infected through the mother's milk, but not through the umbilical vein.

Hookworms can infect humans. The most well-known form of infection is cutaneous larva migrans, commonly known as "creeping eruption". This results in red, itchy patches on the skin. It is seen mostly in hot, humid regions. Walking barefoot in contaminated areas can result in infection. Children's sandboxes contaminated with infected feces are also a common source of infection. If you suspect infection, see your physician.

Treatment consists of oral medication repeated in two weeks.

Whipworms—Whipworms are intestinal parasites that are about one quarter inch long. They live in the large intestine and are much more common in dogs than cats. Watery, bloody diarrhea, weight loss, and general debilitation can result from infestation. Eggs are passed in the stool. The eggs are very resistant to drying and heat; they can remain alive in the environment for up to five years. Whipworms pass small numbers of eggs, which means diagnosis can be more difficult and may require examination of multiple stool specimens.

Treatment consists of oral medication which should be repeated in three weeks. Whipworms are not infectious to people.

Coccidia—Coccidia is a single-celled protozoan ingested through dirt or the feces of an infected animal. Isospora and Cryptosporidium species of coccidia most commonly cause clinical symptoms; many cases of coccidia are subclinical, meaning no symptoms are seen. Infected dogs pass immature coccidia in their feces, contaminating the soil, where the oocysts (immature coccidia) can survive for long periods. Infection may occur through ingestion of contaminated soil or ingestion of a mouse infected with coccidia. Coccidia are most dangerous to young animals as the disease may cause severe watery diarrhea, dehydration, abdominal distress, and vomiting.

Treatment consists of oral sulfa-type antibiotics given for 5 to 25 days. In severe infections, it may be necessary to repeat treatment. The most common species of coccidia do not have any effect on humans, however, Cryptosporidium may be transmitted to people. This parasite has also been found in the public water supply of some major cities and poses a health risk for those who are immunocompromised.

Giardia—Giardia is a single-celled parasite that inhabits the intestines of mammals, birds, and amphibians. Mature giardia organisms live in the small intestine where they multiply and become cysts. The cysts are the infective stage and are shed into the feces of the infected animal. They can survive for several weeks in the environment as cysts; when they are eaten by a new host, they repeat the life cycle.

Giardia is spread through feces and contaminated water, soil, or grass. The most common symptom is diarrhea. Giardia can also be spread to humans, although human infection usually occurs secondary to drinking contaminated water. Severe infestations may result in weight loss and dehydration secondary to watery diarrhea. This parasite is easily transmitted between pets within the household.

Treatment consists of oral medication given daily for seven to ten days. Multiple treatments or medications may be needed. All pets in the home should be tested and treated as needed. This parasite can be difficult to diagnose and may be responsible for chronic bouts of diarrhea suffered by many pets.

Toxoplasmosis—Cats are the primary host for toxoplasma, although the parasite can affect nearly all warm-blooded animals and humans. The main source of transmission is raw meat and unwashed fruits and vegetables. Symptoms of infection can include vomiting, diarrhea, and abdominal pain, but neurological symptoms such as tremors, seizures, uncoordinated gait, muscle weakness, and partial or complete paralysis can also occur. Some cats may only be carriers of the parasites and not show symptoms for a long time or the infection may burst out at any time. Dogs can become infected through ingesting infected soil or cat feces. Cats are infected by eating rodents, contaminated soil, or feces.

The parasite is carried in the blood of the pet; diagnosis is made with a blood test.

Toxoplasma parasites can live for up to one year in the environment. The parasite cannot be destroyed by frost or chemicals; only high heat will kill the parasite.

Humans may get infected with the toxoplasmosis parasite. Healthy humans are immune to the parasite; however, pregnant women should be cautious as the parasite may harm the fetus. Women that have been in contact with the parasite before getting pregnant are not at risk; however, if the contact with the parasite has taken place after the beginning of the pregnancy, the fetus is at risk.

Treatment consists of the antibiotic Clindamycin and anti-protozoan drugs. Treatment may have to be repeated if symptoms recur.

Natural Treatments for Intestinal Parasites

- **Fasting with raw organic apple cider vinegar**: One day of fasting can be highly beneficial for your pet. This is because the body has a greater and better predisposition to detoxifying when it is not exerting energy on digestion. Add two teaspoons of apple cider vinegar into a sixteen-ounce bowl of water. This potent antiseptic will help eliminate the presence of parasites when it passes through the digestive tract.

- **Garlic** is a highly medicinal food since it has potent antibacterial, antifungal, and antiviral properties and is also useful for eliminating intestinal parasites. Contrary to internet lore, garlic is not a forbidden food for dogs and cats. For small dogs, feed up to one quarter clove twice a day, medium dogs half clove twice a day, large dogs three quarters clove twice a day, and giant breeds one clove twice a day. Cats can safely be fed a half clove three times a week. Garlic should be freshly crushed before feeding. A word of caution—do not use garlic for pregnant or lactating animals or animals on blood thinners.

- **Ground pumpkin seeds:** These act as an efficient and smooth laxative. Pumpkin seeds contain an amino acid called cucurbitin. Cucurbitin paralyzes and eliminates the worms from the digestive tract. Grind seeds and give one quarter teaspoon per ten pounds of body weight once or twice a day for one week.

- **Thyme** is a plant with powerful antiseptic activity which will help eliminate the parasites in your pet's gastrointestinal tract. Thyme is especially useful for hookworms. Add one teaspoon per pound of food for several days. Do not use thyme essential oil; use fresh or dried herbs. Do not use thyme for pregnant or lactating pets.

- **Dried coconut** can help eliminate worms from the body. Sprinkle unsweetened dried coconut into the food. Guidelines recommend one teaspoon for small dogs, two teaspoons for medium dogs and one tablespoon for large breeds. Coconut oil may also be an effective treatment. Be sure the product used is real coconut, not fake sugary coconut used for baking.

- **Turmeric** is beneficial not only for clearing worms, but also helps repair damage to the intestines due to its anti-inflammatory properties. It can be given as a dried powder or in Golden Paste. The recommended dose is one quarter teaspoon per ten pounds of body weight twice daily. Do not use this in pregnant or lactating pets.

- **Chamomile** can be effective against roundworms and whipworms. It works best when given as a tincture. Give one quarter to one half milliliter per twenty pounds body weight twice daily. Do not use this if your pet is pregnant or lactating.
- **Pomegranate:** This is especially useful for tapeworms. Add one teaspoon per ten pounds of body weight to your pet's meals twice a day.

Medical Treatments for Intestinal Parasites

Sometimes food alone is not enough to get rid of the worms and you may need medical intervention to solve the problem. Natural treatments can be used in conjunction with medical treatments. Work with your veterinarian to determine the most appropriate treatment plan for your pet. Some of the more common treatments include:

- Pyrantel pamoate -This is the active ingredient in Drontal® Plus, PRO-Wormer 2®, Nemex®-2. Side effects include vomiting, depression/lethargy, and anorexia. This drug treats roundworms and hookworms.
- Fenbendazole—This is the active ingredient in common deworming medications including the brand names: Panacur®, Drontal Plus ® and Safe-Guard®. This medication can cause side effects including vomiting, lethargy, anorexia, facial swelling, anaphylaxis, trouble breathing, and collapse. This drug is used to treat roundworms, hookworms, whipworms, and some tapeworms.

- ❀ Praziquantel—This is the active ingredient in Droncit®
  and Drontal® Plus (which also includes pyrantel pamoate
  and fenbendazole). Reported side effects include vomiting, depression/lethargy, diarrhea, and anorexia. This drug
  is used to treat tapeworms and has recently been added to
  many monthly heartworm preventative products.
- ❀ Metronidazole—This drug is used to treat Giardia.
  Reported side effects include nausea, vomiting, diarrhea,
  drooling, bloody urine, appetite loss, pancreatitis, liver
  failure, bone marrow suppression, head tilt, loss of balance,
  lack of coordination, seizures, and paralysis.
- ❀ Combination Drugs—Some drug manufacturers combine de-worming ingredients with heartworm drugs. They
  then market these combinations as preventives for heartworms along with various kinds of intestinal worms. The
  manufacturers recommend using these drugs monthly. If
  you use this medication, you are treating your pet unnec-
  essarily for worms he may not have. It is better to have
  your pet's stool tested twice a year for intestinal parasites;
  treat only if parasites are present.

All anti-parasitic medications will disrupt the gut microbiome
(the good bacteria, fungi, and viruses that are responsible for
a healthy immune system). Gut repair with species-appropriate prebiotics and probiotics is crucial after completing medical
de-worming procedures.

Diarrhea

Diarrhea is unformed or loose stools, usually occurring in larger
amounts and/or more often than usual. Diarrhea is not a disease
but rather a clinical sign of many different diseases. Diarrhea associated with minor conditions can often be resolved quickly with

simple treatments. Diarrhea may also be the result of stress, inflammatory bowel disease, food intolerance, serious or life-threatening infections, organ system failure, or cancer.

Severe or prolonged diarrhea can result in significant dehydration and metabolic disturbances due to fluid loss. Your pet may require hospitalization for intravenous fluid therapy or other, more intensive, treatments. If diarrhea persists for more than 48 hours or is very bloody, dark and tarry, or projectile, it is best to have your pet seen immediately. Testing may include physical examination, laboratory testing, culture and sensitivity, abdominal imaging, or more specialized testing.

The most prescribed medication for diarrhea is metronidazole. It should not be used in pets that are pregnant or nursing, are weak or debilitated, have liver disease, are on blood thinners, or in puppies or kittens. Drugs that interact with metronidazole include chemotherapy drugs, cimetidine (Tagamet), cyclosporine (Atopica), phenobarbital, phenytoin, and warfarin. This drug can have serious side effects including:

- Vomiting
- Diarrhea
- Drooling, nausea
- Bloody urine
- Loss of appetite
- Destruction of the microbiome
- Vasculitis of the skin
- Depression
- Head tilt
- Loss of balance
- Seizures
- Lack of coordination
- Paralysis

- Bone marrow suppression
- Pancreatitis
- Anaphylactic shock
- Liver toxicity, jaundice
- Dilated pupils
- Carcinogenic in mice

Home remedies for diarrhea include:

- Bland diet—see the sample recipe that follows.
- Slippery elm—10 to 20 mg dried slippery elm per pound of body weight can be mixed in water or food. Slippery elm sludge can be made by adding one teaspoon of slippery elm powder to one cup of warm water. Allow to sit for a few minutes until the mixture becomes gelatinous. Give 1 teaspoon up to 2 tablespoons three times daily, depending on the size of the pet.
- Peppermint and spearmint help with gas and bowel spasms. Dried or fresh herb can be mixed with the bland diet—give 1 teaspoon of fresh or 1/2 teaspoon of dried herb per ten pounds body weight or peppermint tea can be given. Give cats 1 tablespoon of tea three times daily and dogs 1/4 cup per ten pounds of body weight three times daily.
- Arsenica Album 30C homeopathic remedy, one per 20 pounds body weight given every 2 to 4 hours may help.
- Probiotics—Species-specific, soil-based probiotics are preferred.
- Bentonite or montmorillonite clay—Clay absorbs moisture from the bowel and adsorbs or binds to toxins. Give 1/4 to 1/2 teaspoon mixed with water a teaspoon of water to form a paste. Do not give herbs, food, or medications within two hours after dosing.

● Coptis herb if the stool has blood or mucus—Give one tea pill crushed and mixed with food per ten pounds body weight twice daily or 0.5 grams (500 mg) powder per ten pounds body weight twice daily. This herb works as well as metronidazole without disrupting the microbiome.

SAMPLE DIET FOR DIARRHEA FOR CATS OR DOGS

☐ 1 pound lean ground turkey or rabbit baked, boiled, or sauteed

☐ 1 teaspoon grated fresh ginger root

☐ 12 ounces well-cooked mashed apple or pumpkin (4 ounces for cats)

☐ 4 ounces Portobello or Shiitake mushroom chopped and sauteed in olive or coconut oil (1 ounce for cats)

Mix all the ingredients together. Feed small quantities multiple times per day until normal stool is observed. Feed the food warm, not cold from the refrigerator. Use this recipe until the stool is firm, then gradually reintroduce the normal diet. If the stool does not return to normal within a few days or if there is blood in the stool, seek veterinary help. This is not a balanced recipe and is not meant for long-term feeding.

If you do not have all the ingredients for the diarrhea diet, feed 50% boiled ground turkey with 50% canned pumpkin.

Vomiting

Vomiting is a common problem in dogs and cats, and there are many causes, some of which can be managed at home and others that can be quite serious and require veterinary care.

A problem that can be confused with vomiting is regurgitation. Vomiting is the ejection of contents of the stomach and upper intestine; regurgitation is the ejection of contents of the esophagus. Regurgitation often, but not always, happens right after eating and the pet will try to eat the regurgitated food. Vomiting occurs a variable time after eating or may occur in a pet who has not been eating.

Pets may vomit for many reasons, ranging from a reaction to medications, exposure to toxins, cancer, foreign objects in the stomach or bowel, infection, constipation, pancreatitis, kidney failure, liver failure, urinary obstruction, ingestion of hair, food allergies, bloating, or even motion sickness. The stomach should be empty by 6 to 8 hours after eating. Vomiting food more than 8 hours after eating may suggest an obstruction in the bowel.

Yellow bile may be present in the vomit. Blood specs are not uncommon if the pet has vomited repeatedly. Coffee-ground-appearance in the vomitus is an indication of ulceration and bleeding in the stomach and upper intestine. If the gums are pale, dry, yellow, or show bruising, emergency care should be sought.

The treatment for vomiting depends upon the cause. Nonspecific treatment for vomiting includes fasting and fluids to correct or prevent dehydration. In episodes of sudden onset of vomiting, food is withheld for 12 to 24 hours and water for 8 to 12 hours. Water should never be withheld from an animal with known or suspected kidney disease without replacing fluids intravenously or subcutaneously (under the skin).

If vomiting stops, small amounts of a bland, low-fat food may be fed 3 to 6 times daily for a few days, with a gradual increase in the amount fed and a transition to the normal diet. Water is also reintroduced in small amounts. You may start with ice chips and gradually increase the amount of water over the day if vomiting does not reoccur.

Dogs and cats who vomit for longer than a day or two, vomit repeatedly without being able to hold down water, or are depressed or dehydrated should be presented for veterinary evaluation.

Home therapies to soothe the stomach include:

- Slippery elm—10 to 20 mg dried slippery elm per pound of body weight can be mixed in water or food. Slippery elm sludge can be made by adding one teaspoon of slippery elm powder to one cup of warm water. Allow to sit for a few minutes until the mixture becomes gelatinous. Give 1 teaspoon up to 2 tablespoons three times daily, depending on the size of the pet.
- Ginger root—1 teaspoon of ginger tea per ten pounds body weight twice daily or a bit of grated fresh or dried ginger root can be added to the bland diet.
- Peppermint or spearmint—dried or fresh herb can be mixed with the bland diet—give 1 teaspoon of fresh or 1/2 teaspoon of dried herb per ten pounds body weight or peppermint tea can be given. Give cats 1 tablespoon three times daily and dogs 1/4 cup per ten pounds of body weight three times daily.
- Coconut fiber can be given to cats vomiting hairballs. Give one to two teaspoons daily. Vaseline, petroleum jelly, and mineral oil are not recommended, as these are all petroleum-based products. Most often, mineral oil is a liquid obtained from refining crude oil to make gasoline and other petroleum products.

- Arsenicum 30C or Nux vomica 30C homeopathic remedy—give one dose every two hours.
- Marshmallow root—To make your own marshmallow root tea, add 1 tsp dried marshmallow root, or 2 tsp fresh marshmallow root to 1 cup of hot water. Once the water has cooled, check to make sure the tea feels slippery. Give 1/2 to 2 teaspoons two to three times daily.
- L-glutamine—amino acid that is the energy source for the cells lining the digestive tract. Give 0.5 grams (500 mg) per 20 pounds body weight twice daily. Avoid using it in pets with kidney failure, liver failure, or seizures.
- Aloe vera juice—The dose is 1/2 teaspoon per ten pounds body weight per day. Be sure it is not preserved with benzoic acid or sodium benzoate.

BLAND DIET WHEN RECOVERING FROM VOMITING—CONGEE

I am not a fan of the usual bland diet of hamburger and rice or boiled chicken and rice. Dogs and cats do not digest rice very efficiently, particularly when the bowel is inflamed. Long-grain, starchy rice can be beneficial when used to make a soup called congee. This healing soup has been used for thousands of years in Asian cultures as a healing tonic. It can be used any time your dog or cat is recovering from illness or surgery. Because it takes some time to make congee, I recommend making it ahead and freezing portions for use as needed.

☐ 1 cup long grain starchy white rice (do not use brown rice or quick rice)

☐ 1 cup diced boneless skinless chicken breast
     (rabbit or pork tenderloin may be used if your
     pet has a chicken intolerance)

☐ 1/8th cup grated fresh ginger root

☐ 8 cups water

Place all ingredients in a soup pot on the stove. Sim-
mer on low for 8 to 12 hours, stirring occasionally and
adding water as needed. Or cook it in a slow cooker
on low for 24 hours, stirring occasionally. The longer
it cooks, the more nutritious it is. When finished, the
grain and meat should be fully disintegrated, leaving
a nice gruel.

Constipation

Constipation is characterized by infrequent stools or stools that are
difficult to pass. Straining and crying may be noticed, along with
blood in the perianal area. Vomiting may occur if the pet is getting
toxic. Anything that causes dehydration can cause constipation,
particularly in cats. Chronic diseases that can result in constipation in cats include kidney disease, diabetes, and hyperthyroidism.

Pets fed raw diets containing too much bone can become
impacted. Foreign bodies, tumors, prostate enlargement, pelvic
narrowing from poorly healed fractures, medications, perineal
hernias with bowel entrapment, pain, and nerve dysfunction can
all cause constipation.

Diagnosing the underlying cause will help determine the treatment. It is critical that pets take in enough moisture to prevent
and eliminate this problem. Dry kibble diets contain only 6 to 8

percent moisture; as stated previously, cats are not big drinkers and do not take in enough moisture to make up for the lack of it in their diet. I have cured many cats with chronic constipation by having the owners change them to high moisture diets and eliminating kibble.

Pets with hernias, tumors, or other obstructive lesions may need to be placed on stool softeners to make it easier to pass stool if the obstruction cannot be removed or repaired. Never give your pet human enemas. Consult your veterinarian for appropriate products for your pet.

Species-appropriate diets, probiotics, and fiber in the diet can help prevent and relieve chronic bouts of constipation. Good sources of fiber include dark leafy greens, pumpkin, coconut, flax seeds, and green beans.

- Aloe vera juice is a natural laxative that may increase bowel movements by up to 30%. The dose is 1/2 teaspoon per ten pounds body weight per day. Be sure it is not preserved with benzoic acid or sodium benzoate.
- Apple cider vinegar may help stimulate intestinal muscles and increase the amount of bile in the digestive tract. 1/4 to 1 teaspoon can be mixed in food or water.
- Fennel stimulates intestinal motility, reduces spasms, and increases movement of the intestinal muscles (peristalsis). Add one teaspoon of fennel seeds to one cup water, boil for ten minutes, strain out the solids, and give 1/2 to 1 teaspoon every 12 hours.
- Beet juice contains a tonic that helps increase bile production. The bile stimulates intestinal contractions and increases intestinal motility. It can be added to food or water.
- Ginger root helps with digestion and reduces stomach pain. Give 1/2 to 1 teaspoon of grated fresh root once or twice daily.

Cancer of the Gastrointestinal System

Gastrointestinal cancers are uncommon in dogs and cats, with stomach tumors representing < 1% and intestinal tumors < 10% of overall neoplasms in the dog and cat. Belgian Shepherds have an increased risk for stomach carcinoma and Siamese cats have increased risk for intestinal adenocarcinoma and lymphoma. Feline leukemia virus has been implicated as an underlying factor in the development of feline gastrointestinal lymphoma. Lymphoma is the most common GI cancer in cats.

Symptoms of cancer may include vomiting (with or without blood), anorexia (lack of appetite), weight loss, diarrhea, and lethargy. Constipation may accompany large bowel tumors. Diagnosis is made with abdominal imaging (ultrasound, radiographs, CT scan, MRI), endoscopy, fine needle aspirates, or biopsy.

Routine laboratory tests are not generally diagnostic, however newer specialized blood tests are available. VDI laboratory has an Advanced GI Panel and GI Lymphoma Panel that includes testing for TK1, HPT, CRP, Cobalamin, and Folate which is excellent for helping rule cancer in or out without resorting to a surgical biopsy. If your veterinarian is not familiar with this test, information is available at www.vdilab.com.

Bloat and GDV

Bloat (also called gastric dilation and volvulus, or GDV) is a life-threatening emergency. It is caused by the twisting of the stomach and the accumulation of gas with or without fluid in the stomach.

Bloat tends to primarily affect large, deep-chested dogs. Stress may trigger an acute episode of bloat. Other risk factors include a lean body size, aggressive or fearful behavior, stress (boarding, veterinary visits, grooming, travel), once daily feedings, dry food diet, and eating quickly. The incidence increases with age. Doberman

Pinschers, German Shepherds, Standard Poodles, Great Danes, Saint Bernards, Irish Setters, Weimaraners, Standard Poodles, Bassett Hounds, and Gordon Setters are affected most frequently but it can be seen in any breed. Dogs that have a parent, sibling, or offspring with the condition also have an increased risk.

Dogs with bloat commonly have eaten a large meal followed by exercise and repeated, unsuccessful attempts to vomit. Signs of bloat may include restlessness, apparent discomfort, rapid breathing, abdominal pain and swelling, repeated dry retching, and excessive drooling. Your veterinarian may note a rapid and weak pulse, pale mucous membranes, and other signs of shock. An irregular heart rate can also develop. Veterinarians usually use x-rays to diagnose stomach rotation, but other imaging techniques can be helpful.

A successful outcome depends on prompt diagnosis and treatment by a veterinarian. The first goals of treatment are to stabilize the animal and decompress the stomach. The dog may require intravenous fluids to counteract shock. The pressure within the stomach will be relieved as soon as possible. This may be done by passing a tube through the mouth into the stomach. Once the tube enters the stomach, gas readily escapes. Excess fluid and food can then be removed via gravity and suction. After the stomach has been decompressed, the veterinarian may rinse it with warm water or saline to remove any remaining debris. If a tube cannot be passed into the stomach, excess gas may be relieved by inserting a large, hollow needle and catheter directly into the stomach through the skin.

Surgery is then performed to assess the condition of the stomach and spleen, to remove any dead tissue, to reposition the stomach to its normal location, and to attach the stomach to the abdominal wall to decrease the likelihood that it will twist again. The spleen is removed in some cases. Food is usually withheld for 48 hours after surgery. Drugs may be prescribed to control pain and vomiting, if necessary.

Complications of the surgery include abnormal heart rhythms (arrhythmias), blood infections, severe inflammation of the lining of the abdomen (peritonitis), and a serious clotting disorder called disseminated intravascular coagulation. Approximately 25%–30% of dogs die because of bloat. Immediately seek veterinary care if your dog exhibits signs of bloat; doing so can improve its chance of survival.

If your dog tends to develop bloat, your veterinarian may recommend that it be fed smaller meals more frequently over the course of the day, rather than a few large meals. Excessive exercise should be avoided, especially after eating, to decrease the likelihood of bloat, and consumption of large volumes of water after exercise should be avoided to limit distention of the stomach. Feeding from elevated bowls has also been associated with increased incidence of bloat. In practice I rarely saw bloat in dogs fed species-appropriate meals; most cases were seen in kibble-fed dogs.

Homeopathic remedies that may provide some relief if you believe your dog is bloating include Carbo vegetabilis and Nux vomica. Potency of 30C or 200C can be given every 15 minutes if you suspect bloat which may help while you are on your way to the veterinarian.

Obstruction of the GI Tract

Gastrointestinal obstruction is the blockage of the digestive tract. The blockage can arise from a tumor or enlarged prostate pressing on the bowel, a mass within the bowel wall, or obstruction inside the cavity of the digestive tract. An obstruction interferes with the passage of food and fluids, can damage digestive tissues, and can result in life-threatening consequences.

Obstruction of food movement out of the stomach can result from tumors, foreign objects, polyps, and overgrowth of stomach tissue.

Intestinal obstruction may be partial or complete and may be caused by foreign objects (corn cobs, small toys, balls, rawhide, rocks, pacifiers, and large pieces of bone are common), intussusception (a condition in which the intestine telescopes on itself), bowel entrapment in a hernia, and tumors. Long, thin foreign objects (such as string, yarn, or fabric) may become attached at the base of the tongue. If the object is long enough to trail into the intestines, normal intestinal movement tends to cause a sawing or cutting motion on the gut, leading to intestinal perforation and abdominal infection. I once had a client who made a ball of yarn into a toy for his large dog. The dog unraveled and ate yards of string. He waited quite a few days before bringing the dog in. Sadly, there was too much damage done to the bowel to save the dog.

Signs of gastric or small-intestinal obstruction vary but often include vomiting and loss of appetite. Other signs include lethargy, drooling, straining to defecate, diarrhea, abdominal pain or swelling, fever or subnormal body temperature, dehydration, and shock. Pets with complete obstruction will vomit repeatedly and be unable to hold down water or food.

To make a diagnosis, your veterinarian will need to know as much as possible about your pet's eating habits. Access to string or sewing needles or missing objects (such as toys) may be important facts and should be reported. Abdominal palpation (gently using the hands to feel the internal organs) can allow your veterinarian to detect organ enlargement, thickened bowel loops, and gas. Abdominal radiographs or ultrasound are often necessary. Examination using an endoscope may also be used to identify the problem. Blood tests are performed to identify complications from the obstruction but will not identify the obstruction itself.

Pets that have generalized signs of illness, such as depression or fever, benefit from intravenous fluid treatment. An endoscope can be used to remove some objects from the stomach. If an obstruction cannot be removed using the endoscope or if it occurs in the intestines, then surgery will be needed. Pets with sudden abdominal signs of unknown cause, and those that continue to worsen, may also require surgery. Many of these animals recover well if they are diagnosed and treated quickly.

Many years ago, our English toy spaniel, Jazzy, became very ill. She started vomiting and wouldn't eat for days. Her lab work and x-rays revealed nothing unusual, and I was stumped. I packed her little bags and set off for the local veterinary college to have her seen by the experts. After two days in critical care and three ultrasounds, they were finally convinced that she had a foreign body in her small intestine. Jazzy had never eaten anything strange around the house, so I was surprised at the diagnosis. I agreed she should go to surgery for an exploratory search of her abdomen. I was shocked when they called eight hours later to say they had removed one third of her small intestine due to a sock being wedged tightly in place. She was critical and they gave her little hope of survival. I was devastated. Little Jazzy spent eight days in ICU with three plasma transfusions given every day to elevate her protein levels. She had a feeding tube placed directly into her small bowel to give her nutrition. She hadn't eaten in twenty-one days. Amazingly, after eleven days the doctors said she was healthy enough to go home. Even in severe cases, there is always hope.

Intussusception

Intussusception is a condition in which one segment of the intestine telescopes or invaginates into the adjacent segment of intestine. Intussusceptions may occur at any location in the gastrointestinal tract but most often involves the middle of the small intestine or where the small intestine joins the large intestine.

Symptoms may include vomiting, diarrhea, decreased appetite, bloody stool, hunched back, or straining to defecate. Causes of intussusception include tumors, foreign bodies, intestinal parasites, infections, dietary changes, surgery of the intestinal tract, or trauma.

Diagnosis is made with abdominal imaging. Treatment requires surgical correction. Promoting a healthy digestive tract with a healthy gut microbiome is the best prevention.

Gastroduodenal Ulceration

My English toy spaniel, George, has had gastrointestinal ulcers multiple times in his life. He is low dog in the household, which means he worries and becomes stressed more easily than others. He has never had clinical symptoms but has had chronic anemia and low iron on blood tests, leading me to have abdominal ultrasonography performed to diagnose the problem. His ulceration has never been serious enough to warrant medical therapy; stress management and holistic therapies have been successfully implemented for him.

Bute, or phenylbutazone, which is commonly used for lame and arthritic horses, falls into a class of medications called nonsteroidal anti-inflammatory drugs or NSAIDS. Other drugs that fall into this category include Rimadyl (carprofen), Previcox (firocoxib), Deramaxx (deracoxib), Metacam (meloxicam), Galliprant (grapiprant), Onsior for cats (robenacoxib), ibuprofen, aspirin, and naproxen, as well as others that are being newly researched and marketed. Some of these have a high toxicity rate, such as ibuprofen and naproxen, for pets. Aspirin is toxic to cats unless given in extremely small doses every three to four days. Acetaminophen is toxic to cats in any dose.

Common side effects from these medications include stomach or small bowel ulceration. One study showed up to eighty percent of dogs given aspirin on a routine basis have evidence of bleeding ulcers in their stomachs. In the past, when animals have shown gastrointestinal upset when taking these medications, veterinarians have dispensed anti-ulcer medications such as sucralfate and antacids such as cimetidine to decrease the side effects. This is a poor way to deal with the problem, as side effects are just being masked. Any pet that stops eating, vomits, develops diarrhea, or has bloody or black stools, should never be given any medication that falls in the NSAID category.

When Rimadyl first came on the market some dogs vomited or showed signs of gastrointestinal distress. Rather than withdrawing the Rimadyl from the patient treatment plan, more drugs were given to mask the symptoms caused by the Rimadyl. Many dogs were given sucralfate to coat the stomach and antacids to decrease stomach acid production. While this helped mask the symptoms caused by the Rimadyl, it did not protect some dogs from the deadly erosion of the lining of the stomach and small intestine, resulting in perforated bowels, sepsis, and death.

For dogs that did not develop bowel perforation, some developed swelling of the stomach wall so that it became so thickened they were unable to eat and vomited nonstop, losing weight, and perishing from this deadly combination. This happened to my business manager's Labrador Retriever, Radar. He was being treated by another veterinarian with Rimadyl and an antacid for a long period of time. When he started vomiting, we assumed he had ingested a foreign object (all Labradors seem to eat everything in sight). During exploratory surgery we found a grossly swollen and thickened stomach wall; biopsy revealed the results of this deadly combination of drugs. Withdrawal of both drugs allowed Radar to recover, and we developed other options for treating his arthritis. I am not saying that Rimadyl is a horrible medication that should never be used, but like any medication, it must be used correctly.

Any pet placed on an NSAID must have laboratory testing to monitor liver and kidney function every three months. Any side effects or increase in liver or kidney enzymes is an immediate cause for withdrawal of the medication.

Many of the NSAIDS are sold in chewable tablet or treat form to make them taste better and easier to administer to pets. Unfortunately, many pets view these as treats and will eat the whole bottle of pills if given the chance. These medications must be stored out of reach, in a closed cabinet.

More than one NSAID should never be given at the same time. Many pets have died because an NSAID was dispensed by the veterinarian and the owner decided to give aspirin along with it. If one NSAID is stopped, there must be at least a one week waiting, or washout, period before starting a different NSAID. I once had a client whose primary veterinarian dispensed Deramaxx. The owner ran out of medication while on vacation, so she started giving ibuprofen. Ibuprofen alone may have been enough to kill the dog, but the deadly combination of starting the ibuprofen without the waiting period after stopping the Deramaxx, caused kidney failure and bowel ulceration resulting in the demise of her beloved pet. A pet that cannot tolerate one NSAID should never be given a different NSAID. The danger of a bad reaction and possible fatality is too high.

The incidence of stomach and bowel ulceration in dogs and cats is unknown but appears to be more common in dogs. NSAID and steroid medications, cancer, pancreatitis, inflammatory bowel disease, Addison's disease, heavy metal poisoning (arsenic, zinc, thallium, iron, and lead), kidney disease, and liver disease are the most often reported causes of ulceration and perforation. Stress can also lead to ulcers.

Ulcers vary in severity. Erosions may wear through a few layers (non-perforating ulcers) or may create a hole through the stomach or intestinal wall (perforating ulcers). Perforating ulcers are the most dangerous because holes in the gastrointestinal tract allow the gastrointestinal contents to spill into the abdominal cavity resulting in peritonitis, sepsis, and death.

The most common sign of gastrointestinal ulcers is vomiting, often with blood. Depending on the ulcer's severity, location, and frequency, other signs may include:

- Weight loss
- Melena (dark, tarry stools)
- Diarrhea
- Decreased appetite
- Drooling
- Dehydration
- Abdominal pain (dogs may look at their abdomen, cry when touched, or go into a "praying" position)
- Lethargy and weakness
- Fever
- Pale mucous membranes

Ulcers are diagnosed with laboratory testing (anemia or low red blood cell count, increased BUN from digested blood), stool testing, endoscopy, and abdominal imaging with radiographs, ultrasound, CT scan, or MRI.

Treatment will depend on severity of ulceration and the underlying cause. Blood transfusions and emergency surgery may be needed for perforated ulcers. Medications that may be causing ulceration need to be discontinued; metabolic and infectious diseases must be treated. Decreasing stress to decrease release of cortisol, which is a form of steroid, is advised.

Traditional treatment of ulcers includes gastroprotectants such as sucralfate which is comprised of aluminum hydroxide and sucrose. It binds to areas of eroded or ulcerated bowel. Medications to decrease stomach acid production include cimetidine, famotidine, ranitidine, omeprazole, misoprostol, or pantoprazole. Alternative therapies for gastrointestinal protection include:

- 🐾 Reduce stress. If your pet is chronically stressed, examine lifestyle changes and provide herbal, flower essence, vitamin, essential oil, or supplement therapy to decrease anxiety. Options may include chamomile, lavender, melatonin, valerian, probiotics, CBD oil, and others.
- 🐾 Gastroprotectants include slippery elm, marshmallow root, and aloe vera. See dosing under vomiting.
- 🐾 Provide a species-appropriate, easily digestible diet until the bowel is healed.

SAMPLE EASILY DIGESTIBLE DIET FOR DOGS

- ☐ 8 ounces cod
- ☐ 8 ounces pork tenderloin
- ☐ 4 ounces turkey liver
- ☐ 4 ounces canned pumpkin
- ☐ 1 teaspoon hempseed oil
- ☐ 1 teaspoon eggshell powder
- ☐ 1 teaspoon ground cinnamon powder
- ☐ 1/2 teaspoon kelp powder
- ☐ 1 zinc capsule 15 mg

Provides 29 calories per ounce. Cook in a slow cooker for 4 to 6 hours. Blend in a food processor when cooled after cooking. Feed according to guidelines in chapter 4.

SAMPLE EASILY DIGESTIBLE DIET FOR CATS

- ☐ 8 ounces cod
- ☐ 8 ounces pork tenderloin
- ☐ 7.5 ounces turkey liver
- ☐ 2 ounces canned pumpkin
- ☐ 2 teaspoons hempseed oil
- ☐ 1.5 teaspoons eggshell powder
- ☐ 1/2 teaspoon kelp powder
- ☐ 1 teaspoon cinnamon powder
- ☐ 1 zinc 15 mg capsule

Provides 32 calories per ounce. Cook in a slow cooker for 4 to 6 hours. Blend in a food processor when cooled after cooking. Feed according to guidelines in chapter 4.

Hemorrhagic Gastroenteritis (HGE) or Acute Hemorrhagic Diarrhea Syndrome (AHDS)

This syndrome is characterized by sudden onset of bloody vomiting and diarrhea, often with profound dehydration which may progress to shock. Young, small and toy breed dogs are mostly affected. It may be seen secondary to stress, parvovirus infection, pancreatitis, inflammatory bowel disease, and unknown causes. *Clostridium perfringens* bacterial toxins have been incriminated in causing ulceration of the intestinal lining and bleeding. Eighty percent of patients experience vomiting approximately ten hours before the dramatic bloody diarrhea.

There are no specific tests for AHDS, but the packed cell volume of red blood cells (or hematocrit) will be dramatically increased. A normal hematocrit is 37 to 55% but in AHDS it can be much higher. Protein levels in the blood will be low.

Treatment for this syndrome requires aggressive fluid therapy. This is an emergency. Do not wait for days to have your pet seen. Medication for nausea and pain control will be administered as well. Use of antibiotics is controversial and not recommended unless there is a fever, elevated white blood cell count, or sepsis.

Slippery elm, marshmallow root, and aloe vera can help the bowel heal. Probiotics should be started after the bleeding from the bowel has subsided. Congee can be used during recovery to provide nutrition.

Exocrine Pancreatic Insufficiency (EPI)

The pancreas is responsible for producing insulin (see section on diabetes mellitus) and digestive enzymes to break down fats, starches, and proteins. Once nutrients are broken down into smaller molecules, they can be absorbed throughout the GI trat. Without an adequate amount of enzymes, food cannot be digested. This occurs when the cells of the pancreas are not producing enzymes.

The disease may develop at any age and in any breed. About 70% of dogs with EPI are German Shepherd dogs and 20% are Rough Collies. Chronic pancreatitis is the usual cause of EPI in cats.

Symptoms of the insufficient enzyme production include:

- Weight loss from decreased absorption of nutrients
- Greasy diarrhea from decreased breakdown of fats
- Dry coat with dandruff from decreased absorption of fats
- Anemia from B12 deficiency
- Blood clotting abnormalities from decreased vitamin K
- Flatulence, gurgling intestines

- Lethargy, depression
- Ravenous appetite

Diagnosis of EPI requires a blood test called Trypsin-like immunoreactivity. Trypsin is one of the digestive enzymes secreted by the pancreas. The TLI test looks for a normal level of trypsin-like enzymes in the bloodstream. A dog or cat with EPI will have almost no serum trypsin-like immunoreactivity in the bloodstream. The patient must be fasted for the test to be accurate. There are specific canine and feline tests.

Treatment requires dietary supplementation with digestive enzymes. Powdered enzymes work better than tablets. Most enzymes are porcine (pig) origin. The enzymes can be mixed with the food and fed immediately. In the past it was believed the enzymes needed to be mixed with the food 10 to 15 minutes prior to feeding; this is no longer the case. Response to therapy is fast, usually within a few days.

Raw beef or lamb pancreas can also be used as a form of enzyme replacement. The pancreas must be served raw as cooking will inactivate the enzymes. Raw pancreas can be stored frozen without losing digestive enzyme activity. Two ounces of raw pancreas replaces one teaspoon of powdered enzyme replacement.

A highly digestible, low-fiber diet may be beneficial to help pets gain weight.

Vitamin B12 (cobalamin) supplementation is recommended. Injectable vitamin B12 can be given at home or by your veterinarian. Injections of 1/4 to 1 ml may be required weekly for the first few weeks and tapered to monthly dosing. Oral vitamin B12 supplements are also available for dogs and cats. In cats, folate deficiency is common and may need to be supplemented. Provide species-specific, soil-based probiotics.

SAMPLE RECIPE FOR EPI FOR DOGS

- ☐ 1 pound 93% lean ground turkey
- ☐ 2 ounces chicken or turkey liver
- ☐ 4 ounces yellow squash
- ☐ 2 ounces turnip
- ☐ 2 ounces parsley
- ☐ 3 ounces fresh or canned (in water) sardines
- ☐ 2 teaspoons hempseed oil
- ☐ 1 teaspoon ground eggshell powder
- ☐ ¾ teaspoon kelp
- ☐ 1 ounce oyster or 1 zinc 15 mg capsule
- ☐ 1 tablespoon wheat grass powder

Provides 33 calories per ounce. Add 1 ounce of raw pancreas per 20 pounds body weight at the time of feeding if feeding twice daily (2 ounces if feeding once daily). May be served raw or gently cooked (do NOT cook the pancreas!)

EASILY DIGESTIBLE RECIPE FOR CATS CAN BE USED FOR EPI

- ☐ 8 ounces cod
- ☐ 8 ounces pork tenderloin
- ☐ 7.5 ounces turkey liver

- 2 ounces canned pumpkin
- 2 teaspoons hempseed oil
- 1.5 teaspoons eggshell powder
- 1/2 teaspoon kelp powder
- 1 teaspoon cinnamon powder
- 1 zinc 15 mg capsule

Provides 32 calories per ounce. Cook in a slow cooker for 4 to 6 hours. Blend in a food processor when cooled after cooking. Add 1/2 ounce of raw beef pancreas to each meal at the time of feeding. Feed according to guidelines in chapter 4.

Protein Losing Enteropathy

Protein-losing enteropathy (PLE) is **not** a specific disease but is described as a group of diseases that cause the loss of proteins from the bloodstream into the gastrointestinal (GI) tract. Primary GI disease, heart disease, and diseases of the lymphatic system can all cause PLE.

Pets with protein losing enteropathy have a net loss of protein, which means they lose more protein than they take in from the diet. This can affect health quite severely, as proteins are needed for numerous roles within the body.

Pets with protein losing enteropathy (PLE) are still able to absorb protein from the diet through the intestines, but these proteins can leak back into the gut and end up being excreted. One of the main proteins lost is albumin. A decrease in albumin will cause breakdown of protein such as muscle. Muscle wasting, along with diarrhea and vomiting, will result in noticeable weight loss.

The development of PLE can be a result of one of many factors. Two conditions that are often involved in the development of PLE include canine inflammatory bowel disease (IBD) and lymphangiectasia (a condition where lymph vessels become dilated).

Lymphatic vessels carry a clear fluid containing white blood cells, called "lymph", through the body. Lymphatic diseases that can lead to PLE include:

- Lymphangiectasia—dilation of the lymphatic vessels in the GI tract.
- GI lymphoma/lymphosarcoma—cancer of the lymphoid tissues around the body, including the lymphoid tissues within the GI tract.
- Infiltration of the GI tract by scar tissue which interrupts lymphatic flow.
- Congestive heart failure causing increased pressure within the lymphatic system.

Diseases that directly affect the GI tract and can lead to PLE include:

- Bacterial, fungal, viral, or parasitic gastroenteritis
- Inflammatory bowel disease (IBD)
- Adverse food reactions or food intolerance
- Mechanical GI disease— chronic foreign body irritation (without creating a blockage)
- Intestinal cancer—lymphoma is the most common cause of PLE in cats
- Ulcers in the stomach or intestines

Dog breeds more likely to develop protein losing enteropathy include:

- Soft coated Wheaten terrier
- Basenji
- Yorkshire Terrier
- Norwegian Lundehund
- Poodle
- Maltese
- Shar Pei

Symptoms include:

- Diarrhea
- Vomiting
- Weight loss
- Lethargy
- Difficulty breathing
- Swollen abdomen or limbs

Diagnosis is made by laboratory analysis. Albumin levels in the blood will be low. Globulin may be low or may be high if there is inflammatory disease. Cholesterol will also be low. Abdominal ultrasound can help rule out cancer or lymphangiectasia of the bowel. Definitive diagnosis requires intestinal biopsy.

Low-fat, highly digestible diets are recommended. Home prepared or commercial raw or gently cooked meals using human-grade food ingredients are much preferred to highly processed food. Most veterinarians will recommend hydrolyzed protein kibble or canned diets, but I have never prescribed them. This is an advanced form of leaky gut. See chapter 5 for supplements that may help.

Lymphangiectasia

Intestinal lymphangiectasia is characterized by dilation of the lymph vessels of the intestines. It is believed to be the most common cause of PLE in dogs. IL occurs in both a congenital form (primary IL) and an acquired form (secondary IL). Primary IL is a developmental abnormality that leads to an insufficiency or malformation of the lymphatics. Secondary IL is due to obstruction of lymph flow. This may develop due to physical blockage of the lymphatics (lacteals). The lacteals may be physically blocked by inflammation or cancer of the intestines. This results in poor absorption of fat from the intestines and loss of protein from the bowel.

Initial symptoms include weight loss, vomiting, and diarrhea. Protein loss can result in blood clots and fluid accumulation in the lungs or abdomen.

Decreasing the fat content of the diet to 10 to 15% reduces inflammation and helps relieve symptoms. It is very important to use high quality protein sources that are easily digestible. Supplements may include B12, folic acid, prebiotics, and probiotics.

Inflammatory Bowel Disease

Inflammatory bowel diseases are the most common cause of chronic vomiting and diarrhea in dogs and cats. The term IBD is used to describe a group of conditions characterized by inflammation of the gastrointestinal tract and persistent or recurrent GI signs. The small intestine, large intestine, or both can be affected.

Multiple factors can contribute to the disease including genetics, immune system overload, environmental factors, and microbial factors (changes in the microbiome). Boxers and French bulldogs are prone to histiocytic ulcerative colitis (large bowel inflammation). Siamese and other oriental cat breeds are suggested to be more prone to developing IBD.

Inflammation of the cells lining the intestinal tract results in swelling of the cells. Normally there are tight junctions between the cells which prohibit pathogenic organisms and large protein particles from reaching the intercellular space. When the cells are swollen, those tight junctions open, eliminating the protective barrier. This is what is called Leaky Gut. The goal of treatment is to eliminate swelling and inflammation, thereby restoring the protective barrier.

Stress, poor quality diet, over-vaccination, over-stimulation of the immune system, pesticides, antibiotics, medications, and environmental toxins all contribute to the formation of leaky gut. Vaccines are made by growing antigens (vaccine immune particles) on chicken eggs or bovine serum. During vaccination your pet's immune system may become sensitized to particles injected during vaccination, including the proteins in the vaccines. This sensitization can lead to an inflammatory reaction in the gut.

Dysbiosis (an imbalance of the microorganisms in the bowels) is seen in the microbiome of animals affected by IBD.

Most pets eat the same thing every day. This repetition tends to create food intolerances and sensitivities. Feeding a rotational diet can help lower the risk of your pet developing intolerance and inflammatory bowel disease.

Clinical signs of IBD can include vomiting, diarrhea, dark tarry stools, bloody stools, weight loss, and decreased appetite. This may progress to PLE (see above) with fluid buildup in the chest or abdomen or swollen limbs.

Diagnosis of IBD is made by excluding infectious and parasitic agents, EPI, partial obstruction, cancer, and metabolic disorders that may produce similar symptoms. Recommended specialized tests include cobalamin, folate, and TLI blood tests. Abdominal ultrasound will show intestinal wall thickening and enlarged abdominal lymph nodes. Endoscopy and biopsy are commonly performed.

Traditional treatment of IBD includes the use of hydrolyzed diets, immunosuppressive drugs, and antibiotics. While these are potentially useful if the pet is in crisis, they cause further dysbiosis and damage in the long run.

Fecal transplants, probiotics, and natural anti-inflammatory supplements, along with a novel protein, easily digestible, human-grade diet may provide more relief and a better outcome overall. It is important to detoxify the liver and kidneys of these animals, as well. (See the chapters on liver and kidney disease.) Acupuncture can help reduce inflammation.

A study was performed feeding whole ground raw rabbit to cats with IBD. The cats' coats improved, as did the stools. In contrast, stools from cats fed premium cooked food remained soft and malodorous. Unfortunately, 70% of the cats developed taurine deficiency.

BALANCED RAW RABBIT DIET FOR CATS

☐ 1 pound whole ground rabbit, including fur, head, and bones

☐ 10.5 ounces raw duck liver

☐ 1/2 teaspoon ground turmeric powder

☐ 1/2 teaspoon kelp powder

☐ 1/2 teaspoon cod liver oil

Provides 31 calories per ounce. Must be fed raw. Follow feeding guidelines in chapter 4.

60 to 70% of pets will have a favorable response to diet change within two weeks. Only 16% of dogs have good outcomes with long-term antibiotic use. Antibiotics cause more dysbiosis and antibiotic resistance.

Supplements to support the bowel and decrease inflammation include:

- L-Glutamine—This is an amino acid that nourishes the cells lining the gut wall, helping with their growth and repair. It is found naturally in spirulina, broccoli, and asparagus. It can be dosed at 20 mg per pound of body weight per day for both dogs and cats.
- N-Acetyl Glucosamine—This form of glucosamine comes from shellfish and can also be found in bone broth. While normally used to support joint health, it also promotes growth and healing of the gut lining. Dose at 15 mg per pound of body weight per day for dogs and cats.
- Licorice root—This is an anti-inflammatory herb. It also helps nourish intestinal cells. It should be given in the deglycyrrhized form. Licorice root tea can be given at 1/2 teaspoon for small dogs and cats up to 2 teaspoons for large dogs once or twice daily. Dried herb powder can be given at 20 to 60 mg per pound three times daily.
- Aloe Vera juice—This juice (must be from the gel of the inner leaves) promotes tissue and cell regeneration and is anti-inflammatory. It can also form a coating to protect the cells of the gastrointestinal tract. Dose at 1 to 4 teaspoons daily, depending on size of the pet. Do not use aloe vera for more than one to two weeks.
- Slippery Elm—This makes a coating that lines the intestines to protect them and decrease inflammation. The dose is 10 mg per pound of body weight two to four times daily. The powder can be mixed with water to make a sludge that can be mixed with a small amount of food. Medications should be given 1 to 2 hours before a dose of slippery elm, since the mucilaginous coating it creates

can inhibit their absorption. Slippery elm paste (powder mixed with cold water) can also be used as a poultice for hot spots and rashes.

- Marshmallow root—This herb provides relief from inflammation and irritation in the digestive tract. It encourages healthy growth of intestinal microflora while lubricating and soothing inflamed mucous membranes in the intestines by creating a coating like the properties of Slippery Elm. This is best fed between meals as a tea but can be added to meals at a dose of 1/4 teaspoon for cats and small dogs up to one teaspoon for large dogs two to three times daily.

- Chamomile flowers—This herb fights inflammation, expels gas, is antispasmodic, expels worms, and stimulates digestion. Be sure to purchase chamomile in forms specifically made for pets, as it can be toxic. Avoid use in pregnant animals. It can also be used as a topical ointment or poultice by mixing with coconut oil or shea butter. Dried herbs should be dosed at 50 mg per pound of body weight up to three times daily or 2 drops per pound of body weight of an alcohol tincture up to three times daily.

- Ginger root—Warms the digestive tract, excellent for nausea and digestive upset. Dose is 25 to 35 mg of fresh grated root per pound of body weight twice daily. It can be mixed with food.

- Boswellia—A human study showed this herb was as effective as standard medications for treating IBD. Give 150 mg for cats and small dogs up to 450 mg for large dogs once daily. These doses may need to be doubled for the first two weeks.

- Quercetin—Quercetin is a natural antihistamine. 5 to 10 mg per pound of body weight can be given twice daily.

Quercetin is found naturally in blueberries, apple skin, and parsley. Quercetin is often combined with Bromelain.

● Curcumin (turmeric root)—This is a potent anti-inflammatory and stimulates circulation and digestion. Dose at 1/8th to 1/4 teaspoon dry powder per ten pounds of body weight twice daily mixed in food. It can also be given as Golden Paste: 1/4 teaspoon for cats and small dogs up to one tablespoon for large dogs twice daily.

● Milk thistle—This boosts the ability of liver cells to filter toxins from the blood and decreases allergic response. The dose is 5 mg per pound twice daily.

● Dandelion root and leaves can help flush toxins from the body.

● Red clover—used for lymphatic drainage.

● Digestive enzymes—These can be plant or animal origin. Enzymes help the body to correctly digest food. Adding beef or pork pancreas is also an option.

● Mushrooms—Reishi is the preferred mushroom to support the digestive system. Chaga is also effective for digestive support. Both also support the immune system. Mushrooms are a great source of prebiotic fiber. The mushrooms can be gently sauteed in olive or coconut oil and added to the diet or can be given as an extract in powder form at 100 mg per ten pounds body weight per day.

● Colostrum—Colostrum contains over 90 immune factors; it inhibits immune cells that cause allergic reactions. It is also anti-inflammatory and can reduce histamine levels. Give 1/8th teaspoon per 25 pounds body weight twice daily.

● Omega-3 fatty acids—High-quality fish, krill, or algae oil can calm inflammation. Give 100 mg of EPA and DHA combined for every 10 pounds body weight per day. One sardine contains approximately 100 mg of EPA/DHA.

- Vitamin B12—250 to 1,000 micrograms orally daily or weekly by subcutaneous injection depending on the size of the pet.
- MCT oil—medium chain triglycerides—are easier to absorb than other fats.
- Probiotics—They block the pathogenic effects of the bad bacteria, regulate and improve immune function, decrease inflammatory reactions to pathogens, and strengthen the intestinal barrier function. Soil-based, species-specific probiotics are preferred.

17 Cancer in Dogs and Cats

When my grandmother was diagnosed with liver and colon cancer my father and his brother sent me to talk to the doctor to get some answers on her condition. Having dealt in the past with medical doctors who looked down on veterinarians, I can say I was not too thrilled with my assignment. As expected, the doctor was not very pleasant and resented having to speak with me. He marched into my grandmother's room and informed her that he was not pleased. Not only was the doctor mad, but my grandparents were furious. In our family we were not allowed to mention the word *CANCER*. My grandparents did not speak to me for a week. I never asked for another update on her condition.

Fifteen years later it was my grandfather who was diagnosed with cancer. Once again, I was assigned the task of dealing with doctors. When my grandfather was placed in hospice care I explicitly explained that we were never allowed to say the word *CANCER*. Unfortunately, the first hospice care worker who arrived, apparently did not get the memo. He chatted on and on to my grandfather about his impending care. When he finally said the word *CANCER* I was waving my arms and jumping up and down out of view of my grandfather, who turned to me and said, "I do NOT have *CANCER*. Get this guy out of here." Yikes.

Many people live in fear of *CANCER*, whether for themselves or their pets. It brings up emotions associated with fear, pain, and loss. Cancer is the second leading cause of death in people in America and the #1 cause of death in dogs over two years of age. We have every right to be afraid. But rather than living in fear we could "take the bull by the horns" and be pro-active in preventing cancer. We live in a polluted, toxic world with questionable food and water supplies, but we can diminish our risk.

Cancer is a disease in which some of the body's cells grow uncontrollably and spread to other parts of the body. Cancer can start almost anywhere in the body, which is made up of trillions of cells. Normally, cells grow and multiply to form new cells as the body needs them. When cells grow old or become damaged, they die, and new cells take their place.

Sometimes this orderly process breaks down and abnormal or damaged cells grow and multiply when they shouldn't. These cells may form tumors that can be cancerous or not cancerous (benign). Cancerous tumors spread into nearby tissues and can travel to distant places in the body to form new tumors (a process called metastasis). Benign tumors do not spread into other tissues. When removed, benign tumors usually don't grow back, whereas cancerous tumors sometimes do.

Unfortunately, dog cancer is common. It is the leading natural cause of death in dogs. Approximately 50% of all dogs will be affected by cancer in their lifetime; one report shows that 50% of dogs over the age of 10 will die from cancer. Cancer in cats is less common than cancer in dogs. It's probably half the rate seen in dogs, but feline cancer tends to be a more aggressive form. Lymphoma is the most common cancer in cats, followed by oral squamous cell carcinoma and fibrosarcoma in the muscle, also known as injection-site sarcoma.

Cancer cells:

- Grow in the absence of signals telling them to grow. Normal cells only grow when they receive such signals.

- Ignore signals that normally tell cells to stop dividing or to die.
- Invade into nearby areas and spread to other areas of the body.
- Tell blood vessels to grow toward tumors to supply oxygen and nutrients.
- Hide from the immune system.
- Have changes in their DNA.
- Rely on different kinds of nutrients than normal cells.

The cause of cancer is unknown but there are contributing factors to cancer formation. Changes in the DNA within cells will cause cells to become cancerous. Known and suspected causes of cellular damage that can lead to cancer include:

- Herbicides
- Insecticides
- Second-hand smoke
- Radiation exposure
- Environmental pollution
- Chemical flame retardants in furnishings
- Viral infections, particularly FIV and FeLV in cats
- Genetic predisposition
- Vaccinations
- Chemical additives and preservatives in food
- Chronic stress
- Chronic inflammation

There are more than 100 types of cancer. Types of cancer are usually named for the organs or tissues where the cancers form. For example, lung cancer starts in the lung, and brain cancer starts in the brain. Cancers also may be described by the type of cell that formed them.

- Carcinomas are the most common type of cancer. They are formed by epithelial cells, which are the cells that cover the inside and outside surfaces of the body. Adenocarcinoma is a cancer that forms in epithelial cells that produce fluids or mucus. Mammary, prostate, and colon cancers often fall into this category. Squamous cell carcinoma is a cancer that forms in squamous cells, which are epithelial cells that lie just beneath the outer surface of the skin. Squamous cells also line many other organs, including the stomach, intestines, lungs, bladder, and kidneys. Transitional cell carcinoma is a cancer that forms in a type of epithelial tissue called transitional epithelium. This tissue is found in the linings of the bladder, ureters, and part of the kidneys (renal pelvis), and a few other organs. Some cancers of the bladder, ureters, and kidneys are transitional cell carcinomas. Melanoma is a cancer of a pigmented skin cell called a melanocyte. It often occurs in the mouth or nail bed.

- Sarcomas are cancers that form in bone and soft tissues, including muscle, fat, blood vessels, lymph vessels, and fibrous tissue such as tendons and ligaments. Osteosarcoma is the most common cancer of bone. The most common types of soft tissue sarcoma are hemangiosarcoma, lymphoma, mast cell tumors, leiomyosarcoma, malignant histiocytosis, histiocytic sarcoma, and liposarcoma.

- Cancers that begin in the blood-forming tissue of the bone marrow are called leukemias. These cancers do not form solid tumors. Instead, large numbers of abnormal white blood cells build up in the blood and bone marrow, crowding out normal blood cells. The low level of normal blood cells can make it harder for the body to get oxygen to its tissues, control bleeding, or fight infections.

I know I repeat myself often, but I will keep repeating eating fresh, organic, locally sourced, antibiotic- and pesticide-free foods is paramount to our survival. Yes, I know they can be hard to find. I know they are more expensive. I know it's hard to find nice restaurants that offer healthy options at an affordable price. I know packaged and processed foods are easier to store and prepare. But read the labels! How many chemicals that you can't even pronounce are listed on the side of the bag, box, or can? Do you have any idea what those chemicals do to the cells that make up your incredibly delicate, unique body? No? Well, neither do I, and neither do the folks at the manufacturing plants, but we do have good evidence that many of the dyes and preservatives in food are carcinogenic. I can assure you there are bad things occurring in food processing because we read and hear reports of problems in the food chain every single day.

We need to stop overdosing on medication and antibiotics. Every drug has side effects, and we take more drugs to alleviate the side effects. Antibiotic resistance is a worldwide problem, requiring the use of bigger, better, stronger drugs. We are producing super bugs that will destroy us, like unstoppable flesh-eating bacteria. We need to become a society in motion; sedentary lifestyles are leading to increased obesity. This includes our pets. Exercise is not a dirty word.

The immune system in our body is incredibly sensitive. Constant stimulation with vaccines, chemicals, pollution, medications, and bad diets that include GMO grains, dyes, and chemical preservatives destroys the immune system. Destruction of the immune system causes poor digestion, endocrine disease, and *CANCER*. It is NEVER too late to improve your pet's diet and decrease toxin exposure. When someone comes to consult about a pet with cancer, the first order of business is cleaning up the diet and decreasing toxic chemical exposure.

Although there are many types of cancer they tend to fall mainly into a couple of categories from a Chinese Medicine perspective. Blood or Qi Stasis causes the congealing and decreased flow of blood and energy, forming a lump or mass. Qi, or energy, must be present to move blood. Traditional medicine studies have shown decreased and abnormal blood flow within tumors, so it would appear the ancient Chinese theory agrees with modern medicine. Many of the herbal remedies used for cancerous lumps include herbs to move Blood and soften hardness. With this condition there will be a lack of energy, fatigue, and a feeling of heaviness. There may be pain or a history of pain. The tumor is only a symptom of a larger underlying imbalance resulting from emotional stress (dogs and cats spending all day alone or housed in crowded conditions), poor diet, toxic chemicals, and pollution. Common cancers of this nature include mast cell tumors and hemangiosarcoma. The tongue of these pets will be a lavender or purple color and may have a phlegmy coating.

The second type of cancer from a Chinese Medicine perspective is a Yin Deficiency with secondary Phlegm formation. When blood becomes too dry (not enough moisture is present), phlegm results (think of mucoid secretions like snot). These animals are hot; they pant a lot. They can't get enough to drink. Many of them are overweight (or were) and have lipomas (benign fatty tumors) and poor digestion with gas, diarrhea, and vomiting. Their tongue is usually dark red (I call it toxic red). Most pets with lymphoma or lymphosarcoma, osteosarcoma, squamous cell carcinoma, and anal gland tumors will fall in this category. Herbs used to treat these cancers will include Yin Tonics to cool and moisturize and herbs to clear heat.

In China, people with cancer are usually treated with Fu Zhen therapy, which is herbal therapy, in conjunction with chemotherapy. Ginseng, astragalus, ligusticum, codonopsis, atractylodes, and ganoderma herbs are combined to protect and stimulate the immune system to fight cancer. Fu Zhen therapy is reported to increase survival times significantly when used in conjunction with modern treatments. In human medicine, patients are rarely treated with herbs alone, but herbal remedies can be used to stimulate the immune system, decrease side effects of radiation and chemotherapy, and to help aid in tumor reduction itself.

Warning Signs of Cancer

Warning signs of cancer in pets include:

- Any new lumps, bumps, or sores. If you examine your pet daily, you will notice if a new lump or bump suddenly appears. While many lumps and bumps are benign, many are not. Have your veterinarian look at the lumps and perform a needle aspiration (obtaining a few cells with a needle and syringe). Cells should be examined under the microscope to determine whether they may be cancerous.
- Any change in old lumps, bumps, or sores. If a mass has been present for a long time, but suddenly starts to grow, becomes ulcerated, seems painful when touched, or the pet is paying a lot of attention to it, the mass may need immediate removal. Sores that just won't heal may be a sign of skin cancer. Body maps can be used to chart lumps when you find them. Calipers can be used to measure the mass(es) to determine whether they are growing.
- Constant licking at one toe or any other specific area. Pets try to heal themselves by licking areas that are painful or infected. Constant chewing or licking at only one toe can be a sign of a nail bed tumor. Constant licking at the anal area could indicate an anal gland tumor. Pets with bladder tumors may lick in the groin area.

- Bloody discharge from anywhere, whether that is nose, mouth, penis, vulva, or rectum. Nose bleeds are not common in pets and should always be a warning sign to have the pet checked. Many pets with dental disease will have malodorous saliva, but pets with serious cancers in the mouth may have a lot of blood in the saliva. While blood in the urine or urinary openings may signify a urinary tract infection, it may also signify something worse, like a transitional cell carcinoma of the bladder or prostate cancer in males. Rectal bleeding may be associated with colitis but can also occur with tumors in the bowel. Dark, black, tarry stools are an indication of bleeding higher in the digestive tract and may indicate a bleeding mass in the stomach or small intestine.

- Weight loss without a diet change. Some pet owners associate weight loss with aging changes. However, weight loss may signify something much worse. Your pet should be weighed at each veterinary visit and any significant change should be noted and the cause determined.

- Bloated abdomen. Bleeding tumors of the spleen or liver can cause abdominal distention. Hemangiosarcoma is a big culprit with this. However, tumors of the liver will often be accompanied by fluid in the abdomen, called ascites. A sample of the fluid can often reveal the underlying cause.

- Loss of appetite. If your pet starts turning up his nose at the usual meals that he loves, something has changed. If they turn down treats or goodies, get them seen!

- Straining to urinate or defecate. While straining to urinate may indicate an infection, it may also indicate a tumor in or around the bladder. I recently had a patient that started leaking urine and the problem turned out to be a huge hemangiosarcoma sitting above the bladder putting pressure on the bladder. Pets that strain to produce very small or flattened stools may be trying to pass stool around a mass blocking the bowel (either in the bowel or compressing it from outside the bowel as in prostate cancer).

- Weakness or loss of energy. If your normally playful, energetic pet is now refusing to go for walks or play with their favorite toy, something has changed. This could be due to pain of arthritis, pain of cancer, metabolic problems like diabetes or Cushing's disease, or general weakness. Make time for a checkup.

- Foul odor. This usually indicates an infection somewhere. But that infection may be secondary to an underlying cancer. Many cancerous masses will have dying cells that release a "dead" odor. Cancers do have a specific odor, as evidenced by dogs used to sniff out bladder cancers in urine samples.

- Behavior changes. If your pet is hiding more, doesn't want to be petted or involved in the activity of the household, or is becoming snippy or rude, these are signs he isn't feeling well and wants to be left alone. He may be struggling with pain.

- Pale gums. This is a sign of bleeding or anemia. Chronic illness will lead to anemia. Blood-based tumors like hemangiosarcoma can rupture and bleed into the chest or abdomen.

- Coughing. That dry, harsh cough that just won't go away. Usually non-productive or only a little phlegm is spit out. Respiration may become labored or rapid. This can be a sign of the spread of tumors to the chest. The cough will usually be made worse with exercise.

Diagnosing Cancer

Cancer is diagnosed through laboratory testing, biopsy, fine needle aspiration, cytology, and imaging. Screening tests can be performed by VDI Lab to determine if your pet is at risk for cancer. Cancer is a form of inflammation; tests that show evidence of chronic inflammation can be used to assess risk. VDI lab offers a canine cancer panel that can be used to diagnose the presence of cancer and to monitor disease progression or therapy outcomes. Common use includes diagnosis of lymphoma, abdominal masses, solid tumors, mast cell tumors (stage II), hypercalcemia found on blood work that may be associated with malignancy, chemotherapy management, and metastatic disease. The test is not recommended for skin masses, stage I mast cell tumors, or brain tumors. Tests include TK1 and C-Reactive Protein.

VDI lab also offers a feline gastrointestinal lymphoma panel which is very useful to help differentiate GI lymphoma from inflammatory bowel disease.

More specific tests for cancer in dogs include the NuQ test, available from IDEXX labs, which has a high success rate for early diagnosis of lymphoma and hemangiosarcoma, but may indicate other cancers such as histiocytic sarcoma, malignant melanoma, osteosarcoma, soft tissue sarcoma, and mast cell cancer.

Some disease problems may interfere with cancer testing. Inflammatory diseases such as immune mediated disease, systemic inflammation, sepsis, and trauma can also cause elevated nucleosome and inflammation levels. Tests may not differentiate between sick patients with systemic inflammatory mediated illness and cancer. For this reason, it is not recommended to run tests in patients that could have these types of diseases. However, the test may be run in dogs without systemic inflammation but with other illnesses such as hypothyroidism, renal disease, osteoarthritis, mild or moderate pyoderma or other such minor illnesses. Pets must be fasted before blood is drawn.

Antech lab offers a test called the CADET BRAF to detect the presence of Transitional Cell Carcinoma in the urinary tract using urine samples.

Pet DX pioneered a test that is available through IDEXX and Antech labs called OncoK9. It is a liquid biopsy test that utilizes next-generation DNA sequencing technology to aid in detecting 30 types of common canine cancers: lymphoma, hemangiosarcoma, soft tissue sarcoma, mast cell tumor, mammary gland carcinoma, anal sac adenocarcinoma, malignant melanoma, and osteosarcoma.

SearchLight DNA by Vidium Animal Health identifies mutations in canine cancer genes and provides insights into a cancer's origin, its behavior, and the optimal approach to treatment. It incorporates advanced diagnostic, prognostic, and predictive biomarkers to provide greater clarity about the behavior of a canine's tumor. It finds mutations in the DNA of dog's cancer cells, identifies chemo-sensitivity gene MDR1, and checks for 120 relevant cancer genes. Cytology and biopsy samples can be used to perform the test.

Any lumps or masses should be evaluated as soon as possible if they are greater than one centimeter in size or have been present for more than one month. Masses felt on or under the skin can be aspirated; cells from the aspirate can be examined under the microscope to determine if they may be cancerous.

Impression smears using a microscope slide can be obtained from masses that are open or ulcerated.

Any mass that appears to be malignant should be biopsied, with full removal including clean margins, as soon as possible. Many times, surgical removal of a malignant mass will be fully curative.

Imaging to find internal masses may include radiographs, ultrasound, CT scan, or MRI.

Treating Cancer

Where conventional medicine is destructive and aggressive, TCVM is reparative and detoxifying. TCVM and other complementary therapies are especially effective at enhancing the immune system and reinforcing the body's ability to withstand disease.

Conventional treatment may be instituted if the pet is likely to live longer with treatment than without, however, financial constraints and difficulty accessing specialty oncology treatment centers may limit the options available.

Side effects from radiation and chemotherapy are variable. Both chemotherapy and radiation may predispose the pet to developing secondary cancers from treatment. For instance, cyclophosphamide is a proven bladder carcinogen and is associated with a 4.5-fold increased risk of development of kidney tumors.

The goal of any therapy is a high quality of life, not necessarily a longer life where the pet's health has deteriorated into a poor condition.

It is beyond the scope of this book to list herbal, vitamin, and glandular treatments for each cancer seen in pets. The list can be endless, as each pet is different. There is no "one-size-fits-all" therapy. If your pet is undergoing chemotherapy or radiation, be sure to check with your oncologist before starting any sort of vitamin, herbal, or antioxidant therapies. Many times, complementary medicines can interfere with the traditional medicine therapies. It is imperative to work with a veterinary herbalist to achieve the best combination. I am including a list of some of the more common treatments:

- For any dog with a tumor that may rupture or bleed, like hemangiosarcoma, use one capsule twice daily of Yunnan Bai Yao.
- Si Maio San and Artemisinin (Sweet Wormwood) are

commonly used for lymphoma and other Phlegm-based cancers. Artemisinin should not be used in pets undergoing radiation. It works by decreasing the formation of new blood vessels in the tumor; it also binds to the high iron content within cancer cells to help kill them. Artemisinin is usually given for 11 days, then withheld for 3 days and the cycle is repeated. Artemisinin dose is 2 to 5 mg per pound of body weight given twice daily on the prescribed cycle. Artemisinin should not be given with iron supplements or within 3 hours of a high meat meal.

- Vitamin therapy can also help stimulate and protect the immune system. Vitamins A, B-complex, C, D, E, and selenium are commonly supplemented. Vitamin A, in particular, can kill cancer cells when given in high doses. It can also cause kidney failure, so work with your veterinarian or a veterinary nutritionist. Intravenous vitamin C infusion is becoming more popular for people and animals. Vitamin C has activity against cancer cells.

- Inositol hexaphosphate (IP-6) offers significant protection against cancer and metastasis. It increases the production of NK (natural killer) cells in the immune system that kill cancer cells. It also binds to iron in the cancer cells which is a major source of food for the cells. It induces apoptosis (cell death) in many cancer lines and inhibits angiogenesis (new blood vessel growth for tumors). Doses for dogs range from 800 to 1600 mg twice daily for medium to large dogs and 400 mg twice daily for small dogs and cats.

- CoQ10 is a strong antioxidant that can also protect the heart if chemotherapy is being used. Give 5 mg per pound of body weight twice daily. Researchers at the University of Miami added CoQ10 to prostate cancer cells—and found a 70 percent inhibition in growth over 48 hours. Adding CoQ10 to breast cancer cells also inhibited proliferation, without harming healthy cells. The team noted that treating a culture of melanoma cells with CoQ10 resulted in the death of all cancer cells within hours—and that applying CoQ10 topically to mice with melanoma tumors caused a 55 percent reduction in tumor mass. There was also a "profound disruption" of tumor vasculature—the structure of veins needed by tumors for oxygen and nutrition.

- Any pets undergoing chemotherapy should have liver support in the form of milk thistle, dosed at 5 to 10 mg per pound daily, which may also help chemo drugs work better. Research shows that milk thistle is an inhibitor to cancer cell cycles, effectively blocking cancer growth. In addition to its direct anticancer effects, milk thistle silymarin compounds may also reduce damage to the heart and liver from chemotherapy drugs. In lab studies, silybin from milk thistle worked even better against breast cancer cells when combined with curcumin from turmeric.

- Omega 3 fatty acids have antioxidant and anti-inflammatory effects when dosed at 30 to 40 mg per pound; dose may be as high as 12,000 mg per day of fish oil. If your pet develops diarrhea with fish oil try evening primrose, olive, flax, or borage oil.

- SAM-e is great for liver support, particularly for pets undergoing chemotherapy. SAM-e has been shown to prevent breast tumors from forming, reduce the growth of the tumors already present, and decrease the number of metastases. It also has cell-killing effects on liver cancer cells. Give 90 mg to small dogs, 225 mg to medium sized dogs, and 400 mg to large dogs.

- Probiotics and digestive enzymes should be added to repopulate the bowel with good bacteria and help with utilization of nutrients in the food.

- Medicinal mushrooms have been shown to have anti-cancer effects. Clinical trials are underway studying the efficacy of medicinal mushrooms in treating canine cancers. Mushrooms can be added to the diet as well. These can include Reishi mushroom, which is known as the mushroom of immortality because it helps modulate the immune system, supports adrenal glands to manage stress, and helps regulate the digestive system. Lion's Mane mushrooms are known for their neuroprotective effects. Chaga mushrooms have strong antioxidant function to protect DNA from oxidative damage, support the immune system, promote muscle strength, and help regulate blood sugar. Tremella mushrooms are supportive for animals undergoing chemotherapy, are an immune system tonic, and help protect the heart. Turkey Tail mushroom has the highest beta-glucan content of any medical mushroom, making it the most-used cancer-fighting mushroom. Turkey Tail boosts the production of the cells the body relies on to kill abnormal cells that can form tumors; it helps support a healthy immune system.

- Melatonin is a mild chelator and free-radical scavenger, decreasing oxidative damage to proteins and DNA. Melatonin directly eradicates various types of tumor cells by inducing apoptosis, or programmed cell death, while inhibiting tumor and cancer cell growth. Melatonin should be given at night. Dosing is 0.1 mg per pound of body weight. Do not use liquids that contain xylitol.

- N-acetylcysteine (NAC) is a dietary supplement derived from the amino acid L-cysteine. It is used as an antidote for acetaminophen overdose. As an antioxidant, it is thought to reduce DNA damage. NAC is also marketed for its liver-protective properties and to support healthy immune functioning. In a 2017 study conducted by researchers from the Thomas Jefferson University, NAC succeeded in slowing down the growth of cancer cells in patients with breast cancer. The natural antioxidant reduced the aggressiveness of tumors by modulating the metabolism of cancer cells. NAC also depleted the cancer cells of nutrients, forcing them to starve and die. Dose is 5 to 10 mg per pound of body weight daily for dogs and cats.

- MCT oil assists with burning fat instead of sugars for energy. Cancer cells thrive by utilizing sugar for energy. MCT oil can help the body make ketones, which the brain uses as an energy source.

- Colostrum—The mix of immune and growth factors in colostrum can inhibit the spread of cancer cells. And, if viruses are involved in either the initiation or the spread of cancer, colostrum could prove to be one of the best ways to prevent the disease in the first place. Colostrum contains cytokines that can help enhance the body's response to cancer and are thought to inhibit the growth of cancer cells. It supports the immune system and helps fight viruses which can initiate the growth and spread of cancerous cells. In addition, colostrum contains lactoferrin, which is an anti-inflammatory substance that fights viruses and bacteria. It has been extensively researched for its role in treating and preventing cancer.

- Homeopathic remedies that match the patterns in the diseased state of the ailing patient may help. Consult with an experienced homeopath.

- While not specifically labelled as chemotherapy agents, many drugs are used off-label to help fight cancer and decrease inflammation. These may include cimetidine, doxycycline, and fenbendazole, among others.
- Energy work can include massage, Tui-Na, acupressure, Reiki, Craniosacral therapy, Vibrational Healing, and TTouch.
- Acupuncture can help pets feel better by improving appetite, decreasing pain, stimulating the immune system, moving blood, decreasing inflammation, and improving energy.
- Electroacupuncture should not be used around cancerous areas.
- Cold laser therapy should also not be used over cancerous tumors.
- Pets with cancer should never receive vaccines, nor should they be treated with topical pesticides and insecticides.
- Prednisone can be used judiciously in pets with cancer and sometimes it will improve their appetite, making them feel better. Most complementary protocols can be used along with prednisone.
- Cats can be difficult to treat, as they do not appreciate being made to take multiple supplements. Ask your veterinarian to choose the most important two or three for the cancer you are fighting.

So, what about the diet? First and foremost, take them off dry food. Dry food contributes to phlegm production. This is the time to pull out all the stops and go in search of organic, fresh, whole foods.

Cancer cells thrive on processed foods and diets high in simple carbohydrates. Avoid white potatoes, white rice, quick oats, or any food with a high glycemic (sugar) index. You can access plenty of glycemic index lists on the internet. High quality proteins and fresh foods that are rich with antioxidants can slow the cancer. Gently cooked or raw diets are best. Most oncologists will demand that the pet not be fed raw food, but I have never found this to be an issue. Ketogenic diets are high-fat, moderate protein, and low carbohydrate. They must be fed raw due to the high fat content.

Many pets undergoing treatment will become extremely picky with their food. It is more important to get calories in than to worry about balance and ingredients if you have a pet that is not eating. Offer different foods and keep rotating foods. Small amounts of tomato sauce (organic, no sugar added), grated parmesan cheese, or dried garlic powder (not garlic salt) can sometimes entice picky eaters. Fish cooked in butter or sweet potatoes sprinkled with cinnamon are other options. If you find one ingredient or food the pet likes, do not offer extra helpings. Overfeeding may result in nausea and the pet will stop eating the one thing they like. All foods should be fed slightly warmed and should never be fed cold, even if feeding raw meats. Do not warm food in the microwave. You can put the meal in a glass container and put the container in a bowl of hot water for warming. Do not put medications in the meals. The pet needs to eat, and many will walk away if the food is adulterated in any way. Pills can be hidden in bananas, organic no-sugar almond butter (no peanut butter as peanuts are high in aflatoxins), liver, gizzards, sardines, or whatever you can manage. Try to avoid processed lunch meats, ice cream or dairy products, and hot dogs for hiding medications.

Ingredients l like to include:

- Grass-fed beef
- Dark meat chicken or turkey—make sure the turkey is not injected with butters or oils

- Fresh caught ocean fish—not farm-raised
- Organ meats like heart or liver (up to 30% of the protein portion of the diet)
- Broccoli and broccoli sprouts
- Spinach, Purple Cabbage, Brussels Sprouts, and Kale
- Dark leafy greens, parsley, basil, and oregano
- Carrots
- Eggs
- Sardines
- Sweet potatoes or yams, pumpkin—for soluble fiber and as Qi tonics to move the Blood and Phlegm, small amounts
- Barley—acceptable low-glycemic-value grain which is cooling and draining for pets with Blood Stagnation
- Ground almonds
- Pears, bananas, or apples
- Medicinal Mushrooms
- Fresh or dried ginger root can be administered if the pet is vomiting or refusing food. Give 1/4 to ¾ teaspoon per meal. Ginger tea also works well and can be given by dropper or syringe if the pet is not eating. Ginger has been found to activate the immune system's T-cells. It helps lower blood sugar to starve cancer cells. It also can reduce the size of cancer tumors and causes apoptosis (death) of both normal cancer cells and cancer stem cells.
- Crushed fresh garlic—to resolve stagnation and dissolve tumors; garlic can entice anorexic pets to eat. Dogs under 20 pounds can be fed 1 small clove per day. Larger dogs can eat a large clove. Fresh garlic is far superior to garlic capsules, dried garlic, or jarred garlic. Animal studies have shown that possible cancer-preventive mechanisms include: inhibiting enzymes that activate carcinogens

(potentially cancer-causing compounds), boosting enzymes that deactivate carcinogens, reducing inflammation that could support cancer development, supporting DNA repair, slowing growth and stimulating self-destruction of cancer cells without disturbing normal cells, and limiting cancer's ability to spread by decreasing a tumor's ability to grow new blood vessels.

🐾 Fresh organic blueberries or raspberries

Processed treats should not be fed. All treats should be fruits or berries, pieces of hard-boiled egg, or pieces of meat. Because this diet is low in carbohydrates pets may have a difficult time maintaining weight. You may have to feed three to four times daily if weight loss is an issue.

High quality probiotics must be added to the diet and I also recommend adding digestive enzymes. Since 70% of the immune system resides in the gut, the gut function needs to improve.

In addition to high quality food and elimination of toxins, exercise and interaction play key roles in healing. All the therapies in the world are not as important as attitude and ability to LIVE while treating cancer. According to Chinese medicine, all cancers are rooted in the emotions. I have seen clients spend every day hauling their pet from one veterinary specialist to the next, having the pet poked and prodded every day, hoping someone, somewhere, will give them a cure or the answer they desperately want to hear. Sometimes they forget that the pet would enjoy a trip to the park or a walk in the neighborhood instead.

One of my clients had a wonderful older dog that was her dancing partner. (Yes, I said dancing. It's a great sport.) Misty developed cancer in her upper jaw, even though she was not vaccinated and was fed an organic raw diet. Even with the best care cancer can still appear. Misty's owner struggled with the decision of how to proceed with treatment. The oncologist gave her decent odds the cancer could be stopped with radiation, so the owner decided to go forward. Six treatments under anesthesia would be the protocol. Misty hated the treatments. What Misty loved was to go for long walks. By the fifth treatment, which didn't seem to be working because the tumor was still getting bigger and destroying more jaw tissue, Misty refused to get out of the car at the radiation center. Once pulled and lifted out, she refused to go into the building. I realize the traditionalists would argue that we shouldn't let the dog dictate the treatment and the treatment wasn't working because she hadn't finished the full dose of radiation. But this owner realized how much Misty was suffering from the treatments; so, she decided to honor Misty's wishes. Instead of going to radiation therapy they went for walks. They walked miles and miles for hours and hours. They went everywhere. When Misty would come for acupuncture treatments I would only use a few needles. If I used too many she would hide and cower under the chair. After each treatment she and her mother would walk to the river near our practice and would walk for an hour or two. Weeks later when it was finally time for Misty to cross Rainbow Bridge, she walked four hours before her owner walked her into the veterinary office. Misty's owner realized it was more important to spend time enjoying each day than to prolong a life of suffering.

Since cancer can be a heart-wrenching subject, I will leave you with a couple of success stories that will make you smile. Deedee, a Standard Poodle, spent the first few years of her life as a breeding female. She was owned by a quality breeder who fed raw diets and didn't over-vaccinate. Deedee was adopted by very special people who also fed a raw diet and avoided vaccinations. Unfortunately, DeeDee developed mammary cancer around age nine. The mass seemed to appear overnight, and it grew rapidly. The biopsy came back with the dreaded news that the tumor was an aggressive form of mammary cancer, and the prognosis was guarded. We had a long discussion about traditional versus alternative therapies and the owners opted to avoid chemotherapy. I had never treated a case of mammary cancer using herbs, so this presented a new challenge. I combed books, journals, and the internet and asked veterinary herbalists how to proceed. I came up with a protocol that included IP6, Artemisinin, Sanshedan Chuanbeiye, mushrooms, omega 3 fatty acids, and CoQ10. The owners continued the raw diet. Deedee became our new, shining star, role model for alternative therapies. She was happy, had no regrowth or spread of the cancer, and lived to age sixteen.

Mast Cell Cancer

Another favorite was Lally, a Cocker Spaniel. Lally had been treated for Mast Cell tumors with multiple surgeries and two rounds of chemotherapy at the veterinary college. When the masses continued to grow after the second round of therapy and became too invasive to be surgically removed, the doctors said no more could be done for her. The owner sought out alternative care as a last resort. Of course, Lally needed a diet change, so her owner opted for home cooking. She started taking probiotics, IP6, Artemisinin, mushrooms, omega 3 fatty acids, CoQ10, and Stasis in the Mansion of the Blood. Within a month the tumors began to shrink. A year later the owner laughingly said if it wouldn't cost so much money, she'd love to make an appointment with the doctors at the university just to point out that yes, something could be done to save Lally. Lally decided at some point that she did not like taking a lot of medications and supplements. We had to choose the most important supplements and decrease the medication load. She had no increase in tumor size or number, even with less supplementation. Lally died many years later of causes not related to her mast cell diagnosis.

Mast cell tumors are the most common malignant tumors in dogs, but are rare in cats. Mast cell tumors can be quiet, locally aggressive, or spread like wildfire. They are great imitators, sometimes appearing to be small, benign growths or skin tags. They can look and feel like a lipoma or benign mass under the skin or they can be pink, raised, ulcerated, and swollen. They may grow and shrink, only to enlarge again later. It is impossible to know whether your pet's mass is a mast cell tumor without looking at cells under the microscope.

Healthy normal mast cells form part of the body's immune system. They can be found in most tissues, but in particular in the skin and the linings of the digestive tract, lungs, mouth and the nose. They are also involved in allergies and allergic reactions. When triggered, the mast cells release large amounts of heparin, histamine, and enzymes.

Mast cell tumors are generally easy to diagnose. A sampling of cells from an impression smear or a fine needle aspirate can be stained and examined under a microscope in your veterinarian's office or sent to a pathology lab for path review. The cells are distinct in appearance, being filled with dark purple granules. Generally, when a mast cell mass is aspirated, the cells will release those granules, resulting in purple spots all over the microscope field. While it is possible to say this IS a mast cell tumor, it is not possible to determine how aggressive the mass will be without a biopsy.

The cause of mast cell tumors is up for debate, just like many cancers. Immune-system suppression or dysfunction and over-vaccination have been implicated by some researchers.

Treatment consists of surgical removal with wide margins. This can be difficult when tumors are located in areas such as limbs where there will not be enough skin to close over areas of wide excision. Biopsy of the mass will determine the grade of the tumor to help predict how the tumor will behave and whether clean margins were realized during surgery. Grade 1 tumors can usually be removed and normally they do not return. Only about 5 to 10% of Grade 2 tumors will return if surgery is done with a wide excision, but about 50% of Grade 3 tumors will return after surgical removal, even with clean margins.

Chemotherapy and radiation may be recommended for higher grade tumors. Other treatments include diphenhydramine (antihistamine), steroids (prednisone), famotidine (histamine blocker), pain medication (as needed), and possibly a new injection called Stelfonta. Stelfonta is injected into tumors that are nonmetastatic (have not spread), skin-based mast cell tumors in dogs, particularly tumors on the legs. Remission rate during clinical trials was 75%. The active ingredient in the injection was discovered in the seed of the blushwood tree native to the rainforest in North Queensland, Australia. The medication works by activating the immune system to destroy tumor cells and tumor blood supply, leading to tumor destruction. Expect a significant wound to form but it should heal within six weeks.

Unfortunately, there is no guarantee these options will prevent recurrence. Many clients came to my office looking for alternative options to help slow the growth of these masses. While each pet is different, I have a few recommendations that I generally recommend.

- A clean, commercial human-grade, whole-food diet low in starchy carbs or a home-prepared diet, or a ketogenic diet.
- Palmitoylethanolamide or PEA, which is a fatty acid amide that supports the healthy function of mast cells and decreases inflammation and granule release.
- Cannabidiol which helps block pain and inflammation through cannabinoid receptors. There is some evidence that CBD can have an anti-tumor effect, as well.

- Mushroom supplements for their cancer-fighting aspects. Mushrooms fight cancer in four specific ways: They stimulate the immune system, help immune cells bind to tumor cells, reduce the number of cancer cells (cytotoxic effect), and slow down cancer cell growth. The Japanese government officially recognizes mushroom cancer therapy as a treatment.
- Omega-3 fatty acids decrease pain and inflammation. Omega-3›s work in conjunction with the endocannabinoid system to decrease spread of cancer throughout the body.
- IP-6 400 to 800 mg daily—an antioxidant that plays and important role in regulating vital cellular functions, helps reduce tumor size and prevent tumor spread.
- Artemisinin—also known as sweet wormwood, 100 mg twice daily for 11 days on, 3 days off, repeat. Cancer cells take up more iron than normal cells. Artemisinin is attracted to these high iron cells and selectively goes to them. Once inside the cancer cells it reacts with the iron causing free-radical formation which kills the cancer cells.
- Xue Fu Zhu Yu Tang (Stasis in the Mansion of the Blood)—Mast cell cancer often arises if there is impaired blood flow to the skin. Without good blood flow the immune system cannot find and destroy the cancer cells that arise. This herb helps promote blood flow to the skin so the immune system can reach the mast cell cancer. In my experience this formula helps to reduce tumor size, occasionally shrink the small tumors completely and prevent formulation of new mast cell tumors.
- Golden Paste—turmeric has been shown to have cancer-fighting abilities. It is synergistic with the Xue Fu Zhu Yu Tang.

From a traditional veterinary medicine standpoint, these tumors are commonly treated using steroids (prednisone, dexamethasone) and antihistamines (most commonly diphenhydramine). Side effects from long-term use of these drugs make them a poor choice for ongoing management, but they may have short-term benefits that might be worthwhile.

When your pet has been diagnosed with cancer, it is easy to feel helpless. It is important to educate yourself about your pet's cancer and how to care for your animal with cancer. Cancer treatment for animals focuses on alleviating pain and suffering, along with extending life, if their quality of life can be preserved. Treatment is typically much less aggressive than in humans.

Try to stick to your normal routine as much as possible, as our pets like routine. It helps them stay active and engaged, especially if they must make many visits to the veterinarian for treatment. Fun activities like exercising, walks, and playtime will help to maintain a healthy mindset for both you and your pet.

Just because an animal has been diagnosed with cancer does not mean its life is immediately over. Our cat, Star, was diagnosed with lung cancer at age 20. She was showing no signs of illness; I found the cancer during routine testing. Because cats are difficult to medicate and Star was already eating a species-appropriate raw diet, I opted to do nothing other than allow her to live a comfortable life, which she did for another year, passing at age 21. One of our Cocker spaniels, Milli, was diagnosed with lung cancer during routine testing at age 16. A few supplements were added to her raw diet, and she also lived for another year, passing at age 17.

Deciding on the course of treatment will vary in every case. You do not have to stress over every little thing. Your love and commitment to your pet will help them enjoy life as long as possible.

Do not be fooled into thinking all cancer diagnoses are a death sentence. Do not be fooled into believing all cancers can be cured with chemotherapy, radiation, or alternative treatments. There will always be outstanding stories on the internet with testimonials spouting miraculous cancer cures. Each case is different and must be treated individually. Do the best you can with the resources you have available and remember to live each day to the fullest.

18 End of Life Care

Old age is not a disease. Old age can be challenging. Old age should be celebrated: you survived your youth.

As pets age, the effects of poor nutrition, over-vaccination, and environmental pollution become magnified. Many pet owners decline to deal with the problems of old age and instead, choose euthanasia or placement of the pet into a shelter. I hear the common complaints like:

- 🐾 He seems to be in pain: This argument might work with me if diagnostics and treatments have been used to try to alleviate pain.
- 🐾 She urinates on my rugs: This argument might work with me if diagnostics and treatments have been used to try to stop the house soiling.
- 🐾 She can't see or hear well: neither can your great-grandmother. It's not a reason to choose euthanasia.
- 🐾 The kids want a new puppy they can play with that can run around: or your kids could learn a lesson in compassion and caring for an elderly being. You could have them walk the older dog gently around the yard. They could read stories to the older pet.
- 🐾 I'm moving three hundred miles away and the trip will be hard on him: him or you? Riding in a car is not traumatic

for most pets, especially if they have been trained to ride in the car over a lifetime.

🐾 I can't afford the veterinary bills associated with aging: you signed on to care for this pet for life. You did not sign on to care for him only during his youth. I understand circumstances can change over time, with loss of employment or housing. But please remember the love this pet has given to you and don't bail on him when times get tough. Find a new home or rescue group where the pet can receive appropriate care. Most rescue groups will take senior pets and there are new senior sanctuaries becoming available.

I know that I am preaching to the choir here because if you are reading this book, you are clearly dedicated to caring for your pets. Perhaps we can educate others to understand there is always hope and there are resources available.

Aging pets will start to fall apart. My English toy spaniel, Lora Lu, developed urinary incontinence. I tried chiropractic treatment, acupuncture, and herbs which helped a little, but she still leaked. Sometimes she leaked a lake in our bed or on our sofa. I solved the problem by having her wear washable cloth dog diapers. Hue said he would never change diapers again after his children were grown. He was wrong. Lora had minimal hearing and usually didn't hear us calling her. She developed glaucoma and needed to have both eyes removed. She suffered from dementia at sundown (like sundowner's syndrome in people) and needed supplements to keep her from pacing and barking each evening. She had heart disease and high blood pressure, requiring a handful of medications and supplements twice each day. Many people would say we should've put her down to end her suffering. I say, what suffering? She loved life. She loved to go for walks in the stroller. She loved sitting outside with us under the shade tree. She LOVED to eat and was the first one to dive into the bowl at mealtime. She loved snuggling in the big chair with Hue. It required extra time and patience to care for Lora Lu. But I made a commitment to Lora Lu when she was rescued from the puppy mill that she would be with me for life, and I stood by that commitment. I'm not shaming people who do not have the resources to care for aging pets. I'm just asking for compassion in all decision-making when it comes to your pet.

General supplements recommended for aging pets include:

- Omega-3 fatty acids—30 mg of DHA and EPA per pound of body weight once or twice daily to support brain, heart, and joint health.
- CoQ10—5 mg per pound of body weight twice daily.
- Vitamin D (test first, but most seniors are deficient)
- Joint support supplements (see chapter 7 under arthritis)
- SAMe—5 to 7 mg per pound of body weight daily given on an empty stomach.
- Mushrooms—Reishi, cordyceps, turkey tail, lion's mane, maitake, chaga, and Shiitake can all be beneficial.
- Probiotics—species-specific, soil-based are preferred.
- Digestive enzymes help with digestion of nutrients.

Cognitive Dysfunction Syndrome

Most people think of this as a disease occurring in dogs, but cats can also suffer with this. Cognitive functions include the mental processes of perception, awareness, learning, and memory, which allow an individual to acquire information about the environment and decide how to react.

Cognitive dysfunction (CDS), sometimes referred to as dementia, as in humans, is directly related to brain aging. Deficits in learning ability and memory, as well as decreased responsiveness to stimuli, are symptoms of the disease. Some pet owners will simply say the pet is acting older. Studies have shown that 50% of cats over age 15 and 40% of dogs over 14, increasing to 68% at age 15, suffer from CDS.

Cognitive Dysfunction Syndrome is a diagnosis of elimination. A veterinarian may diagnose cognitive decline if a physical exam and lab tests do not show the animal's behaviors to have a medical cause, such as cancer, diabetes mellitus, hypertension, hypothyroidism, Cushing's disease, hyperthyroidism, pain from osteoarthritis, or vision or hearing loss. Some behavioral problems can also mimic CDS. These include separation anxiety, aggression caused by pain, and poor housetraining.

Classic signs of CDS can be spelled out with the acronym DISHAA. The letters stand for:

Disorientation—the pet may seem lost or get stuck in corners or may have trouble locating food and water bowls.

Interactions—alterations in interactions with owners, other animals, or the environment

Sleep cycle disturbances—howling, pacing, or crying in the middle of the night

House soiling—they may not remember how to get to the door that leads to the outside or may not be able to find the litter box

Activity changes—sleeping more than usual; and an increase in

Anxiety—separation anxiety, fear in crowded areas or when around other animals, destructive behavior

Treatment for CDS is multimodal:

- Try not to move furniture around too much in your house. Your pet may be having trouble with navigation if they are unable to follow memorized paths.
- Try to keep your routine very similar every day. Try to keep bathroom breaks, mealtimes, and bedtime around the same time.
- Continue with daily exercise and mental stimulation. Puzzle games, scent work, and environmental stimulation will help keep their mind sharper.
- Continue to encourage your pet to socialize with other pets and people. This can help them maintain interest in the world around them.
- Make dietary changes that support brain health. Increased omega-3 fatty acids have been shown to improve brain function. In addition, l-carnitine may provide some benefits.
- Supplement the diet with Vitamins E and C and antioxidants such as SAM-e and COQ10.
- Brightly colored fruits and vegetables contain flavonoids and carotenoids that function as antioxidants. These can include red, orange, and yellow peppers, butternut squash, pumpkin, red cabbage, blueberries, kale, broccoli, and parsley.
- Vitamin D deficiency has been associated with cognitive decline. Have your pet's vitamin D levels tested at least once every six to twelve months, even if you feed commercial diets. Many senior pets are vitamin-D deficient. Supplement vitamin D if the tests results are low.
- CBD supplementation has been shown to be helpful in many pets.
- The specific compounds in Lion's Mane mushrooms promote the growth of neurons and are taken by people to stave off cognitive decline.

My sister had a fifteen-year-old Corgi, Comet, who had not been able to walk for over a year. He had a cart to use but seemed fairly content to pull himself around. He started leaking urine and developed a bad odor. My sister had him checked by her local veterinarian who assured her it was due to his spinal disease and inability to walk, nothing more. By the time she brought him home for the holidays, my parents were dreading the thought of a leaky, stinky dog living in their house for a week. When I saw Comet, it was obvious he had a raging infection with an odor that permeated the house. I cultured the urine and grew some nasty bacteria, which had caused a secondary skin infection. Treatment required shaving all the hair off his belly and hindquarters, washing daily with medicated soap, application of tea tree oil creams, and a long course of antibiotics and probiotics. I also added Adequan for his joints and deer antler velvet for inflammation. Miraculously (or not) the odor disappeared, and the urine leakage stopped. My parents seemed to be the most thankful! Caring for Comet required a huge commitment of time for my sister, but she was committed to giving him a long life free of pain.

Dumping old pets at the local shelter is only one step better than dumping old pets along the road. Older pets with medical issues stand very little chance of being adopted and most of them will be euthanized. Imagine living your life with your family and suddenly being dropped off in a strange environment with people you don't know. Your vision and hearing are not good, and you feel confused. Not a pretty scenario, is it? (Actually, this may be a normal scenario and good comparison to what is done with many older people in our society.) Private rescue groups and breed-specific rescues are usually willing to take in older pets with medical issues. If you truly cannot afford to care for your senior pet, I implore you to contact one of those groups.

Hospice and Palliative Care

While euthanasia was long considered the most humane option for aging or terminally ill pets, the growing fields of veterinary palliative care and pet hospice provide pet owners with options that can extend both the quality of life and the time spent with beloved companions.

While the terms hospice and palliative care are often used interchangeably, pet hospice focuses more on managing the process of dying.

Palliative care focuses on relieving pain and other disease signs. It starts when the focus shifts from trying to cure an illness or extend the length of a life to helping the pet stay happy and comfortable. This is done through medications, therapies such as acupuncture, chiropractic care or laser therapy, dietary therapy, and home care such as administering fluids or applying heat therapy. The goal is to help pets do more of what they enjoy for as long as they're able to enjoy it.

Hospice takes over when palliative care has done all it can do and is no longer effective. The goal of hospice is to provide pets with a dignified death that's as peaceful, humane, and pain-free as possible. That might mean managing pain and making the pet comfortable during a natural death or providing relief for unmanageable suffering via euthanasia.

Palliative care is not used only in cases of terminal illness. Pets with any type of painful or limiting illness or condition can benefit from comfort care, even if the condition is not life-threatening. Conditions that might benefit from palliative care can include:

- Arthritis and joint pain—supplements, pain medications, physical therapy, massage, acupuncture, chiropractic, cold laser, mobility support, and hydrotherapy are just a few of the options available to ease pain and suffering.

- Vision and/or hearing loss—modifications in the environment can be extremely beneficial to help these pets navigate their world.
- Incontinence—this may require diapers, incontinence pads, acupuncture, herbal therapy, and skin care to prevent scalding.
- Cognitive dysfunction- supplements, dietary therapy, environmental modifications, mental stimulation, and re-training can help.
- Kidney, heart, liver, respiratory, and gastrointestinal diseases—dietary modification, supplements, fluid therapy, and acupuncture can help keep these diseases stable.
- Cancer—many pet owners will not opt for surgery, chemotherapy, or radiation, making hospice and palliative care attractive options to keep pets comfortable.

Not all veterinarians have advanced training in hospice and palliative care, however more and more often, we are seeing staff members wanting to provide supportive care for aging or terminally ill pets. The IAAHPC (International Association of Animal Hospice and Palliative Care) is open to veterinarians, licensed social workers, licensed mental health professionals, pet loss professionals, chaplains, aftercare providers, veterinary technicians, and students in those fields.

Pet parents can provide much of the necessary care at home; limiting trips to the veterinary office will decrease stress for both the pet and the family. Providing care in a home setting can help decrease costs involved in care once the pet parent feels comfortable providing care at home. Most pet parents can learn to give injections, administer subcutaneous fluids, and monitor vital parameters such as heart and respiratory rates, body temperature, and blood glucose. The most important aspect of hospice care is education about your pet's medical condition.

At some point, you will know it is the right time to let your senior pet cross the Rainbow Bridge. Things that may help you make the decision include:

- Pain that is no longer responding to treatment.
- Anorexia and weight loss to the point of malnourishment.
- No interest in surroundings or people; depression.
- Uncontrollable seizure activity.
- Respiratory distress that cannot be managed.
- Loss of bowel and bladder control to the point where you cannot keep them clean and sanitary.
- Open wounds or tumors that cannot be closed or removed and have dead or chronically infected tissue.

The decision to euthanize can be extremely difficult. I have seen people struggle with this decision many times. If you have done everything humanely possible for your pet and they are failing and struggling, you will know when the time is right. The decision of when, where, and how the procedure should be carried out, is a personal one. I recommend always having an intravenous catheter in place with sedation and pain medication on board, before proceeding with the final injection. If you want to have the procedure performed in your home or garden, ask your veterinarian if that service is offered. When the procedure is done in the office, ask which time of day is the quietest with the least number of clients in the building. Try to remain calm and talk soothingly to your pet at the end. Let them know you love them, and they will always hold a special place in your heart. This is the final act of compassion you can offer to your dearest friend.

19 The Future

When I first became interested in alternative therapies, many of my colleagues considered me to be "out there". Ridicule, snickering, and jokes were the norm. The American Holistic Veterinary Medical Association was not formed until 1982, only a few short years prior to my foray into alternative therapies. It was easy to ignore the ridicule, as I was seeing such great results with my patients. Over time, those same doctors started referring patients for alternative care, hoping for help when there was nothing left to offer. Or maybe they were just trying to shuttle their hopeless cases to someone else.

I am happy to say, some alternative therapies are becoming mainstream. Acupuncture has become extremely popular, and many veterinary clinics now have at least one veterinarian practicing acupuncture. Unfortunately, as I found in my early days with alternative medicine, having one doctor performing acupuncture while not truly believing in holistic healing will leave the patient with minimal healing effect. Prescribing foods and medications in a traditional practice will continue to cause degradation of the immune system and will continue to contribute to chronic disease.

Food therapy is less popular with traditional veterinarians and the American Veterinary Medical Association has issued a statement against the feeding of raw foods to animals. The Delta Society, one of the largest pet therapy groups in the nation, has excluded any pets that are fed a raw diet, warning those pets may harbor bacteria that could be spread to children and adults with weakened immune systems. I have never seen this happen, but there are many reports of people dying after handling dry pet food contaminated with salmonella. Of course, safe handling practices must be followed when handling any raw meats, whether they are being fed to pets or cooked for human consumption.

The American Veterinary Medical Association started an investigation into the use of homeopathy to treat animals, saying there was no validity that it helps, and pets may be succumbing to diseases that could be treated using more traditional methods. I do not practice homeopathy, but I know many veterinarians who are extremely successful using that therapy. If a governing body becomes successful in outlawing one alternative therapy, what is to stop them from attacking another? Luckily, when the vote came before the AVMA House of Delegates, there was no statement made against homeopathy. For now.

Holistic veterinarians strongly support limited vaccinations in pets. Vaccinations have almost eradicated many diseases that used to kill pets, but repeatedly vaccinating year after year has proven to be unnecessary for many diseases. Each animal has a different level of exposure to disease, so each vaccination schedule must be tailored to the individual animal. For years, good pet owners have followed annual vaccination protocols, presented by their trusted veterinarians, that are outdated.

Chiropractic therapy is less popular than acupuncture, but it has become easier to find practitioners. There has been ongoing debate regarding who should perform chiropractic manipulations on animals. Human chiropractors state they are the only doctors that should treat the spine and veterinarians state they are the only doctors who should treat animals. The stress forces on the spine are very different for two legged humans versus four legged animals, so I feel human chiropractors should treat humans and veterinarians should treat animals. Ideally, those who would like to treat spines of animals should complete human chiropractic school as well as veterinary school, but that would require more years of college than most people would like to attend!

Herbal supplement usage in pets has become very popular. Many clients come to the clinic with a bag full of products they have purchased online or at the store to give their pets. Unfortunately, most of those products are not regulated by the Food and Drug Administration so there is no quality control. Many of the supplements are just placebos, containing no active ingredients. Many are toxic to pets or can cause symptoms to worsen because they are not being used correctly. I can't emphasize enough how important it is to work with a knowledgeable veterinarian or reputable company before purchasing supplements for your pets.

The future is bright for the use of alternative therapies in healing animals. I have had the pleasure of training other veterinarians that are interested in using holistic treatments for their patients and I love the excitement they have toward alternative medicine. For those pet owners seeking a different form of veterinary medicine, it is becoming easier to find holistic practitioners. You can find a holistic practitioner in your area by going to www.AHVMA.org, the website for the American Holistic Veterinary Medical Association. Once you find someone in your area, set up an appointment to meet the doctor and tour the clinic. Ask for references from current clients.

My journey into traditional veterinary medicine, followed by the unusual path that led me into alternative veterinary medicine, has been long and rewarding. I am thankful to all my family, clients, patients, and staff who have been along for the ride of a lifetime. It's been a joy.

Index

Made in the USA
Las Vegas, NV
18 January 2024

84510381R00203